TALE
OF VALOR

A Novel of the Lewis
and Clark Expedition

by

VARDIS FISHER

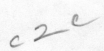

DOUBLEDAY & COMPANY, INC., GARDEN CITY, NEW YORK

1958

Library of Congress Catalog Card Number 58–7356

For Bob—
exploring on another frontier

"The story of this adventure stands easily first and alone. It is our national epic of exploration."

COUES

". . . stands as incomparably the most perfect achievement of its kind in the history of the world."

CHITTENDEN

Foreword

I am aware that some matters in this great story have not yet been settled—that (to give only two instances) Dr. Bakeless says the Lewis dog was a Newfoundland named Scannon and DeVoto says it was a black mongrel named Brewster; that Professor Hebard, a biographer of Sacajawea, spells the name Fraser, and calls him a former dancing-master (another calls him a former fencing-master), that Bakeless spells it Frazer, and that in the Army records it is Frazier. As for the dog, neither DeVoto nor Bakeless gives any evidence to support his statement, and so possibly I may be allowed to suspect that it was an Indian stray which Lewis picked up en route between St. Louis and the Teton Sioux.

I have run into the legend that Sacajawea was every man's woman on this journey, and in any case, Clark's. I've no evidence that she was not. Wheeler, a most gallant gentleman, has said that "not a breath of suspicion was whispered against this unpretentious slave-wife of a frontier Frenchman." I've talked to various old-timers with whom a study of the Lewis and Clark saga has been a hobby and they all agree with me that the morale of the men could not possibly have been maintained if one captain or both had been lying with this child. I call her a child and reason this way: from the day she was captured she was any man's woman. She would have become pregnant as soon as she was nubile, and so far as we know, Pomp was her first child. Possibly she was no more than thirteen or fourteen when she left Fort Mandan with the Corps. If this is true, her part in the journey becomes all the more remarkable.

We still don't know what "Janey" means in the letter Clark wrote to Charbonneau—"bring down your *Son* your famn Janey had best come along. . . ." My conjecture is that he called her Jawey, for the third syllable of her name, when spelled Sacajawea, seems to have been pronounced "jaw" and the accent seems to have been there. Her name, as Bakeless says, has "been much disputed." Basing his statement on the Bureau of American Ethnology, the U. S. Geographical Board, and the DAB, Bakeless says, "If it is a Minnetaree word, it is derived from *tsa-kaka*, 'bird,' and *wea*, 'woman.' If it is Shoshone, it is derived from *sac*, 'boat,' *a*, 'the,' and *ja-we*, 'launcher.'" The bird-woman or the boat-launcher.

VARDIS FISHER

Mandan, North Dakota
October 23, 1957

TALE OF VALOR

1

Régis Loisel's black eyes had been studying their bearded faces, his gaze lingering on the strong jutting jaw of William Clark, on the changing lights in the slate-gray eyes of Meriwether Lewis. He was a shrewd judge of men. He knew that the two captains before him were bold resourceful men, but he also knew the Sioux Indians.

With a touch of impatience he said, "I'm only telling you what I know. You act as though I'm trying to deceive you. After all, it's no business of mine if you're determined to get yourselves killed and every man with you. But I do say this, that if you're fully resolved to go through the Teton Sioux country you'd better write your farewell letters home. The Partisan will never let you do it."

At the moment he uttered those last words he was looking into the eyes of Lewis. He thought they seemed to be amused. He wondered if these captains knew as much about Indians as they pretended to.

Lewis said, "You seem to rate these Sioux pretty high as fighters."

"As Indians they're the best I've known. Ask the Arikaras. They drove the whole Arikara nation out of their homes and up the river. But what I had in mind, Captain, is less their skill than their number."

"How many warriors do they have?"

"I think they could bring a thousand against you."

"All with guns?"

"No, not all. Most of them. The English see to that. You know, of course, that it's the English who are determined that you shall not go up the Missouri."

"Oh yes, the damned English!" Lewis said. "Always stirring up ignorant people while filling their own pockets so they can keep riding to the hounds. They've chased the fox so much they're just like him."

Loisel chuckled. "I assume from what you say that you're really fond of the English."

"Devoted to them," Lewis said. "Captain Clark and I are determined that they shall have some fine fox-hunting domains over here." Loisel chuckled again. Perceiving that the man seemed to detest the British as much as he did, Lewis decided to tell him about the stuffy fat red-faced British minister who had been mortally offended by the informalities of President Thomas Jefferson's dinners. He had blown his wig off and his servants thought he had died of a stroke. Jefferson had had to rush word to James Monroe, the American minister in London, to smooth matters over. It had all been the fault of Washington and Adams, Lewis said: those two Presidents had lived in pomp and splendor and the foreign ministers had loved it. Jefferson had changed all that. Soon the outraged ministers were writing home that in Washington a title was thought of no more worth than an Indian's headpiece—and in fact Jefferson had invited red chiefs in their outlandish garb to sit at the same table with some of the oldest titles in Europe. Then there was the Turkish minister. Good Lord, what a fellow! He came to Washington, a city of mud and leaking roofs, swathed eight-deep in the most gorgeous robes of the Sultan's court and within an hour was simply enraptured by a huge fat Negress. He said she reminded him of his best and most expensive wife.

Loisel snorted with joy and Lewis joined in the laughter. He felt better. He always felt better after telling what he thought of the British.

"Jefferson says the English are humorless because they're always stuffed full of kidney pie."

"That may be," Loisel said, wiping a tear away. "But they usually get what they go after, and right now they're after the whole western part of this hemisphere. If they suspect the true purpose of your mission they'll stop at nothing to force the Sioux to exterminate you."

"What do you mean by the true purpose of our mission?"

"You're not fooling anyone," Loisel said. "The news came up the river ahead of you. Take it as a fact that the English know what you're up to. They may be humorless but they're not stupid and they have spies everywhere."

The captains looked at Loisel and were silent. Then Clark said, "Do the Sioux have a chief who is supreme over all others?"

"Black Buffalo but he doesn't dominate the Partisan." To explain what he meant, Loisel told a story. One day Buffalo and Partisan were walking together when they came to a young squaw who had recently spurned Partisan's advances. He aimed his rifle at her heart and pulled the trigger three times. Three times the gun failed to fire. That was Partisan for you—a hot-blooded ferocious monster, a dull savage brute in a red skin. Even Black Buffalo was afraid of him. The Sioux Indians were a cruel greedy treacherous people whose inordinate lusts sometimes drove them to the utmost audacity. Like all Indians, they were cowards but when full of whisky they would stop at nothing. All the tribes who had come in contact with them—the Arikaras, the Mandans, the Minnetarees, and a half-dozen others—were scared to death of them. He, Régis Loisel, had traded with them for years, yet on his last journey up the river they had treated him shamefully, and had bullied and degraded and half-killed one of his assistants. It had been the Partisan in both instances. That horrible monster was given to moods in which the distilled essence of hell itself was pure innocence compared to the blood in his veins.

"If I knew more about the matter I'd say he is insane."

"And Black Buffalo doesn't try to control him?"

"He knows better."

"Is this Partisan popular with the young bloods?"

"Oh, immensely. They greatly prefer him to any other chief."

Lewis glanced at Clark and then rose to his feet. "Well, thanks a lot for telling us what to expect. It looks like we're going to have some fun."

Loisel was never to know whether Meriwether Lewis was jesting. But then he didn't know at this time that these two captains were experienced Indian fighters almost from childhood. He did know that William Clark came from a military background—that he had five brothers who had served in the war that freed the colonies and that some of them were now generals. He knew that George Rogers was now famous.

The meeting with Loisel had been four months ago and a thousand miles down the river. The Frenchman's words came back to Lewis when he saw three naked Indian boys running toward the river. He watched them plunge in and swim as no man in the white party could swim, heading straight for the keelboat. He had them taken on board and then summoned an interpreter, for it was plain that the lads had a story to tell. It was just as plain that the little thieves were looking round them for something to steal.

The Teton Sioux! Well, he had suspected that. He glanced at Will Clark and said tonelessly, "The Teton Sioux at last—the most merciless Indian nation west of the Mississippi except the Blackfeet." To the interpreter he said, "Find out what the little villains want."

The boys had come to tell the white men that on the next creek upriver there were eighty Sioux lodges; not far from them was a village of sixty lodges; and not far from these were still other lodges. The lads were making signs on the boat deck to indicate great numbers, and when Lewis saw what they were doing he turned to Clark with a wry smile and said, "This is the way they give us the first warning. They don't send a chief or even a grown man but three kids. In all your years dealing with Indians have you ever known anything so insulting?"

"Never," Clark said. His face was grave. He had been closely studying the three arrogant Indian boys. He spoke to Drewyer, the interpreter: "What else do they want?"

"Tabac."

"Of course. Are we invited to a council?"

So far as he could understand the boys, Drewyer said, the captains were not. The boys had been sent to tell the captains that back in the hills were hundreds of armed warriors, who wanted tobacco and whisky.

Clark said to Lewis, "I expect we'd best give them some tobacco and send them back."

Lewis fetched two carrots of tobacco twist and gave them to the two larger boys. He asked Drewyer to explain to them, if he could, that the two white chiefs were commissioned by the great white chief in Washington, whose might was greater than that of a thousand Sioux nations; and that the two white chiefs would meet the Sioux chiefs in council in a day or two. But both captains knew that the little rascals were paying no attention. They were looking round them for something to seize before jumping overboard.

After they were gone, after they had reached the shore and raced away and vanished, Lewis and Clark stood together, looking into the northwest. They knew that they had entered a zone of great danger. They knew that the success of their enterprise might be won or lost in the next few days. They did not have much to say about it to one another. They were not men who talked about the obvious. Before leaving St. Louis they had known that they would have to face the Sioux and back them down, or yield to them—and these two men never yielded. They had been told in St. Louis by traders, and for a thousand miles up the Missouri, and over and over by such as Loisel, that they would all be massacred, or tortured and degraded and driven back. Now and then they had wondered if their informant was a scoundrel in the pay of the British or the Canadians, who wanted to keep all the western trapping waters for themselves. Still, they had plenty of evidence to support their belief that their troubles would really begin when the Teton Sioux came swarming to the river.

And so for a little while they stood together, looking off into the distance and thinking.

Other Sioux tribes they had already met, farther down. On the James River, August 27th, they had sent Pierre Dorion, a trader familiar with the area, to invite the Sioux to a council. Dorion had returned two days later with his half-breed son, five chiefs and seventy warriors. These were the Yankton branch of the Sioux, whose trade relations for years had not been with the British up north but with St. Louis. They had complained and whined and begged. They had asked for ten times as much as they hoped to get, as the red men always did; but they had shown no hostility. The Teton Sioux, it was said, had been pretty decent fellows before the English gave them whisky and weapons and flattered them to death. Now every last man of them, Loisel had said, was a thief and a pirate, egged on by the James River and Des Moines River British. Breaking the British stranglehold on this vast area, yes, even driving the British out, was a part of the dream in the mind under Tom Jefferson's red hair.

In the mind of Meriwether Lewis, as he stood there looking toward the Sioux, was a great worry—a tormenting question that he could not put away. He had not spoken to a soul about it. It was the kind of thing a man had to settle in the loneliness of his own being. It was a thing he had to settle, if he could, before he went to sleep this night. For it had made him bilious and half-sick and he wanted to get it over with.

"I wonder," he said, "how many of them are looking at us this moment."

"A lot of them, I expect."

"They'd give a pretty big pile of wampum to know what we have on these boats."

"They'll never rest till they do know."

Lewis decided to ask his friend a question but he took a few moments to formulate it. He had no doubt that Will Clark knew a lot more about the Indian mind than he knew. Studying the Indian mind had been a hobby with Clark ever since he was a small child, and was almost a passion with him now.

"Will," Lewis said, "how do you see it? Would they strike before they know how strong we are?"

Clark took a few moments to consider the question. "Not," he said, "unless they're full of whisky."

"Well, yes, there's always that—and the British will be sure to bring up the whisky. You think it looks pretty bad?"

Clark was no romantic dreamer. He was a realist. "Pretty bad," he said. Then he turned to look at Lewis. "But we've been in bad situations before."

Lewis knew what he meant. His mind looked back. Clark's people had gone down the Ohio to Kentucky when Will was still a boy and the two friends had not met again until they met as soldiers in the Indian wars. Will had told Merne how on that long journey down the Ohio he had seen Indians in every clump of brush along the way, their black eyes looking out at him. It was about this time that the tribes along the Ohio had become alarmed, and then enraged, as white settlers steadily encroached upon their hunting grounds. They had begged the white leaders to make a permanent line between red man and white.

But what Will Clark had had in mind just now was the wars. He had seen Colonel Logan, on orders from Will's brother, General George Rogers Clark, butcher the Shawnee settlements—ten Indian chiefs had been shot down there, including Dan Boone's foster father, Black Fish. Will had been with his brother when he mowed down the Wabash Indians, and again with Colonel Hardin when he wiped out entire Wabash settlements. He had been in the campaign with General Scott, and one who saw him in the fighting there had written to his people that he was as brave as Caesar. He had been with still other Indian fighters and was barely out of his teens when he became a lieutenant under Mad Anthony Wayne. Lewis had served under him and had seen what kind of man he was. Looking at him now, he recalled the expression in Will Clark's eyes when

General Wayne had one day told his men that it was stupid to fight the red men in the fall, when they were full of corn and venison and high spirits, but wise to fight them in the spring, when they were dispirited, half-starved and half-dead.

This was September.

"Remember," Lewis asked, "what General Wayne told us? About the right time to fight the Indian."

"I remember," Clark said.

"He's full of corn and venison now."

"And British whisky."

"That seems to me to be the big unknown factor here—just how hard the British will push them."

"It seems that way to me," Clark said. "I expect they'll push them pretty hard. They certainly will if they happen to know what our plans are."

Again for a little while the captains were silent, their gaze still fixed on distant rolling prairie. Lewis felt bilious. He supposed it was because he had been thinking of the damned British. He thought it might be a good thing to take a stroll through river woods and chew some willow and kinnikinick bark. His mother would approve that. Lucy Marks—she had married again after her husband's death—was known far and wide in Albemarle County as an herb doctor—a yarb doctor, the people called her.

"I guess I'll take a walk," Lewis said, without looking at Clark. "I won't be gone long."

2

He was a tall man, the one strolling there, his rifle across his left arm and his dog at his heels. In his moccasins he stood a good inch above six feet. He had a rather long face; a high forehead from which at thirty the hair was already receding; heavy black arched brows above eyes that were steady and searching, yet more the eyes of poet or philosopher than of professional soldier. He had a long nose, slightly Roman, and a dimple in his upper lip. He had a mouth that was of almost womanly shape and delicacy. His chin was neither weak nor aggressive, nor his jaws. He had a long neck, shoulders that sloped sharply, and bowed legs. It was a rather ungainly body over which he did not have the control that might have been expected of one who had been woodsman, horseman and mountain boy and man since early childhood.

He liked to be alone with his dog, for he was sensitive, shy, introverted, impulsive and brooding—a lonely man who suffered from dreadful spells of depression and melancholy—who had preferred to live much to himself ever since the tragic death of his father when Merne was only five. Indeed, when he was only seven years old he had often taken his gun and his dog and prowled from dark until after midnight in wild forested areas that would have chilled the blood of boys for whom intimacy with danger and boldness in the face of peril were not an ordinary way of life. Long before he was grown he had local fame as a hunter.

This man walking there, brooding upon his problem, had never married, had never been in love. He had a quick eye for feminine excellence, and now and then he had made remarks which some of his friends had thought romantic; but not once had he seriously contemplated marriage, and when looking into the future he always saw himself as a single man. He did not like to talk about his tastes in this or in other matters; but when pressed he would tell a story in his Albemarle drawl: "I'm like the man you heard about who was riding a horse through the woods and looking for a switch. Every time he saw one that looked fine and dandy he stopped and was about to break it off; but then he thought, Oh no, there'll be a better one a little further on. And so he kept riding and riding, until at last he was clear out of the woods."

His consuming passion, this man once said, was wanderlust. As a boy he had always asked himself when looking at a distant mountain, "What's on the other side?" He had been hardly more than a child when he begged his friend and distant relative, Thomas Jefferson, then Secretary of State, to send him with an exploring party that would cross the vast plains and mountains and go to the far ocean before the British or Spanish could do it. That had been in 1792, and this was Sunday, the 23rd of September, twelve years later, and he had traversed sixteen hundred miles of the journey he had long dreamed of. He had got his wish at last, and with it a problem that now plunged him so deep into melancholy that he felt ill.

It was a simple problem. It was stated in a few words, which he had memorized, in the long letter of instructions which President Jefferson had sent him. Those words said:

> As it is impossible for us to foresee in what manner you will be recieved by those people, whether with hospitality or hostility, so is it impossible to prescribe the exact degree of perseverance with which you are to pursue your journey. we value too much the lives of citizens to offer them to probably destruction. your numbers will be sufficient to secure you against the unauthorised opposition of individuals, or of small parties: but if a superior force, authorised or not authorised, by a nation, should be arrayed against your further passage, & inflexibly determined to arrest it, you must decline it's further pursuit, and return.

There the problem was, in plain words! From all that he and Clark had learned, a superior force, egged on by the British, would be arrayed against them. The President's orders in that case said explicitly that the party should turn back! What were he and Clark to do? They were not the kind of men who ever turned back. On the other hand, they were Army men, under Army discipline and rules, and under the explicit orders of their commander-in-chief, the President.

Captain Meriwether Lewis, Indian fighter, explorer, former secretary to his ruddy freckled-faced Albemarle neighbor and now his trusted adventurer-in-discovery, chewed bark and searched his mind for a way out. He tried to stand all the facts up so that he could see them. There were these: that Thomas Jefferson's dream of a great United States now filled a continent; that for twenty long years, as Minister to France, as Secretary of State, as Vice-President, he had tried with every resource at his command to get the western part of the continent explored and claimed for the United States before the British or French or Spanish could explore and claim it; and that in his Monticello home he had agonized in prayer over what he was doing, saying to Lewis, "I have no right, I have no right, but I must, I must! God grant that I am not making waste paper of the Constitution! But if Louisiana can be bought I must buy it, even though I make ten thousand enemies for every friend! And you, my friend, must explore it!"

But not with too much perseverance! Well, that set up another group of facts. Jefferson had said to him, "My friend, you and your men may never come back"—and he had looked at him clearly as an expendable man. But he had also said, "If you all perish it will be my political ruin. The Federalists will never stop crowing. For they say I expect to find a mountain of solid salt out there, with an eagle of salt sitting on top of it!" He had said, in effect, "Go on— and on, even if you all perish, even if I am ruined!" But he had said, in effect, "The death of you and your party would be a major disaster—so use the utmost prudence in the degree of risk you take." *Which* had he meant? Lewis knew that he had meant both. His dream of a great United States that would be a world power was such a mighty beating force in him that he was willing to sacrifice anything to attain it. At the same time, his reluctance to spend even one man to win half a continent held him back and plunged him into a struggle with himself that Lewis had understood very well.

For it was his own struggle, now. When the men were enlisted for the Corps they had been told that they would go on a journey fraught with great dangers. They had not been told that they were headed for a vast unknown and the Pacific Ocean. They had not been tested in battle. They might not look with any enthusiasm to the founding of a greater nation upon their blood and bones. . . .

In the letter of instructions the President had also said, "To provide on the accident of your death . . . you are hereby authorised . . . to name the person . . . who shall succeed to the command on your decease. . . ." That was another matter that tormented him. If he fell, Will Clark would succeed him, and no better man could be found, he believed, in the whole wide world. When Jefferson called him to Washington and asked him to lead an exploring party, he had told him to choose an assistant who was a frontiersman, with thorough knowledge of the woods and the wilderness; who was bold and resourceful and a practical fighting man; who could endure great strain and hardship without complaint; and who, preferably, had some scientific skills. Lewis's mind turned to two friends, but he had sent the first invitation to Will, outlining the task and asking him to "participate with me in its fatigues, its dangers and its honors, believe me there is no man on earth with whom I should feel equally pleased in sharing them as with yourself."

Clark had replied at once: "This is an immense undertaking fraited with numerous difficulties, but my friend I can assure you that no man lives with whom I would prefer to undertake and share the Difficulties of such a trip than yourself."

But what if Will Clark also fell under Indian guns? Sergeant Nathaniel Pryor, perhaps—a lean hard loose-jointed man who seemed to have the respect of all the men. The trouble was that though they had recruited their handful of men from hundreds who had wanted to go, they did not yet know them—and here were the Sioux, lusting for battle! It would take a hard winter, and possibly some fighting, to show what kind of men the captains had.

He looked down at his dog, who had pointed his ears forward and was growling. Lewis had no doubt that Sioux Indians were observing him while he walked. There might be a hundred of them, with their black fierce eyes fixed on him now. This whole country roundabout smelled of Indians—as some areas smelled of beaver or muskrat, some of bear or deer. It smelled of danger, and he liked that, for he had made the deliberate pursuit of danger his way of life. On up the river were other savage nations, the traders said—the Arikaras and Minnetarees; and beyond them, somewhere in that unknown which no white man had ever entered, were the Blackfeet, the most ferocious of all. These redskins, it was said, made fiendish and diabolical torture of captives their favorite amusement, the women being even more savage than the men. And beyond them, what? Jefferson had said, "You'll surely encounter many Indian tribes who have never laid eyes on a white man. They may all try to kill you." And again his gaze had said, as clear as day, that Lewis was expendable and he was deeply sorry about it.

Jefferson had said, "But what else can I do, except send an exploring party?" For he had known a long time what the British were up to: having lost their colonies in ignominious defeat, and then developed for them such hatred that no American in England was treated with anything but contempt, they were now determined to colonize as much of this continent as they could. What they could not seize they would let the Spanish or French have, rather than the Americans. With what venom the parents had turned on their children!

Knowing all this, Jefferson had written to George Rogers Clark, "they pretend it is only to promote knoledge I am afraid they have thoughts of colonising . . . some of us have been talking here in a feeble way of making the attempt to search that country but I doubt whether we have enough of that kind of spirit to raise the money. How would you like to lead such a party?"

General Clark had declined, for reasons unknown to the man chewing green bark and turning an inner ear to the rumblings in his stomach. Talking in a feeble way! It had not been in a feeble way that the President had talked to his secretary. He had said, "We must have all that country for the United States. *We simply must!*" He had read about it everything he could find, and night after night in a big room lined with books he had talked to Lewis about it, saying that there might be untold wealth out there in minerals, lands, forests, as there certainly was in pelts.

What an elated man he had been when the whole of Louisiana had fallen into his lap! He had sent ministers to Paris hoping to buy New Orleans for two million dollars, and right out of the blue Napoleon's minister had asked them what they would give for *all* of Louisiana. How large was *all* of it? Jefferson had wondered aloud when talking after midnight with his secretary, or wandering with him in the grounds, their two tall ungainly forms looking to servants as if at any minute they might topple over. Did it rightfully include a part of Canada? Did it include what was known as California? "The Constitution gives me no right to buy land but we must have it, all of it. . . ."

We must have it, Lewis thought, chewing bark. He knew that

the whole matter possibly rested upon his judgment and Clark's. For if they did not push through to the ocean and claim it—if they perished or in defeat turned back, Jefferson's enemies would never allow another party to go, never, and the whole enormous wealth of it would lie there for the British to take. Yes, good Lord, he was aware that the whole matter rested in his hands, now, right here in Sioux land!

you must decline it's further pursuit . . . That was an order from the commander-in-chief. If only he knew whether he had meant it, or had merely put the words down in a moment of compassion! Perhaps he should go back and ask Captain Clark what he thought. He was not Captain Clark, really, and what a pity it was! Jefferson had intended that he would be, but the thickheaded brass of the War Department had denied the commission. Sensing his chagrin and hurt, Lewis had said to him, "Between us it will make no difference: you're to be absolutely equal with me in all things. We mustn't let the men know. You'll be Captain Clark to me and Captain Clark to them." When before their men the two captains always addressed one another by title, and often when together alone.

Returning to the keelboat and going to his friend, who still stood watch, looking toward the east bank, Lewis said, "Captain Clark, the woods over there smell like solid Sioux. I expect maybe a hundred of them were watching me."

"At least that many," Clark said. He nodded his head to the northeast, where clouds of smoke lay low above the autumn woods. "Signal fires. They're calling them in to hold a big powwow."

Lewis grinned faintly and said, "We should have brought the Hill of Devils with us." A month earlier the captains had been shown a conical hill, in which, the Indians said, lived a multitude of devils. These fiends, only eighteen inches high, had huge heads and the sharpest arrows on earth, which they shot into anyone who approached their home. Indians had been seen running away as filled with arrows as a porcupine with quills.

Sensing that his friend was in no mood for levity, Lewis said, "Will, there's one thing I can't make up my mind about. In his orders to us the President said that if we meet a superior force we must decline battle and turn back."

Clark looked at Lewis, his face showing astonishment. "You never told me that."

"I never thought of it, I guess."

"Why would he imagine we wouldn't meet superior forces, or that we'd turn back if we did? We might meet superior forces a dozen times before we reach the ocean. As for turning back, I'd never heard of that."

Lewis felt a warm glow inside. This was his kind of man, the kind who never turned back. But he said, "You and I didn't undertake this enterprise to turn back but there are two things that worry me. One is that the President told me that if we are all killed his political life would be ruined. The other——"

Clark interrupted. "His political life would be ruined? If we're all killed——"

"Yes, we'll be ruined too," Lewis said, his eyes full of mischief. "But what he meant, my friend, is this, that if he's ruined politically there would never be another exploring party. Then the British would gobble it all up."

"I expect that's right," Clark said.

"The other thing is, do we have a right to sacrifice all our men? I mean it's all right for you and me. Our lives belong to us. But at what odds are we going to risk our men?"

William Clark was looking at him, looking straight into his eyes. It was not that he doubted for a moment the courage, or the valor, of this man who had fought with him in one Indian war after another. He knew that they didn't come any bolder than Merne Lewis, or any more reckless—and it was because the man was so reckless that he looked at him now, wondering what change had come on him, or if the President had given him secret instructions. Then he thought he knew what it was.

He said, "From the start I've figured we're all expendable men. I'm sure the President looked at it that way. We certainly don't want to take foolish risks. On the other hand, we set out for the ocean and that's our goal. As for our men, every one of them was told that his life would be in great danger on this journey and that he might not come back."

"That's true," Lewis said. "Still, some of them are so young."

Clark had turned back to the signal fires. He now looked again into Lewis's eyes and said, "You told me the President left the matter to our judgment."

"He said he couldn't prescribe the degree of perseverance. He also said he valued too much the lives of citizens to offer them to probable destruction. And he said without qualification that we are to turn back if we meet a superior force—and by that I expect he meant such a force as all the Sioux warriors, if they should come against us. Believe me, Will, I've been out there in the woods all this time thinking about it. I want to obey orders, and I know you do. We also want to win this great unknown land for the United States. Maybe it's a bigger gamble than we yet realize, but I would say here and now that no matter what comes we'll go on. We'll go on as long as there is one of us alive to lead and one to follow."

William Clark put out a hand and said, "That settles it."

That settled it. Neither captain ever spoke of the matter again.

3

They had come up the Missouri on three river craft: a keelboat fifty-five feet long, with a squaresail and twenty-two oars; and two pirogues, one of seven and one of six oars. The keelboat had a deck in the bow, with a cabin, and a row of lockers in the middle that could be used as a breastwork against attack. All three boats were heavily laden with supplies and were anchored in mid-river.

The captains had agreed that until this crisis was over they probably should both stand watch, for they didn't yet know their men well enough to know which were dependable and which were not. Only the other day they had heard a sneering remark from big John Newman. They expected trouble from him. Three months had passed since the courts-martial of John Collins for drunkenness, while standing guard, and Hugh Hall for stealing whisky. The first had received a hundred lashes on his bare back; the other, fifty. A few days later a private named Willard had been found sound asleep at his post and had been given twenty-five lashes a day for four days. Not long after that two of the men had deserted, a member of the Corps named Reed and a Frenchman employed as a laborer. His patience running out, Clark had sent three soldiers after Reed with orders to kill him if he resisted. Reed's punishment for desertion had been only the running of the gantlet four times, with some of the men hardly touching him with their lash. The captains had decided that the lash was not enough.

The man standing watch on the keelboat at midnight was thinking about the problem of discipline. He was a rugged man, with coarse and slightly wavy red hair, a skull that looked abnormally long because of a high forehead, a narrow face and a jutting chin. His nose was large and strong, his mouth large and firm. It was a face that looked stern when unrelaxed, even arrogant, but William Clark had never been known to quarrel with any man. He was quiet-spoken, even-tempered, methodical, painstaking. Unhappily conscious of his older and far more distinguished brothers, he was resolved to make a name for himself. A legend in the Clark family said that every Clark born with red hair would someday be famous.

Older than his friend Lewis by four years, like him, he was a Virginian; had had only a little formal schooling; had been on the frontier since early childhood; had acquired an extensive knowledge of woods, rivers and wilderness, Indians and warfare. Like him, he had never married and had never been in love. Unlike him, he fully intended to marry and had in fact chosen his wife, a twelve-year-old lass whom he had once helped with a balky horse, though whether her name was Julia or Judith he could not for the life of him have said. Unlike Lewis, he had brought along a personal servant who had been part of his inheritance, a gigantic coal-black Negro named York.

William Clark most of the time looked stern because he was at heart a disciplinarian: he had learned during many years as a soldier and in many campaigns against the Indians that the deadliest enemy a soldier faced was lack of discipline, in himself or in his ranks. He had seen want of discipline half-destroy, or send into shameful rout, one army after another. He had seen and studied the methods of Mad Anthony Wayne. He had discussed these matters with two of his soldier-brothers. Nobody knew better than he that his life and the life of his friend Lewis and the lives of all the men in their command would depend, during this long and dangerous journey, far more on discipline than on numbers or straight-shooting. The Corps had to be a tightly-knit precise mechanism, with each and every man a thoroughly dependable part of it.

It was not yet that kind of machine.

While his woods-and-mountain and far-sky eyes looked all around him for sign of skulking savage or signal fires he considered the problem of discipline. No, the lash was not enough. It would not be enough even if the offender's back were cut to the bone. The switch used was not enough either. The captains had not favored the brutal leather whip used by the British Navy, but only light green branches that stung without biting deep. But even the British leather would not be enough. They'd have to punish a man in a way that would wound his pride, fill him with shame, send him away in disgrace; and what could do that but dismissal from the Corps? He would speak to Captain Lewis about it.

It was after midnight and new signal fires were being set off in the northwest. They were really stirring themselves, Clark decided, but they'd never strike in the dark or before they had determined their enemy's strength. They would first ask for powwows, the sneaking two-faced rascals, so that they could count the men and the guns. Well, let them see the white man's weapons! The keelboat had two swivel guns, one at either end, loaded with scrap iron. There was enough iron in either gun to tear the guts out of a dozen Indians. There was also an airgun, which had fascinated the red men down the river. Invented by the British, it was still a curiosity, even to white men, for the reason that it expelled bullets with compressed air, and could be fired as fast as a hand could drop balls into the muzzle. When fired, the sound it made was not an ear-shattering explosion, as with the swivel, but a pop, like the bursting of an inflated paper bag. It was almost as accurate as the Kentucky rifle and ten times as deadly. Captain Lewis was inordinately proud of it.

They would show off the swivel guns and the airgun to impress the chiefs when they came, but even with these, and all the rifles, and forty men as brave as men anywhere, it was folly to think of surviving a massed Sioux attack. Their only chance to go through alive lay in absolute firmness from the first moment of meeting. An Indian understood that. On the other hand, he was swift to strike if he saw a man falter. He and Lewis would give presents and medals, possibly even commissions, because Jefferson had asked them to commission the top chiefs and make them feel they were a part of the great Army of the United States. They would be firm but courteous; aloof but sensible of the red man's prejudices and rights. Not for a moment would they take any nonsense. . . .

About one o'clock Clark entered the cabin to get some sleep. Lewis was there, stretched out on his back and snoring. When Clark arose at four he found Lewis dressed and standing watch.

"Captain Lewis," he said gravely, "I think we both better try to sleep some more. We might get no sleep at all in the nights to come."

"That's right," Lewis said, and turned with Clark back to the cabin.

But both captains were up at daylight. After scanning the prairies east and west and talking to the guards, who said they had seen nothing suspicious, the captains decided to lift anchor and go up-river. They liked to have their men row an hour or so before break-fast, to whet their appetites and work the drowsiness out of their blood. Besides, they had decided that it would be best to go right to the mouth of the stream on which the Sioux lived. The Indians would understand that kind of boldness.

On the way upstream the captains opened lockers and chose a few medals and garments for the principal chiefs; then inspected both swivels and the airgun. Downriver they had traded for a few horses, and these in the care of a sergeant and one or two privates had been brought upstream along the bank. Sergeant Pryor now called to the captains to say that one of the horses had been stolen during the night.

Lewis looked at Clark and said, "I expect we might as well anchor here and wait for them to come."

Anchor was dropped, and in a few minutes five redskins came skulking out of riverbrush on the west bank. Lewis asked the inter-preters, Drewyer and Labiche, to tell them that the white men were their friends. The interpreters called to the Indians in a French-Indian jargon that no other men on the boats could understand. The five red men stood stock-still, like wild things listening and smelling.

Disgusted, Lewis said, "I don't think they understand a damn thing. Tell them they stole one of our horses and they'd better bring it back. Tell them if they don't we'll never speak to them again." He turned to Clark. "What a silly thing to tell them. It's like talking to children."

"They are children," Clark said. "I expect they were sent down to spy on us and report our number." To the men in the pirogues he called, "Get down and up and move around." At once there was re-markable activity on the pirogues as the men there tried to make their number seem ten times what it was. The five Indians on the bank turned and silently vanished.

"Let's go on up the river," Lewis said.

Again anchors were raised, men bent over their oars and the three boats moved off. On a river island they saw a small herd of elk, and because all the men seemed in a good humor, Clark named it Good Humored Island. The keelboat and one pirogue moved on ahead of the third and soon came to the mouth of a stream flowing in from the west. After looking at it a few moments the captains decided to call it the Teton River. There was no sign of Indians at its mouth or anywhere on either side of it. This was ominous.

Lewis said, "I'll bet a thousand of them are watching us. There's probably a face behind every bush and tree. You think they'll come today?"

"It's hard to tell. A few of them might."

It was toward evening before a living thing came in sight. Three Indians came out of riverbrush and stood on the bank looking over at the boats, and Lewis and Clark in turn gazed at them through glasses. By their manner of dress, Clark said, they looked like chiefs. He guessed he would take some tobacco and go over and have a smoke with them.

"We'll all be on the alert here," Lewis said, observing that the second pirogue had come up. "If you get in trouble try to duck out of our fire."

"In that case we'll dive into the water, if possible. But I don't expect any trouble today. It's too early."

Taking one of the interpreters and three picked men to act as a bodyguard, Clark entered a pirogue and was rowed to the west bank. He and his four men stepped out, and he told the sergeant in the boat to go back fifty yards and anchor, but not in the line of fire from the keelboat. Then he turned to face the three Indians. They also had a guard, a considerable body of men, standing back in the riverbrush.

He didn't like the look of them. For one thing, it was obvious to his experienced eye that they were minor chiefs: it was a mark of special insolence to keep the generals hidden and to send sergeants to talk to generals! For another thing, they looked surly and stupid and brutal. He gave them tobacco and then had Drewyer tell them in signs that these white men were their friends. While the Indians smoked, Clark puffed at his pipe and studied them. No, he didn't like these Indians at all. He knew now, even if he had doubted it before, that the Corps would be in trouble before it passed through Sioux land.

So many things told him this. There was the way they kept staring, with bold open childlike eagerness, at the boats, looking back and forth at them, as though trying to count the guns and the men and estimate the booty. There was the way they looked at Clark himself, turning sullen black eyes on him, eyes filled with contempt, and wonder about him. Each time the contempt faded away after a few moments and there came in its place an uneasy curiosity. Clark was also studying them, coolly, while smoking his pipe. They did not impress him as men. They looked scrawny and undersized; their arms and legs were small. But he had to admit that they looked wild and savage. They did not impress the three young men of his guard. He heard Reuben Fields mutter to a companion, "Mebbe this is where I get me a redskin. The one in the middle would do."

Clark said to Drewyer, "Ask when their big chiefs are coming."

Drewyer again spoke in jargon and signs. He said that as nearly as he could understand them a lot of Indians would come to the river tomorrow.

"They're hoping to scare us," Clark said. He drew a carrot of tobacco from a pocket and gave it to the Indian who had been the spokesman. And there it was again, that insolence and contempt. He thought for a moment the man intended to strike the tobacco from his hand, as a sign that it was not enough. He looked into the black eyes and his own expressed the contempt he felt.

Turning, he signaled to the pirogue and it came to the bank. Clark and his four men entered and were taken to the keelboat. On the way over he did not look back at the three Indians and he told his men not to look back. With an Indian, it was necessary to show respect or contempt at the right moments, and this was a moment for contempt.

Clark went to the cabin with Lewis, his friend's eyes on him, eager and questioning. Clark told him that there was no doubt that the Sioux intended to make trouble but he didn't think the trouble would come before tomorrow, and possibly not that early. These three had been sent, with an immense bodyguard back in the woods, to size up the white men and report to the top chiefs. The top chiefs would hold a council soon. Partisan, no doubt, would demand that the young hotbloods be turned loose for a massacre. Black Buffalo or some other chief might advise prudence. They would never attack the Corps while its men were on boats in mid-channel. They would try with subterfuge and stratagem to lure all the white party to an Indian village, or in some other way to catch them off guard.

The captains decided to take turns standing watch. The two pirogues they put under the command of Sergeants Pryor and Ordway, with orders to stand themselves the two hours before daylight and to choose only dependable men. "Try to make your men understand," Clark said, "that the Corps is in very grave danger.

Captain Lewis and I expect serious trouble. Be sure your weapons and men are in order at all times."

Lewis took the first watch on the keelboat and looked for a while at the smoke rising in the west above hidden lodges and melting into the night-sky. Thousands of Indians there knew that the white man had come in greater force than ever before. What would they do about it? Would four or five hundred young hotbloods be turned loose, with orders to capture for torture as many white men as they could, and to kill those they could not capture? Or would wiser counsel prevail? Any guess about it was a wild guess. At the age of four Will Clark, to the amazement of his people and neighbors, had become interested in the Indian mind and had been studying it for nearly thirty years. He had no doubt that the Sioux would make trouble. "Our only hope," he had said in the cabin, "is to stand absolutely firm. Any faltering that they take to be weakness or fear will mean the death of all of us. . . ."

Lewis had no reason to doubt that his friend was right. Well, if it came to a showdown would all their men stand up like men, and sell their lives for every Indian they could get out of them? If they all fought coolly and efficiently they would pile up a lot of red bodies before the last white man fell. They should be able to kill two or three hundred of them in any case. No Indian tribe would willingly pay such a price for victory but, being children, they would sometimes go into battle with the most incredible optimism. One thing to be done was to let them know how much a victory here would cost them, and one way to do that was to show off the swivels and the airgun.

It was a dark night that steadily deepened. Off in the west there was in the sky a faint illumination from lodge fires down below but there was no sign of light in the east or north. In the north were the Arikaras, who in recent years, Loisel said, had become murderous devils; and northwest of them were the Big Bellies, with a chief ten times as mean as Partisan. It looked as if the Corps might as well get used to the idea of trouble with the red men, possibly for thousands of miles. If these who had known white men were so eager for their death, what would the tribes be like who had never seen white men but who now would see them invading their hunting grounds? "If we survive," Lewis said, looking down at his dog.

Because their survival would depend on the coolness and straight-shooting of every man he fell to thinking about the men, having

nothing better to do. Some of the men had seen Army service; some
had not. Some of them seemed to think that discipline was a matter
for old men to argue about. Most of them seemed to be as bold as
Caesar, and though some were clumsy with a rifle, others could shoot
almost as far and true as Clark and Drewyer, the best shots in the
Corps.

Some of them were queer ducks. There was George Shannon.
George was only a boy really, only seventeen, and with no more
beard on his apple-rosy cheeks than a baby. The previous winter his
father had got lost and had frozen to death, and now this Scotch-
Irish lad had the strange habit of getting lost. Was he, Lewis wondered, trying to join his father? There was something pretty queer
about it. August 26th Lewis had sent him up the bank with the
Corps' two horses, and one day passed and another and there was
no George. After nine days a landing party went ashore to search
for him; and still later, John Colter, only a youngster himself, had
been sent to find him. John came back alone. Then, after almost
two weeks, after everybody concluded that George was dead or
captured by Indians, he walked in, leading one of the horses, his eyes
as quiet and abstracted and his face as apple-cheeked as ever.

Questioned, he said he had lived on grapes and one rabbit. Having
no lead, he had shot the rabbit with a bullet made of hard wood.
Some of the men were flabbergasted. "Mither uv God!" Sergeant
Paddy Gass had cried, bugging his eyes at George. "We niver worriet
so since the pigs et the baby!" "Grapes and one rabbit in two weeks?"
another said. "You don't look so skinny." A third said, "Why in hell
didn't you come to camp? You just like being alone, huh?" George
said he had gone far up the river and then had sat by the river
waiting. Bob Frazier gave him a hard look and said, "We know what
you been doing. A form dee-vine said Georgie be mine! One Sioux
for you, one bed for two . . . !"

The most extraordinary thing about this youth, for Lewis, was not
his remarkable self-reliance but his extraordinary ear. No other man
in the Corps could match him at spelling out the sounds of Indian
words, or at pronouncing them. One of the interpreters was George
Drouillard, whose name the captains did not even try to pronounce.
They called him Drewyer, some of the men called him Never Talks
but George called him Drouillard. He did not pronounce the name
the French way to show off—the captains had learned that he was not

that kind of person—but only because his excellent ear detected nuances that others missed. . . .

While he was thinking about the man Lewis kept searching the black night and the black water. It was useless to look at the timbered banks. It was, he supposed, useless to search the river, because the idea that Indians in force would come swimming to the boats was simply fantastic. White pirates might, but not red men. Just the same, one lesson he had learned in the Army was that the good soldier stood watch as though attack might come at any moment. Besides, it *was* possible that twenty or thirty expert swimmers could come softly through the darkness and mount and overpower and make off with a pirogue. The thought sent him clear around the keelboat to look searchingly at the waters.

At the other end, back to the swivel gun, Joe Fields, Reuben's sturdy and fearless brother, stood watch.

"Private Fields, have you seen anything suspicious?"

"No, sir, Captain."

"It's almost eleven. You'll be relieved soon."

"Yes, sir."

Lewis stood watch till one. Then Clark came out, as straight as a gun barrel and striding like an officer. "Captain Lewis, have you seen anything?"

"Not a thing, Captain Clark."

"You better sleep now and I'll take over."

William Clark stood watch as though the fate of the world depended on it but he knew that there was not one chance in a million of trouble tonight. He moved constantly round and round the keelboat, his eyes searching the black waters. The other watchman on this boat he sent to bed, and those on the pirogues, reminding the two sergeants that they were to rise an hour before daylight. He wanted his men to be alert and able, and not groggy with fatigue, if trouble came with the morning. A half-hour before daylight Lewis came out of the cabin and joined him. Lewis said he thought it would be well for all the Corps to have a daylight breakfast, so that eating would not put them off guard while Indians were around. Clark agreed, and just at the break of day sent orders to the mess cooks to serve bread and cold meat on the boats.

When the men learned that they were not to go ashore to eat by campfires they looked at one another and at their sergeants, and then those on the pirogues looked over at the keelboat, where the two captains stood.

"I guess they expect trouble this morning," Bob Frazier said. He looked up at the coal-black Negro standing above him. "York, have you got your squirtgun ready?"

"Yawsuh!" said York in a deep bass voice, his eyes rolling in black and white, two rows of strong teeth gleaming.

"How many you figure you can shoot down before they split your big black head with a tomahawk?"

"Twunty-two, suh," said York, his grin spreading from ear to ear.

Frazier looked round him. "Twenty-two, that's the guy's age. He kallates on one for every birthday."

"Twenty-two will make quite a pile," George Shannon said. "I don't expect I'll be shooting that fast."

"Twenty-two," said Bob Frazier with a deep sigh, "and if they're York's every one will be female. There's the breakfast whistle. If you're gonna be scalped, I'm told, it always helps if your belly's full. York, is that right?"

"Yawsuh, Majuh!"

Frazier burst with laughter. "To hear us," he said, "nobody would think we'll all be dead before sunset. All but York. He'll be off in a wigwam somewhere with two squaws on each arm."

4

No sign of the red man's intentions came before daylight, nor for some time afterward. Breakfast had been eaten and the dishes washed in river water, and all weapons again inspected, before the first Indians came in sight—a lone one there, straight and motionless and staring; then another, then two or three, then small bands and larger bands, until at last they came pouring in from all directions west of the river. The men in the boats turned tense and many an eye looked over at the captains. Clark had had a few of his men go to a sandbar at the mouth of Teton River and erect an awning, under which he hoped to hold a council with the chiefs. When the river-bank was lined with the red people three who seemed to be chiefs came to the sandbar and after looking round them a few moments went over to the awning and seemed to be staring at the American flag. Lewis was studying them through glasses. He handed the glasses to Clark and said, "One of them looks like the Devil himself. It must be Partisan." Clark gazed at them a few moments and then said it was time to go over; and after gathering up some medals, a flag and some articles of clothing the captains entered a pirogue, with Drewyer and an armed escort. One of the soldiers carried the airgun. The big boat had been anchored so that it stood only seventy yards from the sandbar, with both swivel guns broadside. On the keelboat as the captains pulled away, a score of men stood at attention facing the sandbar, their rifles across their arms; and at each swivel gun stood a sergeant. Armed men also stood on the other pirogue, which had been anchored close to the keelboat. While crossing the two hundred feet of water both captains looked back now and then, to see if their men on the other boats looked formidable and ready.

As the white party beached and the captains, interpreter and armed escort left the pirogue, the hundreds of Indians who had swarmed to the bank fell back and broke away to open a path. Neither of the captains looked at them and both had instructed their men with them not to look at them. It was best with Indians on occasions like this to stride forward as though oblivious of them or indifferent to them. The captains went straight to the awning and made signs of greeting and peace, their eyes swiftly passing over the three chiefs. One of them, they learned, the big one who looked like Satan himself, was the Partisan; the elderly smiling one was Black Buffalo; and the other one had a name which sounded to them like Beffe de Medison.

The captains first gave tobacco to them and prepared to light their own pipes, knowing that formalities had to be observed before an Indian would do business at all. They then presented to the head chief, Black Buffalo, a red coat and a cocked hat with a feather in it, as well as a medal, a commission and a flag; and to the other chiefs they gave medals and commissions. All the while the eyes of the captains were looking as deep into the red souls as they could. They both thought that Buffalo seemed to be a rather good-natured fellow: he was fat and gross, with round fat cheeks, and eyes that twinkled with humor. Partisan had a scarred face, half-lidded eyes that glowed with evil, and menacing gestures, especially after Buffalo got a fancy coat and hat and he got none. Beffe de Medison, obviously third in rank, also looked twice as savage as the wolverene and ten times as greedy. The chiefs, both captains knew well, were trying to look into the souls of the white men, and Partisan's gaze was so fixed and deadly that Lewis had trouble restraining a smile. Deliberately he met the man's eyes and held his gaze until with a quick abrupt movement Partisan turned to look at Clark.

"Should I give my speech?" Lewis asked.

Clark did not look with favor on his friend's wish to give pompous speeches to the red men but he said quietly, "It might be all right."

The chiefs and the white men were all sitting now, except the armed escorts, red and white, who stood back. To Drewyer, Lewis said, "Try to make them understand all this." He then looked into Buffalo's black eyes and said, "We have been sent by the great chief of the seventeen great nations of America." While Drewyer in sign language tried to make the meaning plain Lewis observed that Partisan didn't give a damn about it. Nor did Beffe de Medison. Buffalo was the only one who paid any attention. "A great council has been held with the French and the Spanish. Your old fathers the French and the Spanish have gone beyond the great lakes toward the rising sun, from whence they will never return to visit their red children." Paying no attention at all, Partisan and Beffe were staring over at the keelboat; or at the faces or weapons of the white escort; or at the weapons and clothing of the two captains. Each captain wore a long sword and these seemed to fascinate Partisan. "The red children must now surrender French and Spanish flags and medals and receive American flags and medals. The great American chief now controls all the rivers, on which you must allow only American vessels to pass. You must never——" He broke off. He had been looking into Buffalo's eyes and had decided that the chief didn't understand a word of it. While wondering whether to go on he saw Partisan reach under his robe, though whether to feel for his weapon or to scratch himself he was unable to tell. Disgusted and despairing, he said to Clark, "This is no damn good. Shall we show them the airgun?"

"They'd like that a lot better," Clark said.

"Tell them," Lewis now said to Drewyer, "that we'll show them some big medicine, then maybe we'll take them to the boat."

The red men were quick to understand that. His eyes glowing with black wonderful fires, Partisan turned toward the river and made signs that he was eager to go. Right on his heels was Beffe.

"Not yet, tell him!" Lewis signaled to the pirogue for the airgun, and Clark had a piece of driftwood set on its end at a distance of a hundred feet. Lewis aimed the airgun at it and turned to look at the Indian faces. He hoped to startle the whole multitude with the sudden and amazing sound of it, and was as delighted as a child when at the first *pop!* Partisan's eyelids shot up and the feathers on his headpiece stood taller. A few of the Indians in the throng roundabout began to run away. With Drewyer feeding bullets in, Lewis kept up a rapid fire, hitting the chunk of driftwood every time. Then Drewyer brought the target over and the chiefs examined it, and two other red men who seemed not to be chiefs but had some rank. Clark thought of them as Considerable Men. Buffalo made no sound but the other four grunted and rumbled with astonishment as their hands felt over the wood, trying to determine how deep the bullets had gone.

Standing back with Clark and watching them, Lewis said in a low voice, "Have we impressed them?"

"Not much," Clark said. "The British have shown them too much."

"And told them too many lies. Shall we take them to the big boat?"

"I expect we better."

And so the captains took the three chiefs and the senior Considerable Man to the keelboat; and the first thing they did there was to give the Considerable Man a certificate. He seemed to look at it with contempt. The captains then showed off their swivel guns. Though all four Indians stared at the guns and felt over them and seemed to be interested, they kept looking round them, their gaze pausing now and then to rest on the soldiers standing at arms; or on the captains as though for a fresh appraisal; or at the huge black man over in the second pirogue. At this time it never occurred to either captain that they thought York was a painted white man, and obviously ready for war.

"Shall we give them a drink of whisky?" Lewis asked Clark.

"It's hard to tell if they'll be harder to put off the boat with a drink or without it. But they expected one, so I guess we better give it." Clark didn't like at all the way the red men were behaving. He had no doubt that trouble was coming.

Lewis had a sergeant pour an ounce of whisky into each of four tin cups and present them to the four Indians. All four of them drank the whisky off at a gulp. They then tongued around inside the cups, sucked at the rim, turned the cups bottomside up to see if another drop would run down, looked appealingly at the captains for more whisky, and again sucked at the cups. Perceiving that their mood would get ugly if they were not given more whisky, Lewis said to Drewyer, "Tell them we have a long way to go yet today and must be off."

They understood that! All of them stiffened and stopped licking their cups. Then Partisan put on his act. Suddenly he pretended to be staggering-drunk; he rolled his eyes and licked with his tongue over his lips back and forth. He shuffled over to Clark, and even while Clark was moving back and away from him the big brute pitched forward and pretended to fall against him, at the same instant digging Clark with a vicious clawing up his ribs. The captain's face became as red as his hair. Partisan was moving fast now.

Again he pretended to stagger, and went reeling toward Clark, and when the captain swiftly stepped aside, the big Indian went sprawling.

"Let's get them off here!" Clark cried to Lewis, his voice hard and cold.

To Drewyer, Lewis said, "Tell them they're to go home now! Make them understand it and be quick!"

The score of soldiers in the keelboat and the fifteen in the pirogues had all turned tense and wide-eyed as they watched a big red Indian deliberately show his contempt for the white men. They had fingers on trigger-guards and eyes on their captains.

All four Indians pretended now not to understand Drewyer. They hung back. They pouted and sulked. They were so completely child-like in their behavior that again it cost Lewis an effort to hide a grin. He had never been able to take this kind of situation very seriously, though he needed only to look at his friend's red face and the hundreds of armed warriors on the bank and the tenseness in his own men around him to know that it *was* serious.

With an imperious gesture at the Indians he cried, "To the pirogue! Come! Off you go!"

Black Buffalo, whom Loisel had called a decent man at heart, came forward and descended to the pirogue. After looking back and forth between him and Partisan, Beffe and Considerable Man followed him. Partisan all the while continued to act drunk, and was so comical, staggering and reeling, while his black eyes studied the ship, the lockers and the cabin, that Lewis grinned in spite of himself. He had never been able to take danger very seriously. Clark was in a different mood. Still smarting under this big brute's insolence, he went over to him and, taking him by an arm, roughly propelled him toward the pirogue. Buffalo was calling to him. Partisan went to the pirogue and, still keeping up his act, almost fell headlong into it; and then sat, sullen and hostile, his eyes glowering up at Clark.

For a moment the two captains spoke together. Clark said he would take an interpreter and a picked bodyguard and go to the shore with the Indians, and possibly there he could get some sense in their heads. Lewis said, "So far, as I see it, they're more determined than ever to stop us."

Clark said, "I'm afraid that's true."

"If they give you any trouble there, we'll all be ready to fire. Try to get out of the way. We'll kill all the chiefs the first round."

"If I lift my left hand once, it means get ready to fire. If twice, it means to shoot." Clark called to John Colter, the Fields brothers and Joseph Whitehouse to come with him as bodyguard. He knew and the men knew that they were expendables, for if there was trouble they would be the first to fall. The scowling Reuben muttered to his brother, "If they start anything, the big red bastard is mine. You take someone else."

The pirogue moved away, and after a few yards Clark glanced back and received a reassuring sign from Lewis. On the bank the red chiefs were waiting for the white men. It was Partisan, whom Loisel called a monster of iniquity, who had Clark worried. He knew Indians well. He read their eyes and their emotions as he read those of children. He stood in the forefront of the boat as it approached the bank and he was the first to step out, with Drewyer next behind him, and then his guard. He was not at all surprised the moment the pirogue touched land to see three powerful young bucks seize its cable and an Indian policeman its mast. Through his mind flashed the thought that he had blundered, that they intended to take him and his men as hostages. He had learned from Loisel that a Sioux policeman would never let go of what he had been told to seize, except on orders from his chief, even if you ran a sword through him. "That will be one sign you're in trouble," Loisel had said, "if a policeman puts his arms around or sits on something that belongs to you." The policeman was hugging the mast, and the three bucks were sitting on the cable.

Clark glanced over at the keelboat and the other pirogue and saw that Lewis and all his men were ready. He turned to his bodyguard to say in a low voice, "Be on the alert." As though they were not! Buffalo came out of the boat. Partisan, Beffe and Considerable Man sat in it, sullen, scowling, their eyes on Clark. "Come!" Clark said, and waved them out. Beffe rose and came, then the Man, and then Partisan, again staggering, the preposterous child, as though drunk. The next moment Clark was astounded when Black Buffalo himself grasped the cable and sat on it—this, the one chief they had counted on for friendliness! Buffalo had no more than eased his fat body down when Partisan, waving his big copper-colored hands and shouting in a loud arrogant tone, staggered up to Clark and breathed deliberately into his face, while continuing to shout at him. His manner was so menacing, the whole situation in just a few moments had become so critical, with Buffalo and three braves sitting on the cable, with a policeman hugging the mast and sneering, with Partisan all but thrusting the captain back and with warriors roundabout putting arrows to their bowstrings, that Clark knew that he must act decisively and at once. He spoke, his voice sharp and clear but his words in a headlong rush, "Drewyer, what is he saying? Privates Fields Colter Whitehouse step back four paces be ready make no move without orders if I give orders drop the chiefs first!" The same instant he raised his left hand once. The next moment, with Partisan still breathing in his face, and Drewyer saying that Partisan was saying that the white men had insulted them with cheap presents and must give much more and would not be allowed to go up the river even if they gave everything they had, Clark stepped swiftly back and in that instant drew his sword, its blade flashing in the sunlight. Also in that moment there was dramatic movement on the keelboat and the other pirogue as more than thirty men raised rifles and took steady aim.

Clark was then speaking, and if the red men didn't understand his words they at least understood his tone, for he was very angry. His voice trembled and his eyes flashed. He was saying to them— he was almost shouting to them: "You Teton Sioux had better understand now, right now, that we're not squaws but warriors and we're ready to fight! We will die but we will take none of your insolence! We may not be the kind of men who've been coming up this river—the kind you've bullied and degraded and robbed! We're not the French, not the Spanish, not the British! We're Americans and by God this is our land, our country, our nation! We'll share it with you in peace and friendship but don't try to bully us or we'll wipe you off the earth!"

He would not have spoken so strongly if he had not been so deeply angered and outraged.

He spoke, there was a moment of tense silence, and then an astonishing thing happened. Drewyer and Black Buffalo were both talking. Drewyer said that Buffalo was saying that the Sioux had many warriors—as many as the lights in the sky or the leaves on the trees. Then Partisan was gesturing wildly and shouting; and Drewyer said he was saying that if the white men went up the river they would be followed and killed, every one of them. Then other chiefs and two Considerable Men were shouting, and Partisan was again breathing insults and threats at Clark and moving toward him, so that Clark had to point his sword at him to hold the man back. Believing that he would have to run the sword through him, he again made the signal to Lewis, though he well knew that every man on the boats was tense and ready. "Back!" he shouted. "Back or I'll run you through!" And to Drewyer: "Tell the fools we offer friendship but if they insult and bully us our country will wipe the Sioux nation off the earth! Make them understand it!"

Partisan continued to advance, slowly, his black eyes looking with contempt at the sword.

"Back!" Clark said. But he knew that this man would not stop. He knew that this was a brave Indian. And he had just about decided that he would have to run his sword through him and give the order to his men and kill as many Indians as he could before he died, when there was a guttural shout from Buffalo. The fat chief rose swiftly to his feet. He shouted again, and the awful tension was snapped.

Buffalo was now waving with both arms, waving his hundreds of warriors, some with guns and some with strung bows, back from the scene. He was shouting to Partisan. But he had not yet spoken to the policeman who held the mast. All this had happened in only a few moments and Clark was a little bewildered, not knowing what turn the events were to take. One thing was clear: Buffalo had decided that Partisan had gone far enough. But what did they intend now?

Partisan was shouting. He seemed to be very angry. Buffalo was shouting. Beffe and the Considerable Men were shouting. Clark sensed that they were furious at Buffalo, and Buffalo at them. Buffalo told the three warriors sitting on the cable to get off and the policeman to step back from the mast. This seemed to anger the warriors with strung bows and about a hundred of them moved in. Thinking they intended to take him captive, and now so surrounded by them that he could not have got to the boat if he had tried, Clark shouted to his bodyguard to enter the pirogue and go to the keelboat. "Tell Captain Lewis to send men to rescue me!"

The men moved quickly, and at once the pirogue was off and away. The Indians were flabbergasted and silent, their black eyes fixed on Clark. He had sheathed his sword. He stood with arms folded, his eyes looking into Buffalo's or Partisan's or Beffe's eyes when they met his gaze. Did they think he had sacrificed himself to save four men? That would not make sense to them. Indeed, they soon knew what the move meant, because on the keelboat Captain Lewis was shouting, and a number of men, heavily armed, stood at the edge waiting for the pirogue. The Indians now watched what was going on out in the river, looking only now and then at Clark; and when they saw the pirogue aswarm with armed men head for them and the bank, a few of the warriors turned and ran, and then more and still more. But not the chiefs nor most of the warriors.

Lewis had given one simple command: "Go and bring Captain Clark back and don't return without him."

As the pirogue approached the bank, with a dozen men standing, rifles across their left arms, daggers and pistols at their waists, all the Indians moved back except the chiefs and the Considerable Men. Looking at them, Clark again reflected that these Sioux were indeed braver than most of the Indians he had known. Warriors had moved back but most of them still had arrows to their bows. Buffalo, Partisan and Beffe never once took their eyes off the pirogue after it left the keelboat; and though they did not falter and back up, as their men had, there was a change in them. At first, Clark thought, it was astonishment. Then it was a kind of relaxing of face and body, a quieting of emotions, and possibly a kindling of respect. He saw the two Considerable Men slip hands under their leather jackets. He saw the policeman look at the mast and then back farther away from it. And then he heard Drewyer saying something. Drewyer was saying that Black Buffalo, head chief of the powerful Teton Sioux nation, was mumbling apologies. He wanted the white chief to know that his women and children were naked and hungry, and needed many of the things on the big boat. Astonished, Clark looked at Buffalo's face and, concluding at last that the man had had a change of heart, he advanced to him and offered his hand. With an elaborate gesture of contempt Black Buffalo spurned it. Flushing again with anger, Clark turned and offered his handclasp to Partisan. He was not surprised when that sullen monster also spurned it. His flush deepening, Clark then called to Drewyer to come and walked swiftly to the pirogue. He entered, with Drewyer on his heels, and at once the boat moved away.

Then Clark was again astonished. Beffe de Medison set up a dreadful lamentation, as though he had suddenly lost all his friends and kinsfolk. At the same moment Black Buffalo and the two Considerable Men plunged into the river and at first waded and then swam to the pirogue, all the time setting up a great clamor. With a terrible cry Beffe followed them.

Clark told the men to give them a hand and they were hauled wet and floundering into the boat. Sullen, hostile and looking as murderous as an Indian could, Partisan stood in scornful majesty on the bank. Beffe kept up his wailing. Clark, feeling weak and a little shaken now that the ordeal was over, was saying to himself, "We give these damned rascals whisky, medals and commissions, and now that monster will go from village to village to bring all the warriors against us!"

Lewis was at the keelboat edge to receive him, anxious eyes on his face. Telling a sergeant to watch the Indians, Lewis took Clark's arm and led him to the privacy of the cabin. In the cabin Lewis said, "Captain Clark, was that a close shave or did my eyes deceive me?"

"It was probably the closest shave I ever had."

"I think we should go on up the river."

"Give the order."

Anchors were raised and the boats moved upstream. Returning to the cabin, Lewis again studied his friend's rather pale face and said, "How do you size it up now?"

Clark had poured himself a small drink of brandy. He sipped it and looked at Lewis and said that in his opinion the trouble had just begun. Having failed to frighten and bluff the white men, they would try another stratagem.

"But why did Black Buffalo jump in and follow you? That has a special meaning."

"Yes, very special. It could be he did it to stop Partisan from bringing all his hotbloods against us. Or the reason could be the very opposite. It might be some kind of ambush."

"Would Partisan sacrifice Buffalo and the others?"

"I've been wondering. I think he might."

5

With the four Indians aboard the boats went up the river about a mile and anchored off a small island, which Clark promptly named Bad Humored Island. He had been so deliberately humiliated that he was in an ugly temper. Cooks, with an armed guard to stand over them, went to the island to prepare supper; and after supper had been eaten and night had come, the two pirogues were lashed to the keelboat. Except when sharing the supper the four red men had kept moving about, staring at the lockers and lamenting over and over, Drewyer said, that their children and women were hungry and naked. What childlike dissemblers they were! The captains knew well that the lamentations hid the real purpose. Had they come to the boats to try to determine how much booty there was? Or did they have a plan with Partisan for a massed attack between midnight and morning? If this was it, they all must have realized that the four on the keelboat would be among the first killed. Or had they been moved by no more than a sudden and childlike impulse, with the hope of begging or stealing a few things?

They had earlier given Buffalo a red coat and a cocked hat with a feather, and he had been strutting around the deck to show himself off; now looking down over his coat to admire it; now taking off the cocked hat to see what a miracle it was; and a moment later turning his sly black gaze to the parts of the boat where supplies were hidden. What was the rascal thinking? He knew—for he was no fool—that if his people attacked a lot of them would be dead Indians before the last white man fell. Indeed, as though with precisely this thought in mind, he tried to learn, after supper, how many guns there were, how much ammunition and whisky, how many pounds of beads.

Clark said, "I expect the fool realizes that if they attack he'll be the first to fall."

"I've observed," Lewis said, "that a strange optimism fogs the minds of men when consumed by greed. It's when they hope to plunder their neighbor that they think God is most with them."

Clark looked startled. He had never known what to make of Lewis's sly philosophical musings.

The captains were sitting in the cabin, an hour after dark. Lewis said: "Could it be that Buffalo decided to come on the boat to keep Partisan from attacking?"

Clark considered the matter a few moments. "I'd wondered about that. I don't think that would keep Partisan from attacking."

"Why did Beffe de Medison come?"

"I think just on impulse. If any plans were made they were between Partisan and Buffalo."

Lewis was looking a little curiously at his friend, as a man will who thinks that both he and the friend may soon be dead, and wonders what his friend is thinking. "If they attack they'll come to the island from all directions."

"I expect so."

"The four could jump off when they knew the attack was about to come."

"I had thought of that."

"Should we put them in irons?"

"Well, that would be a matter of pride with them. I'm afraid——"

Lewis said quickly, "A guard would be better. We'll want dependable men for that." Lewis filled his pipe. Then he said, "They refused to shake your hand, that's what looks bad. Usually, even if they plan to scalp you the next day, they'll shake your hand."

"Yes, that's what looks bad. Hatred of white men runs deep in them."

"If Buffalo, the best Indian of them all, wouldn't shake your hand, I expect that's just about a declaration of war. But why in the world did he come on the boat?"

"It could have been just a sudden impulse."

"Perhaps greed shoved him in. But not Partisan. I was watching him through the glasses. I don't think he moved an eyelash."

"He's a tough Indian," Clark said. "And a brave one. I think he would have kept coming, and he must have known I would run him through."

"I was watching that. I figured he still thought he might bluff you." Lewis grinned at his friend and said, "After all, he didn't know what was in your mind as well as you did."

The captains decided that neither one of them would get any sleep this night. They would both stand watch. They would have to post guards all the way around the small island. Sergeants Pryor and Ordway would take turn with one or two soldiers guarding the four Indians with orders to keep them on the boat even if they had to overpower them. They assigned Ordway to the first watch, and he soon found that he had his hands full. Buffalo, Beffe and the two Men were not sleepy at all! They kept prowling back and forth on the boat, their black eyes staring a thousand times at the same things—the cabin, the lockers, the swivel guns, the armed men, the pirogues; and the armed men, at least such as the Fields brothers, Colter, Shannon, Willard, Whitehouse, Collins, Gass, Windsor, looked at them hard, if by chance they met their eyes, their own eyes saying, "Just start something, you red bastards, and we'll finish it!" Because all the men knew that the party had almost met its end when Clark drew his sword over on the bank. They knew that their captains for all their gallantry were two deeply worried men. They knew that their troubles with the Sioux had just begun.

"There won't be any sleep for anyone tonight," Reuben Fields said.

His brother said, "York. I never knowed a servant has some things better than his master. And by God, can that nigger snore!"

"You're jealous," Reuben said. "Just 'cause the squaws like him better."

George Shannon, the better-educated, quieter, more philosophical one, was saying to Joe Whitehouse, "All night we walk round and round this island; and over there a thousand black eyes will be watching us."

"That's only five hundred redskins," Joe said. "You mean four thousand. They have at least a thousand warriors."

"It makes little difference," George said, "whether it's five hundred or ten thousand. After we kill so many that's the end of us."

Bob Frazier, taking a stretch of island watch with Silas Goodrich, blew kisses to all the invisible Indian maidens and sang his foolish little ditties, his low baritone drawing out the last syllable of each

verse in a mournful breath: "Let's me and you, my adorable Sioux,
play Ma and Pa, my bowlegged squaw! You know, a lot of white
men marry squaws."

"Don't ask me to understand it," Silas said.

"When you enlisted did the captains tell you that a thousand redskins would be after your scalp?"

"They told me what they told all of us, that there'd be a lot of
danger."

"You know where we're heading for?"

"About as much as you know. For the western ocean, I reckon."

"You know how far that is?"

"No man does."

"You know how many Indian tribes we'll meet on the way?"

"Oh, about a thousand—if we ever get past this one."

Again Frazier blew kisses into the dark and the night. "You
red-faced gazer at Robert Frazier! Let's me and you play peeka-
boo. . . ."

On the keelboat Clark stood by a swivel gun, looking over at the
black shoreline. Stretched out behind him on the deck were the four
Indians, on blankets which the captains had given them. Clark had
passed them a few minutes ago and had paused to listen for snores
but there had been no snores. He had supposed that they were all
awake, because most Indian bucks snored like pigs when they slept.
Not far from them Drewyer lay on the hard deck asleep. Deer
poacher, barge peddler, riverman, hunter, trapper, scout, he had
lived all his adult life with danger and it took more than threat of
Indian attack to disturb his sleep. In one of the pirogues Clark could
see his black servant, sitting on baggage, his huge hands clasped
around his knees. He wondered how York would behave under fire.

He had suggested to Lewis that he try to sleep awhile but he
knew that Lewis was standing at the other swivel. About two hours
past midnight Lewis came over and the two captains stood together,
listening to the snoring of Drewyer and the Indians, and the lapping
of river water against creaking boats; and smelling on a breeze the
frostiness of autumn and the wildlife of the river bottoms. After a
while Lewis yawned and spoke. He proposed that the boats should
leave just before daylight, to see what the four Indians would do.

"I had the same thought," Clark said.

"It would call their bluff or force a showdown."

"Did you sleep any?" Clark asked, looking at Lewis.

"No. I don't expect we'll sleep tonight."

"Or tomorrow night either," Lewis said, and returned to his gun.

A good hour before daylight the four Indians were up and prowling around. Clark aroused Drewyer and told him to watch them. He could see no sign of daylight yet, not a streak or a lightness anywhere. He decided to pace his watch, back and forth from the swivel almost to Lewis's position at the other end. Only by keeping an eye on them could he be sure of what the Indians were doing. They weren't doing anything at all, except prowling, their restless black eyes peering at what in broad daylight they had looked at a thousand times. Aware that Clark was watching him, Black Buffalo shuffled over in his moccasins, his large fat shoulders drooping, his voice wheedling, his eyes reminding Clark of a raccoon's. Buffalo wanted whisky. He tipped back his head and swallowed and gurgled, as though drinking, and the other three redskins looked back and forth between him and Clark. Clark kept walking and seemed to pay no attention. The four Indians were following him and presently all of them were begging.

Then there was a break in the sky, the first sign of daylight of a Wednesday morning; and the dog-tired captains gave orders to unlash the pirogues and move all boats upriver. Lewis had hoped to go four or five miles before breakfast but the boats had hardly cleared the island when hundreds of squaws and children on the west bank were setting up a din worse than that of ten thousand waterfowl. Buffalo was begging the captains in turn, and seemed actually to have tears in his eyes. Drewyer said he wanted the boats to put in close to the bank so the women and children could see what big medicine they were. He said the chief wanted the white men to camp on the west bank and remain near the villages at least one night so that he could show them how friendly and hospitable they were.

The captains exchanged glances. "I expect," Lewis said, "we could put in a little closer." And when Clark agreed, Lewis gave orders to the steersmen to go within about a hundred feet of the bank and stop. Among the women and children were two or three hundred men, also making shrill cries. The din was so dreadful that Bob Frazier shoved fingers into his ears and said the red people must have eardrums like iron bathtubs. The women and children were positively shrieking now and beckoning to the white men to come over; and York stood on top of a pile of baggage to make himself seem taller than he was and rolled his eyes and grinned like a man about to swoon with ecstasy. It became clear to the white men at last that he was the one most of the women, and possibly all the younger ones, were beckoning to. "I can't imagine," Frazier said glumly, "what idiot got the notion that a white skin is best." And George Shannon said scornfully, "They think he's painted. For them he's the only real fighter among us."

Buffalo brought Drewyer to the captains and began to talk in a loud shrill voice. His women and his children, he said, were poor and ragged and hungry, and were begging the white chiefs to see the boats and the things in them. They would look only once and then go away. Clark had turned to the riverbank and was staring at the Indians there. He thought them scrawny and ill-shaped, with bugged-out eyes and bowed legs. Lewis came over to him and, acting on one of his impulses, said he guessed he would snatch a bite of breakfast and with a picked guard go ashore. Maybe if he got these four Indians off the boat things would quiet down.

Clark did not like the proposal but he said nothing. He had never known what to say that might restrain his friend in his more reckless impulses. Lewis had said he wanted to see how Partisan was feeling and what he was doing. Clark had no doubt what the rascal was doing: he was hiding back somewhere and listening and watching and searching his fertile brain for the master stratagem.

"How long will you be there?"

"Oh, not long."

On second thought, Lewis decided that he would have to feed the four morose Indians or they would not go with him; and so he had the cooks bring them cold bread and meat. He chose five men and told them to get some breakfast and make themselves ready to go with him; and then, impatient, his ears splitting, his nerves raw, he paced back and forth while the four red men dawdled at their breakfast. "Come!" Lewis would cry, beckoning to Buffalo; and at last they came.

The moment Lewis stepped ashore, his rifle across his left arm, his long sword dangling, the shrieking women and children closed round him, clawing at him, pushing at him, some of them wanting him to take them to the boats, some of them wanting him to bring York over. For York still stood there, tall and black and grinning; and the younger squaws still pointed to him and shrieked with infernal joy.

Followed by his guard, Lewis elbowed his way through the mob, his nostrils almost paralyzed by their wild Indian odors, his brain reeling from the racket in his ears. He went away from the river and the throng followed him; and his friend Clark, watching from the keelboat, soon became anxious. Because within only a few minutes the tall ungainly form had vanished. He was back in the river thickets, Clark supposed, because there was bedlam there, and the smoke from morning fires. Would they take him and his men as hostages to one of their villages and hold him for ransom? If they tried to take him, would Lewis and his men shoot it out?

Sergeant Ordway came up, his face and eyes bleak with fatigue. He was a well-built good-natured intelligent man but for Clark's taste he had too much interest in Indian women. His voice grave, Ordway said, "Captain, what do you think they'll do?"

"I wish I knew," Clark said, staring through glasses. He could see Indians everywhere but no sign of the mob that had surrounded and escorted Lewis. Was this throng moving through the timber to Teton River and the Indian villages? For an hour Clark looked through the glasses and waited, his alarm and his vexation rising.

At last he turned to Ordway. "Sergeant, you better go find Captain Lewis and see if he's all right. Report back at once."

"Yes, Captain."

After Ordway had been put ashore, Bob Frazier said in a low voice to George Shannon, sitting with him in one of the pirogues, "How does it look to you? Looks to me like we're going to let them pick us off one by one."

"It doesn't look good to me," George said. "If Captain Lewis and his men are prisoners, then Sergeant Ordway will be."

"Then you'll be sent to see how they are and I'll be sent to see how you are."

"I've got a lot of confidence in Captain Clark," George said.

"You mean," said Frazier, sneering, "that when he sends you to look for me you'll have a bodyguard."

George was silent. He needed a few moments to put down his sudden uprush of anger. "I mean that Captain Clark knows Indians."

Like Frazier, like all the men, he was tired and when tired he was quick to anger. He had stood two watches and had been allowed to sleep one but he had not slept. He could tell that Frazier had not slept. He could tell that the Fields brothers and the other three who had gone with Lewis had not slept, and he suspected that this was one of Clark's worries now, because men half-dead with fatigue had nervous fingers on trigger-guards.

After half an hour Ordway came back and his first words on approaching Clark were about the Sioux squaws. He said they were not bad-looking at all.

"Never mind the squaws, Sergeant!" Clark said sharply. "Did you find Captain Lewis?"

"Yes, sir. He says they're treating him real friendly. He said to tell you they plan to give us a big dance tonight and they want us all to stay a few days."

"I don't doubt that," Clark muttered. "Is Captain Lewis coming soon?"

"Yes, sir."

Lewis came a few minutes later and reported, with a grimace, that even Partisan was friendly. This was the second act, Lewis said: friendliness. What would the third act be? He had learned that the Sioux had a few Maha prisoners, one of whom had got close enough to Drewyer to whisper something that Drewyer had not understood.

"Where was that?"

"In the first village."

"It might be worth a lot to us if we knew what he said."

Clark stood in the prow, looking over at the Indians. He was tired, so tired that he wanted to go to sleep on his feet, but he said he guessed he would go over to see if he could learn anything. He was dying to know what the Maha had said. He wouldn't be long.

Clark had barely set foot on shore when he heard a blood-chilling scream. It was a woman's cry and it was so dreadful that he felt the flesh move up and down his back. Hastening forward, he saw one of the Sioux policemen, his badge of office two ravenskins attached to his girdle behind in such a way as to make the tails stick out, and two ravenskins on his head with the beaks thrust forward—he saw the man just as he was stripping the leather skirt off a young woman and making ready to flog her. Another young woman cowered near by, her terrified eyes on the policeman. Indians roundabout were fleeing in all directions. When giving evidence of the ferocity of the Sioux, Loisel had told the captains about their policemen and the brutality with which they enforced the tribal laws.

This man now flogged the girl with a heavy green hawthorn and she screamed with such violence that Clark expected her to hemorrhage from the mouth. The blows were swift and strong, falling across her naked lower back and rump and thighs, raising welts and splashing blood over her; and when he was done with her he turned away from the broken crawling thing to seize the other one, moaning and quivering. He stripped her and hurled her down and laid the club on her. It was all Clark could do to keep from interfering, but this, he kept telling himself, was none of the white man's business. Never had he seen anyone so cruelly beaten. When the second whipping was over with the quivering bloody wretches began to crawl away, their voices whimpering like those of children.

Clark had gone only a little way farther when suddenly a group of men surrounded him and before he knew what was happening, or could draw his sword, they had him up off the earth and sprawling in a huge painted buffalo robe; and with a half-dozen men seizing the robe he was borne away to a large council chamber in the nearest village. There he was put down. With smiles and signs the red men seemed to be telling him that he was a distinguished guest whom they were delighted to honor. He didn't believe a word of it.

Looking round him, he saw several prisoners and supposed they were Mahas. Hoping to discover what the Sioux chiefs had in mind, Clark began a loud speech to those present, telling them that they would have to return these prisoners to their homes. Had they no shame and no mercy? They had to be friends to the Mahas if they wished to please their Father in Washington. He spoke in strong imperious tones, gesturing at them, making his tired eyes flash, his lips curl to show his teeth; and the Indians who heard him gave every possible sign that they understood him and agreed with every word. The whole thing became so silly that Clark broke off and was silent.

How could he get close enough to the Mahas to learn what they wanted to tell him?

There now appeared ten gorgeously adorned young bucks who swept him up into a decorated robe and to a chorus of shrill cries set him down at the side of Black Buffalo, who looked over at him slyly and seemed to be full of laughter. They were in the center of a large chamber. Looking curiously round him, Clark saw that he was under a ceiling of dressed skins sewn together and that about seventy warriors sat in a circle. In front of him and Buffalo a pipe of peace was set on sticks, which stood in a small area of swansdown. Immediately in front of the grand chief was a flag of Spain, and the American flag which the captains had given him. Not far away was a huge roaring fire. The odors of roasting flesh filled the room.

Clark was still gazing round him and wondering what all this portended when suddenly he was astonished to see the same six young bucks enter with a robe on which was sprawled Meriwether Lewis. They set him down on the other side of Buffalo. Lewis looked across Buffalo's broad fat chest and grinned at Clark, but Clark was not sure that this was a matter to grin at. The scoundrels were in their second act, all right, and they were playing it beautifully.

Several hundred pounds of buffalo flesh were now piled in a gory heap on a white robe before the captains. Then Black Buffalo heaved himself up, stretched each leg a time or two to get the kinks out of it, and burst into a loud amiable speech, concluding with elaborate ceremonial gestures and taking up the pipe of peace. He pointed it to the heavens and then to the four quarters of the earth and the earth, and after kindling it and taking a few whiffs which sucked his fat cheeks in against his teeth he presented the stem to the captains. His next gesture of friendliness was to offer to them and their flag certain parts of a cooked dog. The captains and chiefs then smoked together, after which Buffalo staggered up to make another solemn little speech. Then they all ate of dog flesh and pemmican and a kind of potato. After they had eaten they again smoked. Now and then the captains glanced across at one another, and though Clark's face was grave—for he knew all this was intended only to beguile and deceive them—the irrepressible Lewis could not restrain a grin.

Now in sign language the captains were told that a great dance would soon be held in their honor and that all their men were to come watch the dance.

Lewis said, "How wonderful if they could get us all off the boats!"

"And off into the deep brush with their squaws," Clark said.

"And every squaw with a sharp knife under her girdle."

A few moments later a dozen musicians, over at one side of the enormous skin-tent, were making a fearful racket on taut skins, beating the skins with heavy cudgels and at the same time striking off jingling sounds from dried deer and elk hooves. Most of the musicians were chanting while pounding on the hides.

When Lewis was invited over he had chosen a half-dozen men to follow him under the command of Ordway. The sergeant and his men, all heavily armed, now stood over at one side of the tent.

Lewis said to Clark, "Shall we let some of our men come over?"

"If you wish to, Captain, but we need strong guards on the boats."

"You want your black servant?"

A little sharply Clark said, "Of course not."

It was common knowledge among the men, and with some of them a matter for lewd jest, that it was the gigantic Negro upon whom the squaws fixed their enraptured eyes and their longing. The furor over him among the Yankton Sioux had so distressed Clark that he had thought of sending his servant back down the river.

Lewis called Ordway over and told him to leave the most dependable men on guard and to bring the others to watch the dance.

About sixty-five Indian women entered the tent an hour later, all colorfully adorned, and each bearing a fresh scalp on a tall stick. These, the captains knew, were Maha scalps. While the musicians beat out an ear-splitting din the women danced round and round the fire, waving the scalps, shaking them, rolling their black shining eyes up at them; shrieking and screaming; waving the scalps at the captains and mocking them, as they steadily became wilder in their movements as the music became wilder; and at last showing off their bodies with such wantonness and such rolling of their black liquid eyes that Lewis fixed his gaze on the fire. Clark continued to look at them but told himself that they were simply terrible.

"Strange," Lewis muttered, "that women will embrace you in one moment and knife you in the next." He wished he could be away from here and on his own hard bed asleep but he expected no sleep this night. This was all very well, this pipe of peace, this feast in their honor, this dance to entertain them; but all this was only part of the red man's strategy. They thought to lull the white man's suspicions; to gorge him with weariness and food; and then to raise his scalp high with the Maha scalps! They were cunning children but they were not cunning enough.

During the long evening Clark managed to get close to the Maha prisoner who looked to him the most intelligent, and gave him a few awls for the Maha squaws taken captive. He hoped this would encourage the Mahas to convey to the captains, by some means, whatever it was they had to tell. Black Buffalo had already boasted to the captains that his people had recently destroyed a Maha village, killed seventy-five men and children, and taken captive forty-eight women and boys.

About midnight Lewis made his host understand that he and Clark were tired and would go to their boats now. Buffalo readily assented, and said that he and three other chiefs would spend the night with them! Lewis muttered to Clark, "God only knows what that dog meat and dancing are going to cost us!" For it was plain enough in his manner that Buffalo now assumed that he and the other chiefs would be royally fed and entertained. The white men had no women to offer—but they had whisky!

On their way to the boats, with their bodyguard right at their heels, Lewis said to Clark, "Captain, I don't like the looks of this, not at all. All day and all evening Partisan never said a word but he never takes his eyes off us."

"It looks very bad," Clark said. "They expect to wear us down and then strike."

6

On the keelboat Lewis gave a half-cup of whisky to each chief, and
to each a piece of bread and a thick slice of cured pork. The four
chiefs gulped the whisky down and then ate, the eyes of all of them
fixed on the lockers. Did they imagine, Lewis wondered, that all
those lockers were filled with ardent spirits? Well, possibly yes, as a
child might.

The captains decided to give them only the one drink, for if they
gave them more they might be troublesome. It didn't take much to
make an Indian drunk. Clark withdrew to the cabin to write in his
Journal, and Lewis stood watch, taking up a position by the larger
swivel gun. The four chiefs sat on their blankets in mid-decks, still
looking round them, still looking. Lewis was recalling the day's
events and trying to find the meanings in them. He had seen about
twenty-five squaws and boys, all Maha captives, and he thought the
women looked as dejected and hopeless as a person could. He had
felt a pang deeper than pity when he looked into the eyes of the
smaller lads. What did they think would be done with them?

Then he was thinking of the Sioux squaws and their dancing, and
of the look on the faces of some of his men. He wished that he and
Clark could find some good way to discharge the passions of the privates—or of the sergeants for that matter: Ordway seemed as eager
to make a fool of himself as Goodrich or McNeal. These Missouri
Indians, he reflected, had been visited for years by British and Canadian trappers down from the north, and most of them now had
the white disease. That is what Loisel had said. Lewis had talked
this matter over with Clark, and the captains had agreed that dis-

ease might prove to be a deadlier enemy than Indians. For how could they proceed if half their men came down? It would be madness to head up a wild river through a vast unknown if half the men were doctoring the other half. Yet how could they make their men understand this? What discipline on earth could prevail over a young man's lust? Not that he wanted to be a preacher or a moralist: he was neither, he hoped: his task was to reach the ocean and return, and in that enterprise all enemies had to be recognized and faced. It was simply fantastic—from the white man's point of view anyway —with what indifference the red husband allowed his wife to offer herself to white men—indeed with what eagerness he encouraged her, hoping for a drink of whisky or a few blue beads. . . .

He was wondering what he could do to keep the men away from the squaws when he felt the presence of Clark at his side. "You'd better go sleep awhile," Clark said.

"Did you?"

"No. I've been writing. Have you seen anything unusual?"

"Not a thing. Are they asleep?"

"They seem to be."

"You better try to sleep awhile," Lewis said.

Clark returned to the cabin and Lewis to his thoughts. It was a habit with him when standing watch to look over recent events, commands and communications and search them for meanings he might have missed. He was aware that his methods were rather haphazard and his memory faulty. He liked to recall what Jefferson had told him, in person during those long nights of talk in the Monticello library, and by letter. Jefferson thought that if the United States could find a watercourse with a single portage, in a milder climate than the Canadian, most of the furs might then come down the Missouri instead of the Saskatchewan. The British in time could be driven out. The British——

Lord! he thought, for he had found himself staggering. He guessed he had dozed off and almost fallen. To bring himself wide awake he breathed fast and deep and then paced back and forth on the boat deck. He had passed the man a half-dozen times before he realized that Partisan was sitting up, looking at him. This so startled Lewis that abruptly he stopped and, after gazing at Partisan a few moments, went over and looked down at him. Black eyes looked up, steady and inscrutable. For perhaps ten seconds Lewis looked into those eyes and then turned away and resumed his pacing. He felt a little angered. He went to the other swivel gun to see if the guard there was awake.

It was Robert Frazier. "Is everything all right?"

"Yes, Captain, as far as I can tell."

"Partisan seems restless. Keep your eye on him."

"Yes, sir."

Well, Jefferson had written of "An intelligent officer, with ten or twelve chosen men, fit for the enterprise and willing to undertake it." He and Clark had picked up about forty men, a third of whom they intended to send back down the river, a third leave with the Mandans to grow corn, and a third take with them. He and Clark were now wondering if a dozen men would be enough. After all, the President had given them a pretty big job: they would explore the Missouri, he had said, and all its principal streams, clear to the ocean. That might take two or three years. They were to bring back precise information on the soil and face of the country, its vegetation, its animals, its minerals, its climate. They were to be kind to all the Indians, allay their jealousies and suspicions and convince them of the white man's honor and innocence. Just how were they to convince them of the white man's innocence and honor when more than half the Indians were literally rotting with the white man's disease! And how could they convince them of anything without a good interpreter? They had Drewyer, who was pretty good in sign language; and Peter Cruzatte, blind in one eye and half-blind in the other, who understood only the Maha tongue; and Francis Labiche, who could translate English into French. They had——

Damned if that Partisan monster wasn't still looking at him! What was a man to make of that? Annoyed, Lewis again walked over and looked down into those cold inscrutable black eyes. Why did the fool just sit there and stare at him all the time? Did he expect him to go to sleep and topple over? The other three were snoring. They were asleep all right but this monster of iniquity had been staring for about an hour now—never moving, not even his head, but just staring! He would tell Clark about it.

Back at the swivel gun he tried to pick up his thoughts. Of sergeants the captains had three. Nathaniel Pryor, the lanky loose-jointed man, seemed bold and able but Lewis actually knew little about him. John Ordway was one of the best-educated men in the Corps. Ordway had the strange habit of carrying his Journal under his buckskin shirt. Sergeant Floyd had died down the river and in his place the men had voted in Patrick Gass, a short thick hairy man of Scotch-Irish descent, gnarled and hardened by heavy labor as a farmer, river-boatman, carpenter, soldier. Paddy was older than most of the men; he was turning gray. He chewed tobacco all the time except when he was eating; swore like a pirate; laughed like thunder; gave advice whether you asked for it or listened to it; fell into Dublin or some other kind of brogue to delight the men; detested Negroes; and always spit on both palms before picking up an ax. . . .

Well, the monster had lain down at last. He had got his fill of looking.

Of twenty men in Captain Bissell's Company down the river at Kaskaskia who had volunteered for the journey, only Ordway and two others had been accepted. And Ordway, it turned out, was a fool about women. Lewis had heard him talk one evening about two girls back in New Hampshire whom he pined for. One of them had written him that she was offering herself as a sacrifice at the shrine of Hymen, and Ordway had said, "I'm a dog if I marry anything but a virgin. What man would?" And in his dry way George Shannon had said, "You mean what man is?" Lewis smiled, a gray smile that made his fatigue look deeper. He was remembering Clark's startled look when, on seeing a buck take a squaw into the bushes, Lewis had said, "I expect he's counting on a rapturous wedding of wills— a mutual exchange of good offices, so to speak." Clark had looked so flabbergasted that, recalling his expression, Lewis now laughed out loud. A moment later Partisan sat up. Ho-ho! Lewis thought. So you were just pretending!

When Clark came out to relieve him, Lewis said: "The monster of iniquity just sat and looked at me for an hour. What would that mean?"

Clark's pale eyes looked at Lewis several moments. "I've no idea," he said. "Maybe he was just wondering about you, as a child might —wondering if you mean it or if you're bluffing."

"He's counting on fatigue to get us all down."

"I expect so."

"You think we should go on up the river at daylight?"

"I doubt it. Indians are like animals, you have to let them get used to you. That takes a little time. If you confuse them they get angry. As soon as they decide we're not bluffing they'll make up their mind."

"You think the longer we stay the more they'll realize we're not afraid of them."

"The more chances we'll have to show them we're not afraid. You'd better try to sleep now and I'll take the watch."

On his way to the cabin Lewis stood for a moment and looked down at the sleeping Indians. The Sioux men shaved their heads but for a tuft on top, which they wore plaited down their shoulders. They were much attached to this braid of hair and adorned it with feathers and quills, but shaved it off to show deep bereavement. They covered their face and body with a mixture of grease and coal dust that gave them a horrid appearance and a foul odor; and they hung their handsome buffalo robes down over the rancid smear. The robes they also adorned with quills, so fixed that they made a clicking sound when the men walked. Under the robe they wore a kind of shirt of skin or cloth that covered the arms and most of the body; and around the waist an elkskin girdle an inch or so wide, to which at front and back was attached a leather strap that went between the thighs. Their leggings, decorated with tufts of hair taken from dead enemies, reached from their ankles almost to their hipbones. When in full dress, as these four sleepers were, the Sioux brave dragged behind him the hide of a skunk fastened to a moccasin. Another skin served as a tobacco pouch, and this he tucked inside his girdle or carried in his hand.

Though so tired he felt nausea Lewis found himself unable to sleep. Loss of sleep always made him ill; or was it that Indian pemmican, which had in it rancid meat and too much fat? Anyway, he was sick. He thought he ought to take a dose of calomel and a pinch of laudanum. Daylight would come soon. He decided to go out and stand with Clark.

"Loss of sleep is making me sick," Lewis said. "I think I'm going to vomit. How many days and nights of this you think we're going to have?"

"One or two more," Clark said.

"You think then they'll decide to attack or let us go?"

"So far I just haven't any idea. It will depend on whether Buffalo or Partisan gets his way."

Partisan was up before daylight and prowling around. When morning came Lewis wondered aloud if they should give each Indian a peck of corn. Clark said that would be all right but he doubted that gifts, no matter how generous, would make any difference in the Sioux plans. Lewis measured out a peck of corn for each of the chiefs and invited them to sit with him and Clark at breakfast. While Clark

ate he seemed to pay no attention to the four red men but Lewis
studied the faces of Partisan and Buffalo. Indians tickled his sense of
the incongruous. With the unself-consciousness of children they fixed
their black stare on one captain and then the other; and when Lewis
met the gaze of one he went right on staring. It was not curiosity.
They looked at him or Clark exactly as they might have looked at a
herd of buffalo or elk. He felt a little queer, having four red men
looking at him that way, but he restrained his mirth and said, "Listen." The Indians along the riverbank were making an awful racket.

"I'll not be surprised," Clark said, "if this is our critical day."

Lewis stood up and a wave of dizziness engulfed him. He had had
no more than two hours of sleep the past two nights and he was not
in a good mood. "I'm going over to see if I can learn anything," he
said to Clark. He then summoned Drewyer. "Tell them to come with
me." As soon as they understood Drewyer the Indians backed off, behaving for all the world just like sullen children. Sharply Lewis said,
"Tell them I won't be put off! Tell them they must go off now!" Buffalo then came forward and the other three followed him, each
clutching his blanket and peck of corn.

The moment Lewis stepped ashore a buck hastened forward with
two young squaws, and while the man fawned and with signs indicated the uses to which the women could be put, the girls wantonly
exposed themselves. "Go on away!" Lewis barked at them. He hated
them this morning. He was so tired and sick that he wished he could
have the showdown now and get it over with.

Looking round him, he wondered if the whole Sioux nation had
come to the river. There were twice as many Indians as there had
been yesterday and practically all the men seemed to be armed. He
walked up the bank, pushing his way through the throng of copper
skins, his eyes looking for the Mahas. Still fighting against an urge
to vomit, he felt so mean that he wished he had one of the chief
Federalists here—Aaron Burr would do—so that he could give him a
hell of a kick in his hindend and say, "You stupid gorilla, while we
risk our lives to build a nation you can think of nothing better than
an eagle of salt on a salt mountain!" He wished he had William Pitt
here. He had heard that when Pitt learned that Jefferson had bought
Louisiana from Napoleon he fell over on his face as stiff and red as
a cooked lobster.

Still walking up the river with a huge herd of Indians following
him, Lewis stripped bark off willows and chewed it. He soon sensed

that the Indians liked him for that. They were bark-eaters too. Some of them now peeled bark off and chewed with him, their eyes filled with nothing but the solemn wonder of the child.

It was past noon when with the four chiefs and a policeman Lewis returned to the keelboat. "I didn't learn a thing," he said to Clark. "I think the whole Sioux nation came in last night."

"I'll go over," Clark said. He wanted the chiefs and the policeman, whose name was On His Guard, to go with him but the five of them sat like sulking children, their arms folded. Clark was also dog-tired and half-sick and in a bad humor. "Tell them to get along!" he said. Drewyer explained to the five Indians that they would again have to leave the boat, but could return later, if they behaved like good friends. Again Buffalo was the first one to move. He got morosely to his feet and followed Clark to a pirogue. Then the others followed him, all of them looking back with comical innocence at the lockers.

Clark took Drewyer and a guard with him. A few minutes after he landed he was followed by a mob so huge that he was fenced in. Indian boys pressed close to him to stare at his hands, for they had expected him to come with gifts. Indian girls giggled and made signs that they could be wooed. Armed young men, more than two hundred of them, formed a ring around him and Drewyer and his guard of five men, all of them looking sullen and hate-filled.

Clark paused now and then and had Drewyer explain with signs that the white men were their friends. At last he reached a village and the lodge of a chief and again the squaws shrieked and danced for him, with the same filthy scalps on the same filthy poles. While sitting he put a hand to his face and pretended to doze but he was looking between fingers for a Maha. Why in the world hadn't he brought Cruzatte along! I'm so full of fatigue, he thought, that I'm losing my mind. I'd better go back.

On the way he met Lewis, also with a guard, and the two captains strolled up and down the bank until at last Clark said, "I'm just too tired to walk any longer." While he was entering a pirogue one of the chiefs and a policeman shoved past him and leapt in. This angered Clark but he said nothing. A few moments later the clumsy steersman lost control and the pirogue swung broadside against the keelboat's bow, breaking its cable. The results were astonishing.

In a loud voice Clark ordered all hands to the oars, and not until this moment did he perceive that the chief who had pushed in ahead of him was Partisan. Clark's loud command Partisan seemed to take as a sign of battle, for he leapt up and stared wildly round him, while the chiefs on the riverbank all began to shout at the top of their voices. What were they saying? Clark asked Drewyer, and Drewyer said they seemed to be calling their people to arms. They seemed to think that they were about to be attacked. This notion was so absurd that Clark looked round him, trying to discover the real reason. The entire riverbank for a distance of several hundred yards was now covered with armed men, Black Buffalo at their head, and Clark had no doubt that the showdown had come. There was wild screaming from the squaws and children and there were loud angry shouts from scores of warriors, all of whom pressed forward and into the river. Clark gained the keelboat as fast as he could and then stood on top of the lockers, looking over at the tumultuous throng of red people. Had they struck Lewis down or taken him prisoner?

"Captain Lewis!" he shouted, but knew that Lewis could not possibly hear him. Nothing could be heard because of the wild screams of the squaws. They usually behaved like that before their men attacked.

Then Ordway was shouting. "Captain Clark, I can see him . . . ! There!"

And there he was, suddenly, with his guard, entering the pirogue that had gone back for him. "My God," he said, clambering up to the deck, "I thought that was the end of all of us. What happened?"

Clark told him what had happened.

"Was it a signal?"

"I expect it was. Drewyer says they thought the Mahas were about to attack them, but that doesn't make sense."

"Who gave the signal? Partisan?"

"I don't think so. He was with me."

"Well, this means another night without sleep."

The captains took stock of the damage. When the cable broke they lost an anchor, and this meant that they'd have to spend this night much closer to the bank, where the river's current was weaker. They would then offer a much easier target to the Sioux than they had offered when anchored in mid-channel. It looked bad. The captains could not hide their anxiety, or pretend that they were not in a bad humor. Clark was also half-sick now from want of sleep and worry, and wondered how in the world he could stay awake another night.

They had Black Buffalo and Partisan with them but this now meant little: they had had to anchor the keelboat under a high bank, and though they were on the east side of the river and nearly all the Sioux were on the west, the warriors could easily swim across any time they chose to. The two chiefs could easily jump overboard and disappear. Whether Buffalo was still friendly they were unable to tell. He acted rather queer, Clark decided, watching him with blood-shot eyes—acted worried and anxious, as though he expected trouble to break out any moment.

The captains had decided that neither one would dare to sleep a wink this night. Most of their men were dog-tired too; they didn't know what was coming and a few of them like Reuben Fields had turned sullen, and others sat as if half-asleep, guns across their laps, lidded'eyes staring over at the hundreds of Sioux on the west bank. Even the most faithful men, like Ordway, were so nearly dead with fatigue that they dragged their feet and moved clumsily, like men drugged. "We're sure in fine condition to repulse an attack!" Lewis said grimly to Clark. "Half our men are so sleepy they can't see their gun sights."

It was about three hours after dark and Clark was standing watch by one of the swivel guns when Cruzatte approached him. He was a strange man, this half-blind Frenchman. Some of the men called him St. Peter and some called him Master of the Paddle. Cruzatte said he would like to speak to Clark where the watchful chiefs could not see him.

"Is this something important?"

Cruzatte said it was.

"Then I'll call Captain Lewis." Clark went to Lewis, who was by the other swivel gun. "Private Cruzatte wants to talk to us. He says it is important and he doesn't want the chiefs to see him with us."

"Important?" said Lewis, looking at the half-blind boatman with his black ragged beard. "Then let's go to the cabin."

Cruzatte spoke English with great difficulty. Groping for words, he said that while he was with the Indians today a Maha prisoner slipped up and spoke to him. The Maha said the Sioux chiefs had all met in council and come to a decision. They had decided that the white men would not be allowed to go up the river. They had de-cided to kill all of them.

For a long moment there was silence, as the two captains looked at Cruzatte in the cabin's gloom. Then Lewis said, "You speak the Maha language, don't you?"

"Oui, Cap-n."

"Are you absolutely sure you understood him?"

Cruzatte nodded his head yes.

"Then why in hell haven't you told us before?"

Cruzatte said he had had no chance to. He had not returned to the boats until late in the evening. Besides, he had thought there was no great hurry, since the time agreed on was not this day but the next.

"Tomorrow? They fixed the time tomorrow?"

That's what the Maha had said.

Lewis turned to Clark. "Then why did they give that signal today?"

Clark said he expected it was just to keep the hot blood up.

Lewis turned back to Cruzatte. "What time tomorrow?"

The Maha had just said tomorrow. That was all.

"Did all the chiefs agree to this?"

All but Black Buffalo.

Lewis dug out a candle and lit it. He then held the light before Cruzatte's face and for several moments looked into his eyes. To Clark he said, "I guess he's telling the truth. All but Buffalo. Then why hasn't Buffalo warned us?"

"I expect he's afraid to."

Lewis turned to the boatman. "You can go now." After Cruzatte had left the cabin the captains gazed at one another in candlelight, their faces gray with fatigue, their eyes bloodshot. "Would Buffalo be in on the plot?"

"He might be. He's acting queer, though what he knows is enough to make him act funny."

Lewis opened the cabin door and listened. He closed it and said, "You think there's any chance they'll strike before daylight?"

"Not much chance of that. Not unless they think we're asleep. In that case I expect Partisan would give a signal."

"I think at daylight we'd better settle this once and for all. We shouldn't let them pick their own time and situation."

He agreed, Clark said, but the first thing at daylight was to try to find their anchor and then get out in mid-channel.

"Should we ask Buffalo about this?"

"I doubt we should."

"You know what we need, Captain? Something to keep us awake. Three-fourths of our men out there are snoring like hogs. They're in such deep sleep they'd all be killed before they could get their eyes open. I don't feel like even half a man myself."

"None of us," Clark said, "and the Indians know it. They're just waiting for all of us to fall asleep."

"What I'd like is to let most of our men sleep five or six hours and then give them something to really wake them up. And I expect we'd better tell them before daylight."

"I expect."

"Well, I'll dig out the list of medicines." He brought forth the list and by the light of the candle studied it. Clark returned to stand watch.

15	lb.	Pulv.	Cort. Peru		$30.00
½	"	"	Jalap		.67
½	"	"	Rhei		1.
4	oz.	"	Ipecacuan		1.25
2	lb.	"	Crem. Tart.		.67
2	oz.	Gum Camphor			.40
1	lb.	Assafoetid			1.
½	lb.	Gum Opii Turk. opt.			2.50
¼	lb.	"	Tragacanth		.37
6	lb.	Sal Glauber		10	.60
2	"	"	Nitri	33½	.67
2	"	"	Copperas		.10
6	oz.	Sacchar. Saturn. opt.			.37
4	"	Calomel			.75
1	"	Tartar Emetic			.10
4	"	Vitriol Alb.			.12
½	lb	Columbo Rad.			1.
¼	"	Elix. Vitriol			.25
¼	"	Ess. Menth. pip.			.50
¼	"	Bals. Copaiboe			.37
¼	"	Traumat.			.50
2.	oz	Magnesia			.20
4	oz.	Laudanum			.50
2	lb.	Ung. Basilic Flav.		50	1.00
1	"	"	e lap Calimin	50	.50
1	"	"	Epispastric		1.
1	"	"	Mercuriale		1.25
1.		Emplast. Diach. S.			.50

1.		Set Pocket Insts. small		9.50
1		″ Teeth ″ ″		2.25
1.		Clyster Syringe		2.75
4.		Penis do.		1.
3.		Best Lancets	.80	2.40
1.		Tourniquet		3.50
2.	oz.	Patent Lint		.25
50.	doz.	Bilious Pills to Order		
		of B. Rush	10	5.00
6.		Tin Canisters	25	1.50
3.		8oz Gd. Stopd bottles	40	1.20
5.		4″ Tinctures do		1.85
6.		4″ Salt Mo.		2.22
1.		Walnut Chest		4.50
1.		Pine do		1.20
		Porterage		.30
¼ lb.		Indian ink		1.50
2	oz	Gum Elastic		.37
2	″	Nutmegs		.75
2	″	Cloves		.21
4	″	Cinnamon		.20

That was the list as it had come from Gillaspy and Strong. Up and down it Lewis's sleep-filled eyes roved, while with a sense of chagrin he realized that he didn't now know what some of the items were. Some of them he had bought on the suggestion of his mother, a famous yarb doctor who knew the properties of things. He supposed that there were herbs in the list that would fight fatigue and he began to taste of one thing and another until it occurred to him, with a shock of deep dismay, that there might also be some that induced sleep! He felt such alarm that he staggered to his feet. If he were to topple over and Clark were to find him here sound asleep——! It was such a horrible thought that he smote himself a few hard blows, realizing now that for a few moments he had actually been dozing. He looked at his watch. It was midnight. Why under heaven, he thought, now impatient, almost angry, with himself, had he bought so much of some things and so little of others? Of what use was a fourth of an ounce of anything, for thirty or forty men! Only six pounds of glauber for forty men living on nothing much but meat? He peered again at the list and then, disgusted, put it away and snuffed out the candle.

One thing was as sure as sunrise, that if he and Clark were both to fall asleep, all the white men would be dead without awaking. Because on leaving the cabin he found Ordway dozing and roughly shook him; and on looking down at the pirogues, lashed to the keelboat, thought that every man there was asleep. But not Partisan and Buffalo! He next went over where they lay on the deck and stared down at them, and after a few moments saw that Partisan was watching him with one black eye. The other eye was hidden by his robe. Buffalo did not look at him but he was not snoring and Lewis thought he was awake.

Lewis now went over to Clark by the swivel gun. He said he couldn't imagine why three different items of medicine cost exactly sixty-seven cents. He then thought the statement sounded utterly silly and suspected that fatigue was overpowering his senses.

"Did you find anything that keeps a man awake?"

"The truth is I didn't know what to look for. What if the property was to put a man asleep instead?"

"I don't expect we need much of that kind of medicine."

"Partisan is wide awake."

"I know it. I'm watching him. They're all awake yonder along the bank. Look at their fires."

Lewis looked over at the fires and smoke and at a few dim figures around the fires. Then he looked more sharply at Clark. His friend, he well knew, was a more disciplined man, but could he stay awake the remainder of this long night? Could any man, so completely exhausted? Well, they would have to. They would let most of their men sleep until an hour before daylight and then they would have the sergeants arouse them and bring them wide awake. If all the white men were wide awake at daylight and standing at their battle stations the Sioux might change their minds.

Hoping to find something that would fight fatigue, Lewis again examined a few of the medicines, thinking all the while of his mother. She had gathered just about every bitter herb of field and forest, and a swig of some of her concoctions was enough to take a man's head off. Her son shuddered, remembering how she had dosed him when he was at home, and her second husband, poor fellow, until he just pined away. Full of the odor of bitter aloes, he had given up the ghost. Right now Lewis had a homesick wish for a drink of one of her dark steaming brews, while sprinkling his tongue with powdered bark. Tom Jefferson had once said to his secretary that there was a vast realm ahead of mankind in the discovery of the causes of disease and the compounding of medicines. He had admired Lucy Marks and himself had sipped her herb tea. . . .

Well, he had better go stand watch now. He was full of belly rumblings and nausea, and a sense of enlargement and suffocation in his upper chest. At the other end of the boat he could see Will Clark standing erect, the soldier always. Looking over into the pirogues, he thought the men there were all asleep but it was hard to tell, for there was pain in his eyeballs, with a feeling of ground glass under the lids. It was painful merely to turn his eyes to right or left. He glanced at his watch and realized with astonishment that only two minutes had passed since he looked at it. It seemed an hour. What a terrible thing exhaustion of the organism was! It then cared for nothing but rest and rebuilding, and was as insensible of danger as the male in sexual embrace.

He dropped a little powdered ipecacuanha on his tongue, smacked a time or two to get the full flavor, and turned his bloodshot eyes on Partisan. Both chiefs were lying flat. Lewis now tried to push his tall body to its full height, and felt as though he had in his bones and muscles as many aches as could be found in a hospital, and all the dullness and lethargy of a dying world. This was his fourth straight night without sleep. Well, almost without sleep: the first and second nights he had dozed now and then. He had got perhaps three hours' sleep altogether.

He forced himself to look round him and examine their position. The keelboat, or barge, was anchored to a tree on the riverbank. Just beyond this tree, most of them sprawled out but a few of them sitting and staring over at Lewis, were about fifty Indians. Lewis next looked up at the boat's riggings. The moment daylight came Captain Clark intended to make a search for the lost anchor but Lewis thought he would waste his time. This was an extremely turbid river, heavy and dark with upstream silt, even at this time of year. The moment the search was done they would hoist sail and move off, and at that moment the Sioux would strike. If they won, what a dance they would have with all these white scalps! What shrieks of triumph! His tired gray face smiled a little. Lord, with what shrieks they would hoist aloft the red mane of Captain Clark, the black kinky mane of York! His grin deepened and laid a furrow from just above the base of his nose down across either cheek. He was feeling strangely full of lunacy and nonsense. He knew that his giddiness came from physical exhaustion and he tried to stand erect and look like a soldier on guard; but everything inside him seemed to slump and go weak and silly, and when again in fancy he saw a filthy squaw shrieking while waving Captain Clark's red mane he burst with a horrible guffaw. He bent double, filled with cramps, and closing his eyes, it seemed to him that the top eyelids were packed solid with ground glass. While bending over he thought of what a simple matter it would be to scalp a Sioux—for with one stroke of a knife a man could lift the topknot and take the braid away. Again he burst with absurd laughter.

Hearing him, Clark came over. "Captain Lewis," he said, "are you all right?"

With an effort Lewis straightened. He opened his eyes. It was, he supposed, exactly like rolling the lids up over broken glass. "Your eyes hurt?" he asked.

"Horribly," Clark said.

"You full of cramps?"

"From head to feet."

"Well, thank God this is the last night of this kind of thing. Partisan still awake?"

"I expect so."

All the while Clark had been looking strangely at Lewis, wondering what the sound was he had heard. He had thought his friend was in pain. He now went back to his watch and Lewis stared after him, grinning. The time was four in the morning, and the next two hours seemed to fill an eternity. It was a quarter of six when Lewis walked unsteadily the length of the barge and looked at his friend, still standing as straight as a gun barrel. "I think it's time to get them all up," he said. "Let's have the showdown and get it over with and if we're still alive go on up the river."

7

The sergeants were aroused first and ordered to get all their men on their feet. They were to be sure they were all wide awake, even if they had to throw river water in their faces. They were then all assembled on the keelboat, and while they stood four deep, their backs to the west, Lewis spoke to them. He told them what the Maha had told Cruzatte. He told them the Sioux strategy had been to wear them down, exhaust them and then strike, preferably when they were all sound asleep. The showdown would come the moment the boats were headed upstream. There might be five hundred or even a thousand armed warriors, some on one bank and some on the other. They would hope to destroy the white men in a crossfire. As soon as there was enough light Captain Clark would take two or three men and search for the anchor. The cooks would have a cold breakfast ready and the company would then eat. Then they would set off up the river, and at that moment every man was to be at his battle station, his weapons in perfect order.

Not a man spoke. They all stared at their captain in the nightgloom, or at the two Indian chiefs, sitting on their blankets close to the lockers. A little later Clark chose a few men to help him. They attached a long rope to each of the pirogues, and iron sinkers to the rope in its middle part; and with men at the oars the two boats moved back and forth over the area where the anchor had been lost. Kneeling at the edge of one pirogue, Clark grasped the rope, hoping that his sensitive palms would detect the impact if down in the mud bottom iron struck iron. For an hour the oarsmen rowed back and forth, while all the men on the keelboat, except the two chiefs, stood at battle stations, and the hundreds of Indians on the west bank set up an infernal racket.

Black Buffalo all the while supplicated Lewis. He begged the captain to let the women and children come on the boat and look around; and Lewis thought, You hypocrite! He said that all his people wanted to examine the big black man. He said they would all be friends with the white men if they would not go up the river. These are the things he said, according to Drewyer. His arms folded, his gray face like stone, his bloodshot eyes watching the Indians on both banks and the throngs coming from the villages, he gave no sign that he heard. He had decided that Buffalo was as two-faced as Partisan.

Calling to Clark, he said that the enemy now seemed to be coming in force, and he suggested that the search be abandoned. The pirogues drew alongside the barge and Clark came on board. In Clark's ear Lewis said, "I've been studying them in the glasses. A lot of them have firearms, some have bows and daggers. There are more of them than we've yet seen. Should we move now?"

"I think we should eat first. All men fight better on a full stomach."

"Then let's be quick about it."

While the men bolted a cold breakfast, the hundreds of Indians on both banks stood back and watched and waited. The captains knew they were waiting on orders from Partisan or Buffalo. These two chiefs were also eating, but apart, seated on their blankets. Their eyes were studying the faces of the two captains, though again and again Partisan looked to the banks as though to see if all his warriors had come.

Then the captains saw something that they had been expecting. On the east bank three policemen approached the big tree to which the keelboat was anchored, and though they did not touch the rope that held it they looked at the rope and then over at Partisan. Partisan had risen and picked up his blanket. He had seen the policemen approach. Indeed, the captains suspected that they had acted on a signal from him or Buffalo. His face and eyes completely inscrutable, Partisan stood a little distance from the captains, looking at them, back and forth.

In a quiet voice Clark said to Lewis, "This is what we've been waiting for." He glanced swiftly round him to see if all the men were at their stations. Then he said, "We'd better put Partisan off the boat."

It was a moment of great tenseness. All the men, with rifles at the ready, stood as stiff as pokers, including York and the half-blind Cruzatte, their gaze on their captains. Before Lewis could reply to Clark, Black Buffalo rushed up, crying and whining in his supplicating way, his plea addressed to both captains.

Impatiently Lewis said to Drewyer, "What's he saying?" Then there was an outcry from the east bank, only forty yards from where the captains stood; and looking over, they saw what they took to be Sioux chiefs, though the men were so smeared with grease and coal dust that they did not look like Indians but like monsters out of a black bog. Drewyer said they were demanding that the white men leave the boats anchored where they were, until the entire Sioux nation had examined them. It didn't need Drewyer to explain all this; the captains understood the gestures, including Black Buffalo's.

All this they perceived in a moment; and then from the cottonwood thickets fifty yards back from the river, on the east side, Lewis caught a glimpse of armed men emerging. Looking quickly to the west bank and the Indians there, he said to Clark, "Look at them coming out over here. I expect most of the fighters crossed the river last night."

To Drewyer, Clark said, his voice sharp with anger, "Tell them we're waiting no longer, we're going now." To Ordway he said, "Sergeant, run up two flags, a red and a white, to indicate we're ready for either peace or war!" To Pryor he called, "You and the men in your command will be responsible, if an order to fire is given, for all the chiefs on the bank!"

Drewyer, talking and gesturing with desperate urgency, was telling the two chiefs on the boat that they would have to leave it. They first moved as though to take up entrenched positions. Partisan seized hold of a strap on one of the lockers. Turning quickly to give an order to the men in the pirogues, now lashed to the keelboat, Lewis met Black Buffalo's eyes and would have sworn that they were trying to warn him. They were trying to tell him that he must turn back or he would be killed. To Clark he cried, "Captain Clark, let's take these two chiefs to the cabin! Let's settle it!" Calling Drewyer, Lewis strode to the cabin door and, turning there, beckoned to Buffalo and Partisan. They came eagerly, perhaps expecting a cup of whisky or a capitulation.

But in the cabin they found two angry captains. Dispensing with the interpreter, Lewis stepped close to Buffalo and with angry words and angry gestures told him that the Corps was going on up the river. He swung to Partisan and told him. Both captains, very angry now and with their patience exhausted, were telling them; and it was plain that they understood. Drewyer said Buffalo wanted to go up the river with them. Partisan glared and said nothing.

"Make them understand," Lewis said, "that if they start anything they'll be the first to die! I'll take care of that!"

His anger mounting, he left the cabin, followed by Clark. Then both captains stopped cold in their tracks and stared, for there on the bank was the second thing they had expected to happen: three fully armed and savage-looking warriors were sitting on the keelboat rope that was tied to the tree. Black Buffalo came rushing up to Lewis and, pawing at him with both hands, said, according to Drewyer, that all the three men wanted was tobacco.

"Away with you!" Lewis roared. "You hypocrite! Tell them to get off that cable or take the consequences!"

In almost the same moment Partisan had rushed up, demanding tobacco and a flag; and quickly the more levelheaded Clark was saying to Lewis, "Try giving them some. It might work." Lewis then flung a carrot of tobacco at Buffalo, observing in that instant that on the bank the policemen were whipping the Indian women and children to drive them back out of the way. Removing the women always meant that the men were ready to attack. The next instant Lewis saw an Indian brave untying the boat's cable round the tree, and he thought, They're going to let us go! But he was wrong. The moment the rope was untied the three sitting on it seized it and fastened it more securely to the tree.

Anger then came up in Lewis with such violence that his fatigue-gray face turned red and his eyes were dreadful to look at. He glanced up and saw that the two flags, one red and one white, had been run up. He swung to the two Indian chiefs and with a furious gesture told them to get off the boat. Clark hastened over to take the port swivel gun from the gunner there and he swung the muzzle to cover the two chiefs. And still Buffalo persisted. He said he would have to have tobacco for the three men sitting on the rope or they would never forgive him. And so Lewis flung another carrot to him, and at once Black Buffalo left the boat, followed by Partisan.

Buffalo went to the three soldiers and gave them the tobacco. He ordered them back. He then untied the rope. Robert Frazier, standing in the keelboat's prow, laid his rifle down and hauled the rope in. With the pirogues still lashed to the barge so that all the oarsmen would be able to man guns the big boat, with a strong breeze filling its sails, moved out into the river and headed upstream. As soon as it was out of rifle range the captains entered the cabin and flung themselves to their beds. Violent anger on top of four sleepless nights and four nights and days of increasing menace had made them deathly ill. Trying to recover by drawing long deep breaths, Lewis looked back on the experience and wondered how many things had happened in those few tense minutes that he had not seen or heard —for he now recalled the loud furious voice of Partisan and the way the man had jumped up and down while shrieking at the captains. He remembered now that Black Buffalo had also been very angry. So had the chiefs on the east bank and the men sitting on the rope.

"Well—Captain Clark—we're off."

"Yes," said Clark, also breathing hard and deep. "Did you know that—just as we moved off—Buffalo came back on?"

"I didn't know that. I was watching—a thousand Indians."

The captains now rested until they could speak more normally. Then Lewis said: "I expect we owe a lot to Buffalo. If I had cut the cable before giving the second carrot would they have attacked?"

"It's hard to say," said Clark, drawing a hand across his forehead and his bloodshot eyes. "I expect they figured we'd kill too many of them before they could kill us. We had every chief under a gun sight."

"They're not through with us."

"No, they're not. They'll try to get us somewhere up the river."

"Well, it goes to show that the only way to handle Indians is to be absolutely firm."

"That," Clark said, "is the way to handle any children."

Among the men there was earnest talk. Every one of them had expected fighting. They had all believed that none of them could possibly escape, because there must have been five or six hundred armed warriors in sight.

"I had Beffe de Medison right in my gun sight all the time," Reuben Fields said. "Jesus, he has a nice topknot."

Some of the men turned to look at him. They wondered why Reuben was so eager to kill a redskin.

"You know," said the big surly John Newman, "I think our captains lost their heads."

George Shannon turned to look at him. "You'd have lost your head if it hadn't been for our captains."

"You speaking to me?" said Newman, glaring at him.

"Come, come!" said Bob Frazier. And to ease the tension he intoned one of his little ditties: "O beautiful Sioux, I'm not for you!

I'll have to marry Miss Susie McNary!" He blew kisses at a horde of shrieking women, now vanishing in the morning mists of a far shoreline. Then he turned dark heavily-lashed eyes on grinning Hugh McNeal. "Loisel said the Mandan girls will be waiting for us on the front porch. They bathe at least twice a week in the cold muddy Missouri water and never put on more than two pounds of bear grease, except on Sunday."

"Except on Sunday!" cried McNeal, and exploded.

Frazier's nonsense had relieved the terrible tension in some of the men but George Shannon was saying that the crisis with the Sioux was duck soup compared to what lay ahead of them. There were the Big Bellies. If the Sioux didn't get them, Loisel had said, the Big Bellies would. After them came the Blackfeet, the most savage Indians on the continent. After the Blackfeet came nobody knew how many tribes that had never seen a white man.

Newman growled, "How do you know so much?"

"I read, I listen."

"Oh, holy mackerel! What you do——"

"Come, come, boys!" said Frazier. "You should kiss one another and be glad to be alive. If you want to fight wait till you get to old One-Eye. He rapes young girls and then tomahawks them just to get his appetite up for breakfast."

Newman turned his cold gray-blue eyes on Frazier. "And where is this guy?"

"Head chief of the Big Bellies, and you can bet your willow whistle that his scouts have their eye on you right now. I wouldn't be surprised the brush over there is full of them."

Newman turned to look at the river thickets and then back to Frazier. "What happened to his other eye?" he said.

"A squaw knifed it out when she caught him with her daughter."

"You guys sure know a lot," said the angry and contemptuous Newman. "You musta been born that way."

Ignoring him now, Frazier was singing, to the delight of a half-dozen of the men, "It's said that the Rees have knees bowed out like wagon bows—and monstrous bunions on their toes! That's true, Loisel said. He said when a Rees girl puts her feet together a small buffalo can run between her legs."

John Newman scowled at him a few moments and then muttered, "No wonder old One-Eye tommyhawks them!"

8

The captains decided not to camp on land again as long as they were in Sioux country, and to post a dependable watch day and night. This day they snatched an hour or two of sleep and were up again; they took turns standing watch until two in the morning and then they both slept. The next morning Partisan and two young braves hailed them from the bank and asked to be taken on board. Lewis told Drewyer to tell him to run along and mind his business. The second day out the captains saw hundreds of Indians coming down the hills to the river. Putting their best men on the oars, they ordered full speed ahead. When the keelboat struck a sunken log and in a sudden burst of wind almost turned over, Black Buffalo let off a dreadful yell of fright and ran away and hid. A few minutes later he was begging to be put off.

"I guess we might as well put him off," Lewis said. "But shouldn't we smoke a pipe with him and give him something?"

"That would be better."

And so the two captains smoked with the chief what they hoped would be a farewell pipe. Lewis said to Drewyer, "Explain to him that he must keep his warriors away from us, that we are going up the river and the whole Sioux nation can't stop us. Be sure he understands it."

For a few minutes Drewyer and the chief talked in signs. Then Drewyer said, "He zay Cap-n zee hees men no maire."

"Never again?"

Drewyer shook his head and said never.

Lewis said to Clark, "If the old hypocrite was being honest with

us we'd give him something nice, and maybe we should anyway."
They gave Buffalo a blanket, a handsome knife and a foot of tobacco
twist. They clasped his hand in farewell. The Indian's handclasp was
firm, his gaze steady, but they didn't believe him. He was up to some
trick that they hadn't seen through. They set him on the bank and
he grinned at them and waved a hand in farewell, and he stood
and watched them as long as the boats were in sight.

Now and then the next day they saw a Sioux or two or three together but there was no sign of hostility. Near the mouth of the Chien
or Dog River they met a French trader, who said he had just spent
a winter on this river in the Black Mountains. Looking at the eyes
of the captains, still bloodshot, and their faces, still showing the
pallor of exhaustion, he said he was amazed to hear that they had
outbluffed the Sioux, for he knew of no braver red men anywhere.

"We weren't bluffing," Clark said.

The Frenchman studied Clark's face a few moments. Then he said,
"Are you the ones going to the western ocean?"

Lewis said quickly, "We're just exploring in the interest of science."

Jean Vallé smiled and his smile said he didn't believe a word of
it. "Science?" he said politely. "You stick pretty close to the river
for men interested in science."

Even after they knew they were out of Sioux country and in the
land of another nation the captains posted a day and night watch.
In St. Louis, and from trappers up the river, they had gathered all
the information they could about the red peoples farther up, and
had been advised to expect serious trouble from all of them. Loisel's
assistant, Tabeau, they hoped to meet soon. From what they had
heard they had concluded that he was a man of unusual mind and
character, and of broad experience with Indians. He would be with
the Arikaras, Loisel had said. The Arikaras were the next nation upstream from the Sioux. Some called them the Rickarees, some the
Rees. Their language, Loisel had said, was enough to stump an angel:
it had so many dialects that Rees from different villages could barely
understand one another.

The captains hoped that Tabeau would be friendly, though after
their four-day ordeal with the Sioux they were determined to push
on, no matter how hostile the people they met or how treacherous
the white men.

Tabeau had written to Loisel his opinion of the Sioux and the
Arikaras, and the captains had read his words: "They are stupid, su-

perstitious, gluttonous, lewd, vindictive, patient by principle, fierce of temper, cowardly with men of like strength, fearless in assassinations, ungrateful, traitorous, barbarous, cruel, lying, thievish." Lewis had grinned at Loisel and said, "They seem to have all the Christian virtues."

There was one good thing about the Rees, Loisel had said: they held alcohol in contempt and those who used it, and swore by their biggest manitous and most powerful medicine that if the white men wanted them to drink the stuff they should pay them to do it. White men, they said, gave whisky to Indians only to make fools of them. In former times the Arikaras had been a powerful nation but smallpox and the marauding Sioux had humbled them. These two nations had closed the upper Missouri to downstream traders, much to the delight of the British, and now enjoyed huge profits from blackmail and plunder. Lewis had said nothing but he had thought, We'll change all that.

It was the 8th of October when the lookout spotted the first Rees village, a group of cone-shaped lodges made of willow, mud and straw, standing on a river island with tilled fields roundabout. The boats proceeded until they stood close to the island. Then Lewis, with two soldiers and two interpreters, entered a pirogue and put over. A great number of Indians came swarming to the bank to wait for the white men. On the keelboat Clark ordered the men to their stations and got everything in readiness for action, telling himself that it might be peace or it might be war, any day now.

A few minutes later he saw the boat returning, and as it drew near he made out the form of two strange white men. They were Pierre Tabeau, a French-Canadian who had sworn allegiance to the United States, and his assistant, Joseph Gravelines. Gravelines, a rugged middle-aged quiet man, who gave no nonsense and took none, had spent many years among the Arikaras and spoke their language well. Both men at the moment were housed in the lodge of the principal chief, and for a peculiar reason, Lewis now told Clark.

News of the white party's triumph over the Sioux had come like the wind, and had thrown the warlike Arikaras almost into panic. Not so long ago, Lewis said, these Rees Indians had bullied and humiliated Mr. Tabeau here, but now invited him into the lodge of the main chief!

"And all because you called their bluff," Tabeau said. "The news came by runner that a party of white men was coming up who meant business, and the next thing I knew Joe and I were being asked to dine with the chief."

Clark said, "You mean we'll have no trouble with these Indians?"

"Oh, trouble, yes—you always have trouble with Indians. But nothing serious. You realize you're the first white men who ever made the Sioux back down. They won't forget that or forgive it."

"I expect not," Clark said. "We won't forget it either."

"Even Partisan, that brutal monster, backed down. How amazing!"

"He has backed only part way," Lewis said. "He's still plotting."

"Yes, he'll be after you as long as you're within reach."

"Is it true the Blackfeet are more savage than the Sioux?"

"The Canadian traders think so."

"And old One-Eye, will he give us trouble?"

"I expect he'll try."

The captains invited the two men to take breakfast with them the next morning. Tabeau did most of the talking. The captains were eager listeners. Among the three Arikara villages, Tabeau said, jealousy was so strong that it approached lunacy; and right now the chiefs of the two upper villages were dancing up and down like tantrum children, afraid that the captains would commission a first or principal chief in the island village, who would then lord it over the others.

Men were envious and vain, no matter where you went, Tabeau said. The Indian under his copper skin was about like the paleface under his milk. He suggested that they might make the three chiefs of equal rank.

"Why, of course," Lewis said.

Clark said, "Is it true these people never touch alcoholic drinks?"

"Never," Tabeau said, turning his pointed brown beard in the direction of one captain and then the other. He helped himself to a piece of cold boiled elk. "They say it makes fools of people and if they're to be fools they want to be paid for it. I can find nothing to say against their argument."

Lewis smiled at his dry statement. He liked this man. He said, "Still, it's strange to find men who don't like whisky."

"Oh, they like whisky all right. They don't like what it does to them."

"Are they as childlike as the Sioux?"

"More. More impulsive and spontaneous—and the Mandans still more. Your men will learn that when they encounter the women."

Clark frowned. "The women," he said, "do they have the white disease?"

Tabeau at the moment was sinking his teeth into boiled elk. With his teeth still in the meat his eyes looked over at Clark. Clark saw that his eyes were amber-brown and that they were laughing.

He assumed, Tabeau said, when he was able to speak, that the captains were familiar with Indian customs. Among the red people in this area the thing that most distressed such white men as Alexander Henry was the brutality with which the men punished their women for infractions of the sexual tribal laws. What was tribally approved gave them no offense at all. For instance, in the lodge of Chief Kakawita himself, where Tabeau and Gravelines were now housed, a Ricara gambled his wife's favors for a few days, and lost; and then with an indifference that was appalling to white men he had lain on his robe and watched his opponent with his wife. On the other hand, if she tried to deceive him, and was discovered, he would cut off her nose and ears.

They had mentioned One-Eye. That was Le Borgne. They would meet him in due time, up the river—a horrible brute with one eye and the violence of the gray bear when cornered. This monster had been so cruel with his wife that she had left him for another man. One night Le Borgne went to her father's lodge, where he knew she would be, and for a while had sat like a brooding hulk of evil, smoking his pipe. Word went out, and the wise old men of the village came to the lodge and did their best to appease him. They offered him one thing and another. They even offered him more attractive women.

To all their pleas Le Borgne never uttered a word. He sat and smoked, his eyes—or his one good eye really—on his wife, his ears deaf to the wise old men; and when the pipe was finished he slowly laid it aside and stood up. By this time his wife was sobbing with wild fright. With cool deliberation One-Eye had seized the terrified creature by her hair and dragged her over to the lodge entrance, and there he had driven his tomahawk into her skull with such force that he split it open in two halves almost to the collarbone. Not a hand had been raised against him.

"Le Borgne," said Lewis, fixing the name in mind. "He sounds like a playful cuss."

"He's not a Ricara?" said Clark.

"A Minnetaree. In French his name means the One-Eyed."

"The other eye is blind?"

"I assume so. It's covered with a white film and that makes him look twice as savage."

"He hates white men?" asked Lewis.

"As he hates nothing else on earth."

"A coward at heart? He must be if he beats women."

Taking another piece of elk, Tabeau fixed Lewis with a steady gaze and said there was a difference when the beating of women was sanctified by tribal laws. Most Indians were simply cruel. He had known another chief who, catching his wife with a man, had taken all the hair off her head from her nape over her skull to her forehead. The outraged husband had then made an incision across the top of her skull and peeled the scalp down on either side until the two flaps fell over her ears. As though this horrible mutilation were not enough he had then driven a sharp knife into her hands and arms and her shoulder blades. This same man would have offered his wife to a guest.

The captains, he suspected, might find it difficult among these tribes. Alexander Henry had complained that he had deeply, almost unforgivably, offended some Mandan husbands when he refused to accept their wives. You had to accept or have a very good reason, and what you thought were good reasons might sound awfully trivial to an Indian. As the captains and leaders of the party Lewis and Clark would be honored guests, and the choicest of wives, sisters and daughters would be offered to them.

"I'm afraid," Lewis said, "I'm going to offend my hosts. But surely you can buy your way off, can't you?"

That was possible, Tabeau said. But if they were going to be here a whole winter and were importuned every day?

Lewis made a note of the word importuned. Loisel had said that Tabeau was an educated man, and so, Lewis decided, he seemed to be.

"You mean it will take a lot of gifts?"

"For the choicest?" Tabeau smiled. "Doesn't it always?"

"It'll sure be strange," Lewis said drily, "if Captain Clark and I bankrupt ourselves for no more worthy purpose than refusing beautiful women."

Tabeau's smile spread. "Not beautiful exactly but the choicest."

Clark said, "Are they so persistent?"

"The Ricara and Mandan women are very persistent, and from St.

Louis to the head of the Saskatchewan they're known to be very ardent."

"We got clear of the Sioux," Clark said, "without taking their squaws, though Partisan was a big nuisance with two girls he had."

Tabeau glanced quickly from captain to captain, his eyes saying that he didn't quite believe they were innocent of Sioux women. But he said in his polite way, looking round him, "I observe you have a Negro here, a huge handsome fellow. He's going to give you a lot of trouble."

Surprised, Clark said, "Why?"

"Because he's different. They won't think he's black. They'll try to wash his color off. Finding that he really is black—that he was *born* ready for the warpath, the women will swoon with raptures."

"I guess I better send him back down," Clark said.

Lewis said, "You haven't answered about the white disease."

"Have you known Indians who haven't had it, if white men had been there?"

The captains were astonished to discover how true were Tabeau's words about the response to York. The man became a horrible nuisance. It was their third day among the Arikaras that they let the big Negro go ashore with a number of the other men; and the moment the Indians saw the tall figure with the coal-black face and hands they came flocking round him; and York stood still, gazing out over their heads, his big eyes rolling. It was the young women who came in first, twittering and squealing. With a finger one would gently press his naked black skin and then look up at his rolling eyes; then two or more would be pressing and pinching him. Convinced that he was painted black, yet unable to see coal smudge on their fingers after rubbing him, some of them would touch their fingers to their wet tongues and then try to rub the black off. Some of them even put their tongues to his skin, as though to taste the color. Failing to rub or wash away the black, they gave off such shrieks of amazement that the Indian men pressed in, and as many hands as could touch him then examined the huge Negro from his head to his toes. And all the while his big eyes rolled in lecherous joy.

Some of the girls went down on their knees, to wash the black off his legs above his leather leggings; some ecstatically felt the supple muscle-bands of his upper arms; and one, bolder than all the rest, reached up and yanked his cap off. When, looking up, the Indians saw the black shining wealth of his kinked hair, and, reaching up, convinced themselves that the kinks were real, their astonishment was boundless.

The captains and a few of their men had been standing back, watching. York had been almost immobile. But now all the hands over his body were too much for his self-control: reaching out, he seized an Indian brave by a thigh and shoulder and with one effortless graceful movement raised the man at arm's length above his head and for a few moments held him there. With the same superb strength he set the Indian down.

Abashed, and perhaps more amazed than he had ever been before, the red man slunk away.

The feat of strength set the girls to shrieking. York, enjoying himself immensely, looked round him, wondering what other marvels he might perform, to delight and astound them. He saw a hunk of tree bole that weighed possibly two hundred and fifty pounds. Marching over, he stooped, put his long powerful arms under it, hoisted it for a moment to one shoulder and let it fall. Again there were gasps and shrill cries. Speaking through Joseph Gravelines, who had come up to watch, York now told the assembled Indians that he was not a man at all, but a strange wild beast from a far land, that Captain Clark had found and tamed and taught to talk. He said he was stronger than any other man on earth. He invited any two red men to come forward and wrestle with him. When none moved, the girls tried to push some of them forward but all the Indian men backed away, their eyes staring at York with the sober fascination of children.

Again the women pressed forward, to peer, to pinch and feel; to look up at his broad grinning face, at the whites of his rolling eyes, his enormous lips, his hair. Suddenly York gave his master a real start. Because he was double-jointed at both his knees and ankles he was an expert at clogging, jigging and pigeon-wing cutting, and he now became a creature of such fantastic movement and energy that even the white observers were astonished. As for the red people, they had never been more flabbergasted in their lives: for here was the huge giant whose color seemed to be real and who said he was not a man at all but a fierce wild animal—this thing that seemed to have the strength of ten or a hundred was now dancing with such wild abandon that he made the wildest dancing of the red people look tired. Crying like forest birds, the squaws surrounded him, and their eyes actually bugged out when, bending over, they tried to follow the intricate movements of his feet, or determine what in the world he was doing with his knees. The red men now crowded in until the captains could see only the incredible bobbing of the black kinky head and the massive shoulders.

"Holy Moses!" one of the men said.

Again something happened that opened Captain Clark's eyes a little wider. The dancing had ceased and the nature of the female cries had changed. Clark thought he understood what the cries meant and, turning to Lewis, he said, "This is terrible. I'd better send him to the boat." But before he could order York to the boat Gravelines came up with one whom he presented as Red Moccasin, a minor chief. Red Moccasin, he said, wanted to take York to his lodge.

"What for?" asked Clark suspiciously.

"To honor him. He's very impressed by your black servant."

"Or his wife is," said the dry Lewis.

"Where is his lodge?"

"Just over there a little way."

Clark glanced at Lewis but Lewis was having nothing to do with this.

"All right," Clark said, "but I want him back soon. I suppose," Clark added, to himself really, "that he wants to give him a present."

In his driest voice Lewis said, "I'd not be at all surprised."

The group of white men, as well as all the Indians, watched Chief Red Moccasin and a squaw go with York toward the lodges. York seemed to tower two feet above the red man, and three feet above the woman. Sergeant Paddy Gass, who detested Negroes even more than Lewis detested the British, was making grimaces of distaste. "He drivs me crazy wid his nonsince!" he was muttering. Handsome Bob Frazier, the fencing-master, looked less ironic than usual. "At last," he said, "I'm learning something about women."

George Shannon's boyish face with cheeks of apple-bloom and eyes that could never look meaner than the blue of the sky was gazing down at the earth. He was recalling some of the dreadful things that Tabeau had been telling—how a jealous buck, catching his wife with a lover, had methodically cut her up in many pieces, taking her tongue, but only her tongue, with him; and how another had filled his wife's robe with gunpowder and pushed her into a fire. She had made quite an explosion, Tabeau said. They did these things if the wife was caught, yet this chief . . . And so what was jealousy, anyway!

He heard Clark saying in his ear, "Go over and tell my servant York to come to his master."

"Yes, Captain."

"Right now, not later."

"Yes, sir."

George went toward the lodge, dragging his feet. He didn't like this assignment. He didn't particularly care for this giant whom the Indians were now calling the black white man, nor for what he supposed was going on in the lodge. When he was halfway there he raised his eyes and saw Red Moccasin standing propped in the doorway like something the wind had lodged there. The Indian chief waved him away. For a few moments George looked at him and then went on, recalling the sharpness of his captain's command. He went to within eight or ten paces of the chief and said in his rather deliberate way of speaking, "Captain Clark wants his servant." Red Moccasin with a haughty gesture of his right arm repeated over and over was telling George to go away. God in heaven! George Shannon thought. Would his father and mother ever have believed this? For a few moments he stared solemnly at the Indian; turned and looked back at the group of white men; picked up a small stick and began to chew on it; and then, convinced that Clark had beckoned to him, returned.

"The chief is standing guard," George said, glancing into Clark's stern eyes.

Some of the men snickered. Even Captain Lewis had to turn to hide a smile. Pierre-Antoine Tabeau had joined the group during George's absence and seemed to be having difficulty repressing his mirth.

"If you mix white and black, Captain, what do you get?"

Clark was silent. Lewis said, "A fine Virginia chocolate-brown."

"And if you mix black and red?"

"I was wondering about that. You suppose that if a chief had some kinkiness in his long braid he'd be proud of it?"

"Oh, enormously. Ever hear the Welsh story? Are you Welsh, Captain?" Lewis nodded. "You must have heard the story, then—of John Evans who came from Wales to discover the Welsh Indians—for it has been believed by a lot of men that the Mandans are Welsh. A lot of them have fair hair and blue eyes. One of their chiefs is called Big White."

"I have the Evans map," Lewis said.

Tabeau went on: "We who've been around here a long time are a little suspicious of the Welsh legend. We've a notion where the blue eyes came from."

"Not from Wales?" asked Lewis, trying to keep a sober face. "Surely not from Scotland!"

"Nor England, either."

"I expect it would take generations for a blue eye to drive a black one out."

George Shannon looked queerly at his captain.

"The funny thing," Tabeau said, "was the fury of the Canadian bosses when they discovered why their trappers were coming down here. Wouldn't they have suspected it, when the peltries were so few?"

"Oh, not the British," Lewis said. "What did they think?"

"Not having looked inside the British mind, I couldn't even guess."

Lewis grinned. Yes, he liked this man.

York was returning now, escorted by Red Moccasin—the red man looking quiet and full of pride, the black man showing his big white teeth. Two captains, two sergeants and a half-dozen privates were staring at him, and every face was a fascinating picture. Shrill young squaws came running to meet him but Clark went forward, striding angrily, and took his servant away.

"You're terrible," Clark said, looking up at the black face. "I think I'll send you back down the river."

"Uhh-now, massa!" York said. His voice was so deep that it was impossible for him to sound pathetic. "Sholey yo wooden do ut."

"Get over to the boat."

"Yassuh, massa."

Clark stared at the broad back under its golden leather as York strode on ahead of him. Fifty yards distant the big Negro paused and glanced back. When he saw the red women shrieking at him he dared his master's wrath by waving a big black hand.

Lewis was saying to Tabeau, "You said we'd have trouble with him. I see what you mean."

"He's an asset if you handle him right," Tabeau said. "He's worth ten bushels of blue beads."

9

Possibly not a one of the privates and sergeants liked the Negro's easy conquest of the red women. Some of the men were so resentful that they turned sullen and ugly. One of these was the big ham-handed John Newman. Anger and outrage built up in him, and two days after the chief honored York, Newman was striding off toward an Arikara village when Lewis called to him.

"Private Newman, where you going?"

Newman stopped, scowling, and looked over at Lewis. He was mute.

"I asked, Private Newman, where you're going. It's almost dark."

"Who wants to know?"

"What was that?" asked Lewis sharply. "What did you say?"

Then with terrible passion Newman exploded. "I said whose damn business is it?"

Turning a little pale, Lewis swung and looked toward the boats. He saw Ordway and called to him. When Ordway came over, Lewis said, "Sergeant Ordway, place Private Newman under arrest. If he resists, shoot him."

"Yes, Captain."

With almost no delay Newman was taken before a court-martial over which Clark presided. Clark took no part in weighing the evidence or measuring the punishment; these were the duty of the enlisted men who sat as judges. Newman's punishment was seventy-five lashes, all to be given at one time, and expulsion from the Corps, though he would be allowed to remain until some way could be found to send him down the river. It was drastic punishment and

Newman's weather-red face paled a little when he heard the sentence from Clark's lips.

On a small island the next day the seventy-five blows were delivered, with one of the Arikara chiefs present. This chief had been very curious. He watched the men strip Newman and put him in bended position over a bole of driftwood; and before the third blow fell the chief was wailing in loud shrill tones and flinging from his eyes what seemed to be tears. He was raising both hands in protest. At last he rushed over to Clark, his red face convulsed.

Clark turned to Gravelines. "What does he want?"

"He begs you for mercy."

Clark looked over at the soldier with the lash. It was John Collins, who himself had received a hundred down the river. The stinging lash was falling stroke by stroke, and Newman was wincing and trying to burrow his head deeper into his arms. The count was twenty.

"Isn't this the chief who's going to the Mandans with us, to tell them we're their friends?"

"The same."

"Well, explain to him that this soldier was mutinous—that in our nation mutinous soldiers are punished, or there could be no discipline, no command, no security against the enemy. Tell him the British use straps that could cut a buffalo open."

Gravelines talked a few moments to the weeping chief, then said to Clark, "He says this is cruel, says his nation never whips anyone, not even children."

"Oh, not even children," said Clark, grimly amused. "Tell him our people don't split a wife's head open because she prefers another man."

Gravelines was now amused. "Sometimes they do," he said.

The chief had gone round as though to look at Newman's face but the face was hidden in the arms. Alexander Willard was laying on the blows now; he too had received one hundred lashes down the river. The lash used on Newman was only a green chokecherry limb about as thick at the stout end as Willard's forefinger and about three and a half feet long. It stung like fire but did not cut deep. Most of Newman's back was blood-red by the time the fiftieth stroke fell and parts of it were welted and bleeding. Willard backed away with the old lash and Collins moved in with a fresh one. On seeing this the chief gave off a dreadful wail and again ran to Clark, his hands supplicating. Clark could not tell whether he was weeping or only pretending to.

Gravelines was saying that anything the red man couldn't understand was big medicine. Anything he understood but didn't like was bad medicine. This was bad medicine.

Clark gave no reply. He was watching the flogging. John Collins, a powerful young man, was wielding the lash now, his voice calling the number, "Sixty-four . . . sixty-five . . . sixty-six . . ." Clark approached to look at Newman's back. Fifteen or twenty blows did not lacerate a back much, but up and down Newman's back and over his rump the skin in a number of places had been cut through and blood was running freely. With a final wail and a tragic look up at the heavens the Indian chief hastened away and a moment later vanished. "Seventy-two . . . seventy-three . . . seventy-four . . . seventy-five!" Collins tossed the lash aside and stepped back.

Clark said, "Newman, get up."

But Newman did not rise. He turned in a swift convulsive movement and knelt at the captain's feet. He too was supplicating. He raised his anguished face, the weather-red now a gray pallor, the eyes wet with tears, and begged Clark to let him go to the journey's end. He had been a fool, he said, but never again would lack be found in him. "Captain Clark, I beg you! Say a word for me to Captain Lewis!"

"Stand up," Clark said.

John Newman, strong-willed and hot-tempered, rose to his feet. It was easy to see that he was weeping not from pain but from humiliation. Clark told him to put his clothes on. He then turned away. Discipline, General Wayne had told his officers, had to be stern and unbending, even when soldiers were safely bivouacked and the enemy was far away. In times of danger the slightest unbending was a sign of weakness in a commander's mind.

It was a time of danger now, and it would be all the way to the ocean and back.

Tabeau had said, "Don't imagine that the Sioux have forgotten you. They don't intend to let you go up the river. At a time and place of their choosing they'll strike."

"This winter or next spring?" Lewis asked.

"Not while you're in a fort."

"Probably when we leave it to go."

Well, their task now was to get the fort built, somewhere up the river. They would need warm quarters, for the winters here, Tabeau said, sometimes fell to fifty below zero and froze elk or buffalo right where they stood. He had seen big trees split open with the sound of a cannon shot; he had seen a man's hand stuck to his rifle barrel as if steel and flesh had fused.

The two captains met with the Arikara chiefs and Lewis gave a speech that his men were finding tiresome: "We have been sent by the great chief of the seventeen great nations of America. A great council has been held with the French and Spanish. Your old fathers the French and Spanish have gone beyond the great lakes toward the rising sun. . . . The great American chief now controls all the rivers, upon which you must allow no other vessel to pass. The great white chief will welcome your chiefs if you visit him. The great white chief . . ."

Gravelines translated. The Rees, he said, were immensely impressed. These white men seemed to have the biggest medicine they had ever heard of. But they would never dare go visit the white chief, for if they went down the river the Sioux would kill them.

After Gravelines translated, the head chief of a village would rise and speak, and again Gravelines translated: "My fathers, my heart is gladder than ever before to see my fathers. My heart is glad. If you want the road open up the Big River no one will stop you. The Big River will always be open for you. Who would dare to put their hands on the cable of your boat? Not one. No, not one. When you get to the Mandans we wish you to speak good words to that nation for us. We wish to be at peace with them. And when you return from your journey to Everywhere-Salt-Water, if I am living I will be the same man you see now. The red men of the prairie know me, they listen to my words; and when you return they will wish to see you. We will watch the river with impatience for your coming. . . ."

Then the second chief said: "My fathers, I'm glad this is a fine day to talk good talk. I'm glad to see you and know that you will open the Big River road for all. We see that our Great Father has sent you to open the road. We see that our Great Father means to take pity on us. Our Great Father has sent you with tobacco to make peace with all nations. I expect the chief in the next village will tell you to open the road. The Sioux told you the same, I expect. We see you here today and we are poor, our women have no garments, no knives to cut their meats. Take pity on us when you return. You tell us to stay at home and not go to war. We shall do so.

We will go next spring and see our Great Father and receive his gifts. I am not afraid to die for the good of my people. The chief by me will go to the Mandans and hear what you say. We are poor, take pity on our wants."

At a certain point in the second chief's talk there was loud outcry and shrill protests. Sitting by the captains, Gravelines told them that the chief had said, "I am not afraid to die for the good of my people." Then the women shrieked and wailed, and all the children began to weep. What children they were! Lewis said. It was a pity to have to shoot an Indian anywhere, yet you knew that, like children, they were all liars.

The captains had decided to take an Arikara chief up the river with them, for they wished to establish peace among the Arikaras, Mandans and Minnetarees and use them as a buffer against the Sioux. The head chief of the island village urged them to take a few women with them, for what Captain Lewis drily called a mutual exchange of good offices; but Clark thanked him, gave him presents and declined. Tabeau had warned them that all the chiefs would urge on them their handsomest women, hoping in their crafty thieving hearts that they'd give them many fine presents, as balm to their deeply wounded *amour-propre*.

The French term had startled the captains. What was that? they had wondered, but they knew. They had seen a chief bring a few hundred pounds of buffalo flesh, or a robe, or beans, corn and squash, expecting in return twenty times their worth; and they had seen the pain in his eyes when he looked at what was given him. "The pain in his amoor-proper," Lewis said. It was commonplace for the chiefs in council meetings to say, "All our young men were out hunting when you came and they returned from the hunt expecting many presents. They are very disappointed, for you have given them nothing." With Gravelines to translate for them everywhere they were saying, "We are poor, our wives and children are dying of hunger, they are ragged and cold." Then Lewis would study the list of presents brought for Indians and wonder how much to give here this winter, how much keep for the long journey into the unknown.

"What if we find ourselves with a hostile tribe and nothing to give?"

Clark said, "I think we'd better keep just about all of it. A handful of beads may someday stand between us and death."

The friendly Tabeau, wishing in all things to be helpful, had advised them: "For the women they offer, if you decline, they'll expect much but be content with little, so low is their opinion of the female. In fact, they'd be glad to get rid of some of them, especially those who have gone wild over your black man. Bear in mind that to refuse is to wound deeply. The matter balances nicely between a trinket and hurt pride."

It was true, Clark reflected sourly, that quite a number of the young girls had gone simply daft over York. In his Journal one evening he recorded in his fine careful script, "These people are much pleased with my black Servent. Their womin verry fond of carressing our men &c." He thought this strange, after hearing Tabeau tell about the Rites of the Virgins. At the top of a lodge, used as a kind of temple, was fastened a green cedar bough, whereupon to the assembled Indians a few old men, chosen for their wrinkles and shrill voices, proclaimed that all the girls in the village who were still virgins were privileged to climb the temple and touch the bough. At the same time, all the men watching, young or old, were ordered, under pain of extreme denunciation, to tell what they had knowledge of.

Lewis chuckled. "What they have knowledge of! That would be a good custom in the white man's land."

Now and then a girl would start to climb, and a man would rush forth and speak a few words to the old men; and the old men would then challenge her and she would slink away, covered with shame. But Diana, Tabeau said, had not been wholly routed by Venus: it was not uncommon for a haughty beautiful girl to step forth, saying, "Where is the man who can accuse me?" Those whom no man accused were given prizes of vermilion, beads and scarlet cloth.

Sergeants Ordway and Gass made no such confessions in their Journals, nor Private Whitehouse. If they had read their captain's statement they would have turned away to hide grins. Still, the words about York would not have pleased them. Some of the men called him unprintable names, and Gass grumbled, "The red lass goes into extashies over id and bechust hirsel! They better not put him in my mess or I'll have the cook pisen him."

When the captains refused to take women up the river, on their way to the Mandans, two young girls, whose infatuation with York had put them out of their senses, followed along the bank, squealing and waving. The men on the boats stared at them and Frazier blew kisses. "Arikara, you lovely squaw, you be the Ma and I'll be the

Pa . . . !" Most of the men would forget the girls, when suddenly
there they would be, clawing their way through thickets and over
sandbars, squealing and waving their hands. Seeing them, York
would stand up, black and tall, his broad face grinning, his mouth
like a great swelling around two rows of ivory. Seeing him, some of
the men would say spiteful things.

"Lookit!" said Reuben Fields, the more savage of the two brothers.

"Remember that cedar tea?" asked William Bratton, a large and
rather awkward young Irishman, a gunsmith with a talent for picking
at a banjo and singing. Reuben looked at Bratton, but without
friendliness: after the death of Sergeant Floyd three men were voted
for to take his place—Gass, Gibson and Bratton. Reuben Fields had
not voted for Bratton. "Fill him full of cedar tea," Bratton said, "and
he won't even get his buckskin down."

"I'd give him a huge dost of bitter Alice," said Reuben's brother
Joe. He meant bitter aloes.

"Cedar tea with the red berries in it," Bratton said. "Holy grandma,
would that fix him!"

Reuben Fields rubbed at his neck and moved to ease a shoulder.
Most of the men, eating little but meat, were suffering from what
the captains diagnosed as rheumatism; and Captain Clark himself
had one night been so paralyzed he was unable to move. "What's
funny," Reuben said, putting a finger and thumb over the base of
his nose and bringing his hand down across his hairy lip and chin,
"what's funny about these-here red girls is they don't like hair on
a man. That's how the nigger wins. They laugh, but not at him.
At us."

"He's got a horse-sized advantage," someone said. "No hair and
all black."

"You think he's all black," Bratton said.

"Six ounces of bitter Alice," Joe said. "That would really fix him up
for the bushes."

"Poured down him out of a goat stummick," Reuben said. He had
in mind the Indian habit of carrying water in the stomachs of beasts,
without first washing the stomachs out.

"Why you reckon Captain Clark lets him act up so?"

"Just to keep the women happy, I guess."

Reuben Fields rested on an oar and looked over at York, still
standing tall and black, still waving to the shrieking girls. "About a
dozen of Rush's pills," he said.

"Nope," said Bratton, "a quart of cedar tea. Holy grandma, he'd never come out of the bushes."

"A pint of bitter Alice," said Joe Fields. "I once took some and I never got my pants up for a week."

The captains were not unaware of the resentment in some of their men. Nevertheless, one evening, after the two Indian girls had spotted the white man's camp across the river, and had howled and shrieked for an hour, begging to be taken over, Clark sent a pirogue to fetch them. An Indian brave who had been stealthily following them came out of the brush and clambered into the boat with them, hoping to be mistaken for their husband.

The girls had been following York up the river, not the white men, and the moment they touched the east bank they were off to find him. Wild and shrill they ran up to him, but a moment later, full of confusion, their copper color turning a deep dark red, they fell back a little and then gazed up at his face—at his two rows of strong white teeth and his eyes rolling in amorous lights. Then the bolder one plucked at his arm and moved away, indicating that he was to follow; and the other one did likewise; and York turned his head this way and that, his eyes still rolling, to see where his master was. His master was not in sight.

Meanwhile the Indian man who had come with them was pestering Lewis. He knew that York had no presents to give. He knew that Clark was disgusted with his servant and would give none. So he sought Lewis out and through Gravelines presented his case: these were his wives, he said; they had many children and the children were ragged and half-dead from hunger. If he had a gun he would go find food for them. He wanted for the favors of his wives two tomahawks or a rifle, for they were the most beautiful women on earth. Or he would accept a cocked hat, a red jacket and a handful of blue beads.

Lewis, busy writing in his Journal, paid no attention to him.

A little later the red man and one of the girls returned to the pirogue but the other, the bolder one, refused to go. She flung herself to the earth and screamed. She was afraid to go back to her people, Gravelines said. She had a husband and she expected that he would cut her into small pieces. In turn she ran from captain to captain, flinging herself down and beseeching them.

"What's she saying?" Clark asked.

"That if you order her to go back she'll kill herself."

"Will she?"

"They sometimes do," Gravelines said. A red woman crossed in love could be ten times as violent as a white woman.

Clark turned to the Arikara chief who was going up the river with them. "Ask what he thinks."

Gravelines spoke to the chief. He then said to Clark, "He says take her along, she'll cost you nothing."

"Does she have a husband?"

Oh yes, of course, Gravelines said. Only the married women had love to sell. Perhaps the husband was off hunting, or down the river trying to get a Sioux scalp.

He was neither hunting nor down the river and the next day he appeared. A small group of Arikara Indians came up the river and called over to the captains, demanding that the woman be delivered to them. The instant the woman understood what they were saying she ran away and hid. Then across the waters came a loud angry voice. It was the furious voice of a warrior who said that this woman was his wife and he expected to be paid for her devotion to the white men.

Devotion is the word Gravelines used. "Devotion?" said Clark. "Captain Lewis has a number of words for it but I think he has never used that one."

"The sublime reciprocity of wills, I think he calls it."

Clark brought forth a few trinkets. He had sent two men to find the girl, and now they dragged her, clawing and shrieking, out of hiding and over to a boat. They flung her into it and took her and the trinkets to the opposite bank. On receiving the trinkets the delighted spouse began to talk; he was saying, Bob Frazier supposed, that the men could keep her a while longer for another payment like this one. When the keelboat's horn blew, calling the men back, the squaw eluded them and was into the pirogue before they could stop her. There she crouched low, as though hiding from her man. Her man did not seem to mind. He was turning the trinkets over in his hands and uttering little cries of delight.

She became York's woman—or girl really, for Gravelines said she was only about fifteen. Not until the white men came in sight of the Mandans did she decide that it was time to return to her people; and as she walked away, looking back at York, it was with more than reluctance. It was, some of the men felt, with heartbreak. As for the big Negro, he grinned and rolled his eyes while waving goodbye.

He knew that there were women on up the river; he had heard Tabeau say that they loved men with an ardor that made the Arikara women seem cold.

"I guess I'll get my color changed," Bob Frazier said, watching the Indian girl look back at no man but York.

"Holy grandma!" said Will Bratton. "Would my father believe it?"

"Two quarts of cedar berries and needles all steeped ten hours on a coal fire," Reuben Fields growled, "and then poured down him out of a wolf stummick."

"Bitter Alice," said his brother. "I took some and I feel the cramps yet."

Paddy Gass was shaking his Irish head and muttering in Dublin brogue. To think, he said, that he had lived to ondure this day!

10

On the way up the river the two captains, with Gravelines, had now and then walked along the bank with the Arikara chief, who seemed to be a friendly decent sort, they now concluded, in spite of his hysterics over the punishment of John Newman. He delighted them with his knowledge of wild animal life.

One afternoon they saw otter playing. The chief told them that when this beast was frightened, its scream was equaled in blood-curdling intensity only by the cry of two other things in nature, that of the loon and that of the eagle. He said the otter was all pure grit, that it had more grit than any other creature on earth. He told them that when a family was swimming in single file, the strange un-dulating movement just above and under the surface could be mis-taken, and by the foolish was, for a huge serpent.

The captains were more interested in the wild beasts ahead of them up the river. This chief told them what other men, both white and red, had told them, that up the river were bears so monstrous that they scared a man out of his wits just to look at them. His people, he said, would rather face the Sioux than these beasts. If, after long preparation, the boldest warriors decided to attack one of these giants, they went in groups of ten, twelve or even twenty, and then the outcome was likely to be in favor of the bear. This beast was so huge and powerful that with a full-grown deer in its jaws it would rush headlong to attack a hundred or a thousand men. Every other animal lived in terror of it. Wolves fled before it as before fire. Not even a whole gang of buffalo bulls dared to face it.

The captains were incredulous. They had both hunted and killed bears since the age of ten or twelve. They supposed that this chief, more wily than he seemed, was trying to discourage them from going up the river; for when they asked about the Blackfoot warriors this Arikara chief actually shuddered. He actually glanced round him like a man badly frightened.

"These bears," Lewis said to Gravelines, "can't be that big and terrible."

Had the captains seen their tracks? Yes, they had seen them and admitted that they were huge. The chief did not exaggerate, Gravelines said: this grizzled monster could gut a buffalo bull from shoulder to tail with one sweep of his talons. It was almost impossible to kill it, even if you shot it right through the heart. He had known one that was shot clear through ten times, yet ran away and escaped.

The captains glanced at one another. They didn't believe a word of it.

Tabeau and Gravelines told them many things that were calculated, the captains decided, to scare them out of their wits and send them back home. Tabeau even told them they would all get sick and die living on nothing but meat. One night Clark wondered if Tabeau was right: he was seized by an attack of pain in his neck that left him paralyzed. He could move only his tongue. Lewis brought hot stones wrapped in flannels and banked them against Clark's neck and upper spine. "Tabeau says if we eat only the muscle and not the viscera the way the Indians do we'll all get sick and die. I can almost believe it."

Clark suffered dreadfully but two days later was well enough to smoke a pipe of peace with a Mandan chief. The next day a great number of Mandan Indians came to the bank to see the white men, among them a warrior whose small fingers had just been severed at the second joint. This, Gravelines said, was to show grief. If the grief were deep enough over the loss of a loved one, the brave might cut off three or four or even eight fingers, for he had once seen a warrior with only two thumbs.

Looking at the two blood-reddened stubs, Lewis said, "Cutting off eight I expect would be for a wife."

Gravelines glanced at him and saw the droll lights in the slate-gray eyes.

A little later the captains met René Jessaume, about whom they had heard from Tabeau. Jessaume was a squawman who had traded among the Indians a long time. He was an old sneaking cheat, one

white trapper had said; and another had called him a worse thief
than any red man on earth—a skunk and a scoundrel who to the
white man's vices had added those of the Indian. What the captains
saw when Jessaume faced them was a dark, rather short and very
filthy Frenchman, with dirt in his hair and beard and an offensive
odor all over him. He did not meet a man's eyes but seemed to
stare at the point where his hair met his forehead. Because he spoke
some Mandan the captains hired him as an interpreter.

Their first task was to gather from him information about the
Mandan chiefs. The village they first came to was, as nearly as they
could spell it, the Rooptaree, and its principal chief was Poscopsahe,
meaning Black Cat. This chief, they had heard, was a good Indian;
after only two meetings with him Clark decided that Black Cat
had more integrity, firmness, intelligence and insight than any other
Indian he had known. At Matootonha the principal chief was
Shotaharrora, meaning Coal, who was really an adopted Arikara.
Next to him in rank was Shahaka, meaning the Coyote, but known
as Big White because, Jessaume said, he was more white than Indian. Big White, he said, was a loudmouth and a blowhard whom
Le Borgne, the Evil Eye, detested.

A mile on up the Missouri, at the mouth of Knife River, was a
village of the Anahaways, whose chief was White Buffalo Robe; and
up Knife River a few hundred yards was Metehartan, the first of
the Big Belly villages, whose chief was Black Moccasin. The over-
lord of the Big Belly or Minnetaree nation was old One-Eye, called
by Jessaume and some others Evil Eye. Jessaume said he was the
meanest man and the most bloodthirsty monster between St. Louis
and the headwaters of the Athabasca. His one woman was a
Minnetaree but for the captains Jessaume recommended the Mandan
squaws. He said they could really make medicine.

Clark was out looking for timber for a fort when Jessaume trailed
along, still jabbering in a jargon of French and English. If the
captains shied away from copperskins there were the almost-whites,
some with blue eyes, some with gray eyes, and now and then one
who actually had yellow hair. Most squaws were pretty bowlegged
and personally, Jessaume said, he liked them that way; but if the
captains did not, they would find that some of the almost-whites had
legs as straight as any woman in St. Louis. And breasts, *mon Dieu!*
But was it true, as his father used to say, that *on revient toujours à
ses premières amours?* He doubted that, he said. He had once loved

a white girl but now he loved his squaw and his little red children. . . .

Clark paid little attention to the man's chatter. He was feeling in his bones the coming of winter and he wanted to get warm lodges built, so that his men would be at top strength when spring came. No matter how much they discounted the stories of the hazards and perils before them it was no use pretending that the risks were not many and great. Strong men were braver men.

The Mandan lodges had impressed both him and Captain Lewis. From the outside, a lodge, except the entrance, looked like an enormous mound of earth; but on entering the captains saw that it was built of timber, in circular form, and covered over with earth and banked up with earth. Some of the lodges were ninety feet across but most of them were much smaller. In the center of each lodge was a square fireplace, about five feet on each side, set two feet below the surface of the floor. At the apex of the conical roof was a hole about four feet square, which when it rained was covered over with a buffalo hide or a bullboat. This hole served not only as chimney but also as window. The wide door was made of raw buffalo hides stretched on a frame, and hung in such a way that the door at night could be barricaded. The earth floors of the lodges were so hardened by use and heat, and kept swept so clean, that they looked polished, and in spots like marble or granite.

The captains were surprised to learn that these Indians slept on bedsteads: these were made of round peeled poles bound together with leather thongs: a green buffalo hide was stretched tight across the poles and made secure at the sides, and when it dried and contracted it became as taut as a drum. Uppermost was the fur side, on which they lay, with buffalo robes over them, and a folded robe as a pillow.

In the larger lodges as many as a hundred and fifty or even two hundred Indians lived, with their dogs and horses. In the lodge which the captains examined the horses were over at one side, nibbling at cottonwood boughs. Against the huge posts toward the middle, which supported the central part of the roof, leaned canoe paddles, bows and spears; and from poles hung from post to post five or six feet above the floor were suspended green pelts, arrow quivers, moccasins, stomach-pouches, and various garments which the squaws were mending. Here, as with the Arikaras, the occupants sat around half-naked in a chamber warmed by fire and by the heat of the beasts, the bucks sitting against poles and smoking, the squaws busy, as squaws always were.

The Mandans, unlike most Indian tribes, were not nomadic. They had settled down to a life of agriculture and hunting, and they fled their warm comfortable houses only when a stronger nation over-powered them. They lived, Tabeau said, in deadly fear of the Sioux, but seemed to like to wage war against the Arikaras.

The captains had brought the Arikara chief upriver to plead for peace with the Mandans; and when in council this was explained to the Mandan chiefs, one of them said it was all right, they would live in peace with the Rees, for they were tired of killing them anyway. This reason was so quaintly childlike that Lewis snorted. He then gave to the principal chiefs a flag and a medal, and a special com-mission from the White Father; and to the two top chiefs a coat, and a hat with plumes. One Lewis speech was so long-winded, with so many interruptions for translation, that a Big Belly chief sud-denly leapt up and said he must go home, for he smelled deception and double-talk here, and suspected that his village was being at-tacked. A Mandan chief chided him, and he again sat. Le Borgne was there, with the eyes of both captains studying him; he had come by special invitation, and his two eyes, one covered with a white film, the other fiercely black and glowing, kept moving in his skull as he sucked at his pipe and looked from captain to captain.

One-Eye had been suspicious from the start. On his first visit he had seen York and had stood for five minutes looking up and down the black giant. Gravelines said that old Evil Eye thought York was very bad medicine. He called for water, and when a pailful was brought to him he did his best to wash the black off one cheek. Fail-ing there, he scrubbed away at a hand. He looked at a palm and saw that it was whiter than the back of the hand, and for a few moments he washed the palm. He then stared at the fingernails. He told York to take a moccasin off, and then examined the foot, kneeling and grunting. York all the while rolled wild eyes at his master. Le Borgne gave up at last. He went away muttering to himself and turn-ing now and then to look back at York. He was very suspicious, Gravelines said. He knew that bad medicine was being used against him and was beside himself with fury because he couldn't figure out what it was.

Evil Eye decided that the medals and flags and hats with plumes were also bad medicine and he would have none of them. Tabeau had told the captains what to expect when this chief came. He gave them the story of Kakawita, principal chief of the Arikaras, an arrogant ferocious devil who had come into possession of magic. Like Blackbird, the Maha chief, when he foretold that a person would die the person died. There had never been an exception. He used some kind of poison, Tabeau supposed, but no white man had ever learned what it was. For the red people it was magic. Le Borgne, knowing that these palefaces had been with his enemies, the Arikaras, was doubly suspicious when he learned that an Arikara chief had come up the river with them. When a medal was given to him he hastily passed it on to a minor chief, and the bad medicine with it. A sharp observer of Evil Eye's face could have read in it the contempt for all the big brag and boasting of Chief Lewis. By the Great Manitou and the Unseen Spirit, what lies these were! Evil Eye knew that his own nation was the most powerful on earth, and could any day go down the Missouri and over to the village called Washington, and return with the scalp of the Great White Chief and all his preposterous braggarts. And so, smoking and glaring round him to keep the bad medicine away, he said nothing.

Aware of his hostility, the captains were uneasy. They rushed the building of the fort. They wondered if next spring the old murderer might follow them up the river with two or three hundred picked warriors—for these bold people, the Minnetarees, had gone clear to the Rocky Mountains a number of times, and had even fought the Blackfeet. The captains decided to keep an eye on this red giant with his eagle-beak and heavy lips. If things rubbed him the wrong way he might decide to enter a league with the Sioux for the extermination of the white party.

The captains were still searching up and down the river for a site for their winter camp when by accident or design one of the red people set fire to the prairie. Swept by a strong wind into enormous leaping manes of orange-red and smoke-black, the blaze overtook a Mandan buck and his wife and burned them alive while they ran; swept in mountainous red billowing over a man, woman and child and left them crawling away blackened and whimpering, all their hair and clothing burned off; and sent another mother fleeing for her life, but not before she had thrown a green buffalo hide, flesh side up, over her son and told him to be quiet. The boy under the hide was saved, not by the green hide, the Mandans said, but by the Great Medicine Spirit, who had watched over him because his father was white. Smiling a little, Clark entered it all in his Journal, and then went over to Lewis to observe him as physician and surgeon. The three half-burned-to-death creatures seemed to be dying yet made no moan. Even their eyes and eyelids looked cooked.

"I don't know what we have for burns," Lewis said, glancing up. He had been studying the list of medicines.

"A poultice? Have we anything for a poultice?"

"Maybe Juice-um knows of something."

Jessaume was lazy. He said he knew of nothing in the country roundabout that could be used as a poultice. He said the three Indians would die anyway. But Lewis mixed a few things into a paste and gently covered the wounds. Not once did man, woman or child wince under his fingers. He wished his mother was here; she would know what to do. He could amputate a frozen toe or finger, lance an abscess, give a purge or emetic and cut imbedded briars out of festering sores; but he had never seen such horrible burns and he didn't know what to do for them. When he turned away at last he felt half-sick with melancholy. Always he felt this way after ministering to Indians, for, like beasts, they were so mute and helpless. Like a dog's, their eyes looked at you with hope and prayer, and if you could do nothing for them they died uncomplaining.

The next day the father and mother seemed a little better, the child worse. Lewis searched in the woods but could find nothing for poultices. He wished he had enough soda to immerse all three in a big warm soda bath.

Hearing of Lewis as a medicine man, a great many Indians came to the river to see the white men but forgot the white men the moment their gaze fell on York. Like those down the river, they were unable to control their itch to touch him. With York it was becoming a kind of ritual. He loved it. He would let them wash and pinch and rub, his rolling eyes proclaiming his raptures; and at last he would astound them with feats of strength, or with his dancing. He was indeed, the captains decided, worth a bushel of blue beads.

It was York's dancing that held the Indians spellbound. Tuesday evening, October 30th, the captains gave their men a dram of what they called ardent spirits, and around a great fire some of the men danced. They danced square dances, with John Potts calling the turns. Some of the men made their own music by singing and shouting. But not York. He danced alone in his own solitary splendor and the eyes of all the red people were fixed on him. He was so loose and limber in his legs and joints—even, the captains had observed, in his elbows and shoulders—that no other man in the Corps would have thought of competing with him. His feet in his jigging and clogging were faster than the human eye, and on his lower legs the fringes of the buckskin leggings made a fantastic dance rhythm. His eyes rolled as if the swift movements of his feet and legs fed ecstasies upward to his swooning passions, until his whole big frame was atremble and on the point of melting in one overwhelming orgasm of all his senses. And here, as in the Arikara villages, the young wives swarmed round him, eager and squealing; and their husbands stood back, wondering how they could profit from it all.

York became the most talked-about and sought-after person in the whole Mandan area. And how he loved it! Though a slave on call to his master twenty-four hours a day he became more and more arrogant. He felt that if the women preferred him above all other men, red and white, there must be something special about him. He didn't know what it was but he knew that he had it and he was proud of it. The white men who danced and sang strove to fix on themselves the fascinated interest of the young women. Failing in this, some of them muttered threats against York, but Bob Frazier, the handsome fencing-master, composed rimes and sang to the girls. "O form devine wilt thou be mine?" he would sing, and blow kisses. He drew a twitter once in a while but nothing more.

"Just fill him full of bitter Alice!" Joe Fields cried.

But Bob Frazier sang, "Like whisky kegs those Mandan legs! Like pimpernel that bosom's smell . . . !"

Still, Frazier admitted aloud, it was hardly fair to charge these Mandan Indians with offensive odors, for they bathed two or three times a week, leaving their lodges early in the morning and going to the river. He and some of the other men spied on them. The women wore a leather skirt that reached a little below their knees. When a few yards from the water they unfastened the skirt and let it fall, and, running naked to the river, plunged in. They all seemed to be superb swimmers, young and old. Frazier thought the younger women almost beautiful when they unbraided their hair and let it fall in a wide mane down their backs. Some of the men had hair so long that the braids reached the earth, and it was not uncommon to see hair trailing on the ground.

November had come with bitter winds and cold, and Clark still sought timber for a fort. One day he took Paddy Gass and three other men and went back down the river. He felt miserable. He had rheumatism in his shoulders, across his lower back and down his legs; flashes of hot pain down his thighs; a sensation of ache and strain in his eyeballs. He supposed he had been using his eyes too much while bent over his drawings and map-making. The Mandan women had been generous; they had brought bushels of beans which, Juice-um said, they stole from the prairie mice. It seemed that the mice gathered this wild bean by the ton and stored it for winter use. The women, probing with sharp sticks, found the underground hoards and took them away. Oh, not all of them, Juice-um said: they left food for the mice, so that they could live and work again. The women had also brought a few bushels of corn and many squash. Clark hoped that eating this food and less meat would straighten him up.

Paddy was limping. "My ole knee-jints is pure onaisiness itsilf," he complained, limping along and grimacing. "Yisterdee I like to a-died. From me knees up to me chin it was all uv the thing."

"We need a big dost of something," one of the men said.

Clark while walking was looking for both timber and food. Juice-um—the men spelled his name variously in their journals but they all called him Juice-um—had said that besides meat the Indians of this area used black walnuts, hickory and hazel nuts, sweet acorns, prickly pear, as well as all wild fruits, including grapes, cherries, currants, plums, apples and pawpaws. Clark hungered for nuts and fruits. A part of his time he dwelt on the hazards that would face the Corps when, next spring, it entered the vast unknown, and among those hazards he now put a diet of nothing but muscle-meat. All the way up the river it had been meat three times a day, cooked in three big kettles. The flesh was stripped off the bones, cut into large chunks and thrown into the kettles to boil; and the men ate the chunks while clutching them with both hands, the juices running down their wrists to their elbows. They were such big hearty hungry men that they ate two or three elk, six or seven deer, or a big buffalo and a half every twenty-four hours. And most of them were complaining of rheumatism and tight bowels. What, Clark wondered, if across the unknown they were to find nothing to eat but flesh? They might all be laid low with rheumatic paralysis.

A mile downstream from the nearest Mandan village Clark and his group came to a flat bottom above the river, thick with cottonwood trees. The men went through the woods, straining their necks up. Cottonwood did not grow straight, save in the most favorable situations. Here the trees looked as though they had been whipped all their lives by winds.

Clark asked Gass if he could build lodges and a stockade of this timber.

Sergeant Gass, rolling his quid from cheek to cheek, looked up and squinted. The men all thought of him as an Irishman but his family had come from Scotland. He was part Irish. Now and then he talked in an Irish brogue of his own making, because he was a canny man who had learned that most people liked the Irish more than the Scotch. He had gone to school only nineteen days in his life and that was after he was grown, but he had picked up knowledge of a lot of things. He was an expert with broadhorns, scows and square-bows. He was an expert with an ax. For two and a half years he had been a carpenter's apprentice, and it was for this reason that Lewis and Clark had chosen him over a hundred other applicants. Paddy was their carpenter-in-chief.

A shrewd fellow, Paddy knew that a man should take his time before answering an important question. He had observed that the man who popped an answer right out was thought to be a fool. He tongued his quid and took his time, squinting this way and that. He walked deeper into the woods; squirting from one corner of his mouth; looking up and sighting and taking views in all directions. At last he turned to Clark and said the timber would do.

Standing back unobserved by Paddy and watching him was George Shannon. George was amused, but was remembering that Paddy had not amused the Mandan Indians. They had a stuff that they used as tobacco and they were boastfully proud of it. Paddy was a chewing man, not a smoker, and when the bucks pressed some of their tobacco on him he had stuffed his mouth full of it and pushed it around with his tongue, his face looking more and more offended. Then with one terrific explosion he had ejected the whole lot of it, and followed it with such loud curses that the Indians were outraged. Lewis, watching, had said quickly, "Sergeant, wars have been started over insults smaller than that." He told Juice-um to explain that Paddy's taste in tobacco was most peculiar, and then filled his pipe with the Indian weed and seemed to smoke with great enjoyment. The Indians felt better but not one of them had any more time for Paddy.

Paddy had gone around for an hour spitting and muttering to himself about the vile stuff. He was a man of strong prejudices. He didn't like Negroes and he didn't like Indians. As for the Mandan weed, it was not tobacco at all but a prairie plant that they harvested and smoked because they had nothing better. Paddy had learned with horror that if they had neither tobacco nor the prairie weed they then smoked buffalo dung, which they first scented with the sex glands of the beaver. It gagged him to think of the red man's ways. "The pups!" he said, muttering to himself while honing his ax. Pups was his word of utter contempt for all young men and for any older man who seemed full of ignorance and presumption.

The next morning the Corps moved to the river bottom, and Paddy and his men set to work. Clark, who had watched the building of winter forts under General Wayne, supervised the plans, while Lewis day after day, sitting by a cottonwood campfire, worked on the reports which he hoped to send downriver to Mr. Jefferson next spring. The stout log cabins and the stockade were built in the shape of a segment of pie, with the cabins opening inward. The stockade base was walled in with unusually large pickets. While the men labored under Gass, the greenhorns cutting themselves with their tools and raising blisters on their palms, there came down the river a French-Canadian trapper, who the past five years had been living with the Big Bellies. He said his name was Toussaint Charbonneau. He offered himself for hire as an interpreter.

Lewis didn't like the look of the man. He saw before him a Frenchman of above-average height, with long black hair, a heavily bearded face, cunning evasive eyes, and a posture that seemed to have in it the stoop of age. This man, he thought, was about fifty years old. He spoke in English so strongly accented that Lewis could barely understand him, but did make out that Charbonneau knew a lot of Indian languages and knew them well. That was good. The man said all the nations trusted him, including the Sioux. That was also good, if it was not a lie. The man said, "*Ou allez-vous?*" and when Lewis said sharply, "What did you say?" the Frenchman shrugged. Lewis called Labiche over. "Tell him I'll discuss the matter with Captain Clark and let him know."

During the next few days Lewis learned as much as he could about this man. All the red chiefs seemed to hold him in contempt: they had given him a half-dozen names, all derisive: he was the Great Horse from Abroad, the Forest Bear, the Man with Many Gourds, the Chief of Tiny Village, and Old Bean Poop. Juice-um, plainly not a disinterested informant, said that Old Bean Poop was the name Le

Borgne had given him. Old Bean Poop was a coward, Juice-um said; he couldn't swim a stroke, even though he had been on rivers all his life. He was a wife-beater and a raper of young girls—Juice-um said that when a squaw caught him red-handed with her small daughter she had shoved an awl halfway through him; and another had chased him with a flaming fagot right into the river, where the fool would have drowned if he hadn't hooked his chin over a piece of driftwood.

The thing most characteristic of him, Juice-um said, was his uncontrollable passion for immature girls. Old Bean Poop didn't like adult squaws. He wanted the young things, and the young things had been his to use and flog during all his years in Indian land. Had Captain Lewis heard of the Snake Indian girls? When only small children they had been captured by a marauding party of Big Bellies and brought all the way down the long rivers. Since that time the two girls had been any man's women, until they came into possession of Old Bean Poop, who had won them in a gambling game. Did the captains intend to visit the Snake Indians?

Knowing that the question was loaded, Lewis ignored it. He asked how old the girls were.

Juice-um didn't know.

They were Shoshone Indians?

"Oui, Cap-n."

Snake Indians! The Lewis mind was racing westward. "Where do the Shoshones live?"

Juice-um pointed into the west. They were yonder, he said, a long-far-distance. They were a thousand miles farther than any white man had ever gone. They were even beyond La Roche Jaune.

"Farther than the Blackfeet?"

"Ho-ho-ho!" Juice-um had to chuckle at that.

Did these Snake girls want to return to their people? *Mon Dieu, monsieur!* Had there ever been a captive Indian who did not want to go home? What were they now but slaves?—one man's today, another's tomorrow, depending on a game of chance—to be tomahawked at last or kicked out to the wolves.

Did they have children?

Mon Dieu! They were nothing but children themselves.

Lewis took the matter to Clark. It would be wonderful, he said, to have with them a Shoshone Indian, for undoubtedly they would meet the Shoshone nation; but on the other hand, it would be absolute lunacy to take a woman along. As for the squawman, what did Clark think of him?

"I don't like his looks."

"Juice-um says he beats small girls and rapes them."

"He looks about like it."

The first thing Clark saw in the girl when one morning she came to the white man's camp was her pregnancy. She looked grotesque because she was so small and her belly was so large. She had heard that the white men were going up the river next spring, and in her timid birdlike way she approached Clark, her black eyes on his face. She knew only a few English words and at first spoke in a French jargon.

"*La-haut?*" she said, pointing at the west.

Looking beyond her, Clark saw another woman, or child, and supposed that she was the other Snake girl. She was hanging back, watching and waiting. The girl before him—or child, for he could see that she was only a child—seemed intelligent. She had a rather long face, and a nose that was too flattened, but he found her appealing. He had a great love of children but he was not stupid enough to consider taking along a child who was pregnant.

He waved her away and returned to his work but she came again, this time in buckskin. He could now see that though pregnant she did not yet have a womanly form but looked almost pathetically small. Her braid of hair hung to her knees. She had a way of turning her head from side to side when looking at him; of cocking it a little, as though listening with the ear toward him; and then of cocking it the other way, as though to listen with the other ear. It was this in her that reminded him of birds—this and the intentness of her eyes.

The Mandans were calling Lewis Chief Long Knife because of the long sword he wore, and Clark they called Chief Red Hair. Clark was writing when she came up. She stood back and looked at his hair and for a little while he paid no attention to her. Then he sent for Labiche and with Labiche came Charbonneau.

Clark said to Labiche, "What does she want?"

Labiche took the girl aside and talked to her and Charbonneau. Then the three of them came over to Clark and Labiche said she wanted to go with the party next spring.

"She thinks we'd take a woman and baby? She must be insane."

Charbonneau said Indian women were not like white women. If

a nation was on the march an Indian woman could go to the bushes
and have her child and rejoin her people within an hour. A squaw
was used to hard work and hardship, and the baby would make no
difference at all.

"Ask her how far it is to her people."

"*C'est loin d'ici.*"

"I said how far?"

It was many sleeps.

"Tell her we can't bother with women and children."

But Clark again spoke of the matter to Lewis. He said that Indians
never looked on a party as warlike if the men had a woman with
them. It might be a tremendous advantage to have the squaw along.

"But what about the baby?"

"I thought possibly she could leave it here."

"But she might have another baby before we got back."

"I expect she'd want to stay with her people," Clark said.

"Is her man willing?"

"He seems to be."

Clark said he had heard that both girls were weeping most of the
time.

"Maybe their man is putting them up to it."

"That might be."

"I don't think we should bother with a woman," Lewis said.

Lewis had been looking curiously at his friend. Was there in Clark
a deep weakness for women? Or what was it?

Again the girl came to Clark and again Clark laid the matter be-
fore Lewis. Looking at him with mingled astonishment and wonder,
Lewis said, "If you want to take her along it's all right with me but
I wouldn't think we'd want to bother with more than one of them."

When Clark told the slave-girl they would take her she seemed to
take leave of her senses. She ran away shrieking and was so blind to
what she was doing that she bashed her face against a tree and
knocked blood from her nose. Then she was shrieking again, and
when she joined the other girl they both went running and crying
like two demented things.

With the help of George Shannon, who had the best ear in the
Corps, the captains tried to make out her name. Charbonneau made
gestures and they thought he was imitating the flight of birds. He
uttered two or three words over and over, and at last George said,
"Sack. Sack something." He wrote it down. After a while he had sack

a yar wee a and sack a jaw wee a. He wrote the name in still other ways and said he guessed her name was Sacagawea or Sacajawea. He asked Charbonneau to pronounce it again. Old Bean Poop had a thick tongue and spoke with a thick French accent.

"Does he mean bird-woman?" Lewis asked.

When Shannon made flight movements with his arms the squaw-man shook his head no and went through his act again. Sockakawea, Lewis thought it was. That, he said, was her Minnetaree name.

Sacajawea, George said. Clark said he would call her Jawey. That was good enough.

And so she was Jawey, the Snake slave-girl; and for her, Lewis was Chief Long Knife, because of the long sword he carried, and Clark was Chief Red Hair. She soon became devoted to Clark.

He said one day, "I expect we ought to make Shobono marry her."

Again Lewis looked curiously at his friend. He thought Clark must be woman-lonely. He was convinced of it when Clark moved the squawman and his two slave-girls into the white man's fort.

11

November 20th the winter quarters were completed and named Fort
Mandan, and the men moved in. They were now safe from Sioux attack but the captains never for a moment relaxed their vigilance.
They took for themselves a cottonwood cabin twelve feet square,
with a fireplace. For weeks now they had been looking forward to a
quiet winter, during which they would prepare for their President
various maps and data on the country they had traversed. They had
looked forward to a time when their men could get a lot of sleep and
build themselves up for the long dangerous trek that lay ahead of
them. The captains realized little by little that it would be more
perilous than they had thought. When, for instance, Clark called his
interpreters to the slave-girl and had them ask her about the Blackfoot nation she burst into tears and was so shaken by what Clark
took to be terror that she was unable to speak. An hour later Clark
was standing on an eminence and looking into the northwest, where
the Blackfeet lived. Were they, as all the trappers and traders
seemed to believe, the most savage and formidable Indians on the
continent?

Quiet the captains had hoped for but there was to be little of it.
Every day Indians came to pilfer and beg. Nearly every day one of
the white men got himself into some sort of trouble. There was Sergeant John Ordway, who had sense enough to know better but who
was an utter fool over women. A week before the fort was completed
a squaw had come screaming to Clark and had begged him to protect her. She had been stabbed three times and brutally beaten over
her face and throat. She was covered with blood. Because she was

wounded and in deadly fear of her mate Clark allowed her to remain with the two girls. In a few days she returned to her village.

Late one evening the man standing watch called to Clark. He said an Indian brave was ready to murder his wife. He was going to burn her alive. Clark summoned Charbonneau and hastened over. The Indian had his wife by the throat and while choking her until her eyes almost popped out of her skull he was dragging her toward a fire. Clark was surprised to perceive that this was the woman who had fled to him for protection.

Seizing the Indian, he flung him away from the woman, crying, "You damned fool, stand back!" To Charbonneau he said, "Make him understand that we won't have any wife-beating around this fort."

The woman had fallen to the earth and was trembling and moaning. Charbonneau talked to the Indian. The red man, it seemed to Clark, was terribly angry; never had he heard words spill with such fury and violence from a human mouth. The outraged husband was telling his story, not only with words but with wild gestures, now flinging an arm downward toward his woman, now toward the village. This is the story Clark heard from Charbonneau.

Sergeant Ordway had enjoyed the woman's good offices, with the approval of her husband, who had not minded at all until she ran away from him. Running away from her man was an offense punishable by death. But this husband was indulgent and loving and kind: he had not killed her, he had only stabbed her three times and tried to knock some sense into her head. But the fool had run away again. Now there was only one thing that her proud and insulted husband could do—he would have to kill her, and he had thought fire as good a way as any.

The brave said that if the white man wanted her he could have her, but he would not put up with a wife who kept running away from him. Clark sent a guard to fetch Ordway and meanwhile tried his hand at giving the red man a lecture. Through Charbonneau he told him that marriage was a sacred bond between man and woman, to be respected and cherished; that he should take his wife back to his lodge and be kind and gentle to her. Clark spoke further in the same moralizing vein, while Old Bean Poop translated, his astonishment growing.

"He haz zee right—zee right to keel her."

"Rights be damned, we won't have this sort of thing around here."

"He take her zair to keel her." Charbonneau meant to the Mandan village.

At this moment Ordway came up to face his angry captain. "Sergeant, were you with this man's wife?"

"Yes, Captain."

"Did he give you permission?"

"Yes, sir."

"Did you pay him for it?"

"No, sir."

"Then do so, make him feel all right about it."

"Yes, sir."

"And understand this, Sergeant, you're not to molest this woman again, or any of the men. Tell them that. I think it would be well if all of you left the Mandan women alone."

"Yes, sir. You know, sir, they keep after us."

"Oh, I know it but I haven't seen any of you running from them."

At this moment a big chief of the Mandan nation came up. Charbonneau told him what had happened, and at once the chief stepped over and slapped the outraged husband on his red cheek. The crestfallen man slunk away, his wife with him, and the chief marched after them, his angry voice shouting. He was telling them, Charbonneau said, to get to their lodge and be a good husband and wife and not bother the white men any more.

Clark returned to his cabin. A big fire was roaring in the fireplace and Lewis was sitting before it, smoking his pipe. Clark sat on a piece of tree stump by the fire. He ran a calloused hand through his golden-red hair and looked over at his friend.

He told Lewis about Ordway and the squaw. "I ordered him not to touch them any more or any of the men. Did you know we have some bad cases of Louis Veneri?"

Lewis removed his pipe and looked at Clark.

Clark went on: "The French and Canadian trappers say that with these Missouri Indians it's never very serious but it's bad enough to lay a man up. It'll be a fine note if we have to set out with weak men."

"I've been thinking about it," Lewis said. "Will it be like this all the way to the ocean?"

For a little while they were silent. Then Clark said, "Men will be men, we both know that. We've seen them in one campaign after another. If we put the squaws out of bounds would the morale of our men collapse?"

"I expect it would. Bean Poop has three women. Are they healthy?"

"Two of them are pregnant."

Lewis's brows shot up. "The otter-girl too?"

"Besides, they're only children."

Lewis smoked again and looked at the fire. "How old you think Jawey is?"

"Well, from the time she came here she was any man's woman. Shobono says this is her first pregnancy, so she can't be much over thirteen or fourteen." Clark looked behind him at his bed. He was weary. Some of his men had gathered dry moss, buffalo grass and small green twigs to make mattresses for the captains but their beds were hard. Hard beds had never bothered him, Clark said, before he got rheumatism.

Clark said, "Did you know the girl who's going with us is a princess?"

Again Lewis's brows shot up. "A princess?"

"Her brother is the big chief of the Shoshones."

"I'll be damned," Lewis said. "That's better than blue beads. We shouldn't have any trouble with those Indians. Will she go all the way to the ocean with us?"

"She has promised to."

"Well," said Lewis, knocking his pipe out, "I didn't think we should bother with a woman and a baby but if she's really the chief's sister, and we have to have horses to cross the mountains— Do her people have horses?"

"Many horses, she says."

"But if she dies what'll we feed the baby? Buffalo milk?"

"She says we'll all die. Says the Blackfeet will kill us all."

"Yet is willing to go with us."

In their separate beds the captains lay cozily under their robes, thinking of their problems. They had a lot to worry about besides what they called Louis Veneri. Right now, at the end of November, traders were coming down from Canada to poison the minds of the red people. The chief liar and British agent of the whole lot was a man named Larocque, whose name Clark wrote in his Journal as Le rock. Le rock had been busy giving British medals and flags to the Minnetaree and Mandan chiefs. When the captains learned of this they withdrew to their cabin to talk it over.

They simply had to stop him, Lewis said. Jefferson expected them to claim this entire country for the United States, and here were the damned British right under their noses, lying a blue streak.

"Yes," Clark said, "we must stop him but unless we're careful we'll have the whole Hudson Bay and North West companies down here."

"This Le rock is a smart thief and liar. We can't pretend to him we're just studying minerals and reading the stars. Lord, did you see how he looked at us? Like he figures we're bigger liars than he is. What I wonder is if a British party is already up the river ahead of us, or intend to be next spring. If they reach the ocean first this whole vast land will be part of His Majesty's dominions."

"We'd have to fight them in that case," Clark said.

"The President thinks we'll have to someday anyhow."

The captains decided to invite some of the chiefs over. The wide river was full of floating ice and the sky of snow when Black Cat and some other important chiefs came to the fort. The captains showed them all the big medicine, including the swivel guns, the airgun, compasses, watches, thermometers, field glasses; and gave them generously of tobacco, beads, awls, knives and pork; and gently lectured them, saying through interpreters that the British trader Le rock had no right at all to give them medals and flags, that only their American Father had this right. He would be offended if they accepted such symbols from the British and French. The chiefs, paying no attention, hugged their gifts to them and set off under the gray loveliness of winter storm.

The next day, traipsing through snow more than a foot deep, Le rock came to call on the captains. Lewis thought it the right time to give him a piece of his mind.

"By the way," he said, after the formalities were over with, "we've heard you're making British chiefs with medals and flags. Is it true?"

Larocque took his time and coolly studied his man before replying. "I've given them a few things," he said. "It's customary."

"You're making them British chiefs?"

"Oh no, my dear Captain. I've no such thought."

Studying the man with eyes as cool and steady as Larocque's own, Lewis thought, You damned liar you! He said, "We're willing to share Shobono with you as translator, on condition he won't translate anything except what concerns the business of trading."

The more diplomatic Clark spoke up, saying, "Of course we're far from thinking you'd ask him to."

But the damage was done. The blunt Lewis had angered Larocque and he made no effort to conceal his anger. "I deny everything you seem to be charging me with," he said coldly. "I can hardly give flags and medals, since I brought none with me. Good day, Captains."

The captains watched him stride away. Lewis said, "I raised hell that time. Where the British are concerned I don't seem able to keep my mouth shut." He thought a few moments and added, "Well, if they didn't intend to beat us up the river they'll surely try to now. All because Meriwether Lewis has no gumption."

"We have to get the Indians on our side," Clark said, "but I can think of no way to do it."

A way to do it came, as if from heaven. The captains knew that in some of the Indian chiefs resentment toward them had been growing. Lewis one day called on a Big Belly chief and knew he was snubbed when a brave waved him away and said in signs that the chief was not home. Another chief had told Charbonneau that the white men had so much ammunition that they wasted it shooting at targets, yet gave them none. Black Moccasin had never once come to the councils, having arrogantly sent in his place a minor official named Cherry-on-a-Bush. Lewis was convinced that White Buffalo Robe Unfolded, of the Anahaways, had openly sneered at him.

So matters stood for three days after Larocque's call. Then early one morning Clark heard an Indian yelling across the river and sent a boat to fetch him. Through Charbonneau the red man had this story to tell. Five Mandan braves had gone hunting into the southwest and had been ambushed and set upon by a war-party of Sioux and Pawnees. One brave was slain, two wounded, and nine of their horses were stolen. The Anahaways had reported four of their men missing, and said they expected to be attacked by the Sioux any day.

Seeing the golden opportunity, Clark laid the matter before Lewis and he agreed that now was the time to make a stand. If the Sioux were on the warpath and were coming north, all their ancient enemies should march south to meet them. Clark sent word to them that he would march at their head. At once he organized a war-party of twenty-three men, chosen for their courage and their skill with rifles, and within an hour after the red man told his story, Clark was crossing the river with his party and a few minutes later marched into the first of the Mandan villages. He had not foreseen the result. His men, armed to the teeth, presented such a formidable and terrifying appearance that nearly all the Indians ran away, shrieking with fright.

Clark had brought Old Bean Poop with him. He now ordered him to tell two Mandan chiefs, standing off at a distance and shivering, that the white brothers had come to the aid of the red, as the Great Father in Washington had said they would. Now was the time to wipe the Sioux off the earth. So let them come, all the brave Mandan warriors, and with their white brothers in the lead they would all march away.

Charbonneau had barely ceased speaking when there was consternation throughout the village. While most of the warriors were running away to hide, the chiefs went into a conference, their voices becoming loud and hysterical, their gestures frantic. Clark pulled his coat collar up around his face to hide his amusement. He had never had a high opinion of the red man as a fighter or of the red man's courage. Pretending to be inspecting his weapons, he waited, and presently the talkative and flabby Big White stood before him, shivering and gesturing. His people, he said, were pleased to learn that their white brothers had not spoken with a forked tongue when they offered friendship; he said the Pawnees and Sioux were all liars and cheats and bad men; he said his people had made peace with them again and again, only to fall under treacherous attack; and at last, his full round womanly face twitching with emotion, he said that the snow was too deep now, the cold too dreadful, for his men to go to war. It would be better to wait till spring.

Affecting anger and contempt, Clark cried, "Until spring, does this man say? Tell him we go now, right this moment, to shoot his enemies! Tell him to bring all his warriors and march with us!"

But Big White shivered and said again that it was much too cold. He would never take his horses out in such weather as this.

"Horses, does he say? Does he see us on horses? Tell him he and his warriors will walk with us and destroy the Sioux!"

Big White was shivering all over. He said his warriors would have to ride. It was a long way and it would tire them out to wade in the deep snow.

"Tell him to be done with these evasions! Tell him we are here to fight and will he go fight with us, or will he and his warriors go back to the squaws?"

Seeing Big White wince, Clark knew that he had understood. But he wouldn't budge. Again in a loud voice Clark called on him and

all his warriors to come at once and march away to fight, but the
flabby chief shivered and looked over at the warm lodges. He said
they would have to wait till spring.

"Then why," Clark demanded, his voice seeming to ring with
anger, "why did he send the messenger to us?"

The women, Big White said, had been wailing and the children
crying because their brave men had fallen; but now they would scatter their tears and weep no more. Now they would rejoice in the
friendship of their white brothers.

Clark looked at the big fat man with contempt that he hoped
would wither him. Then he gave a loud command and in military
formation his men marched away, with every Indian in the village
gawping after them. This dramatic display of friendship and power
would, Clark hoped, give the Mandans and Minnetarees a change
of mind—for he had no doubt that the Indians for miles around,
perhaps clear to the Sioux, would know all about it before sunset.
Returning to the cabin, he said to the amused Lewis, "Not a single
damn one of them would go."

"You didn't expect they would, did you? What did Big White say?"

"Shivered and whined."

Two days later Clark was working on a map when the heavy door
of his cabin opened a little and two black eyes looked in. It was the
Shoshone princess.

Sharply he said, "What do you want?" The face vanished, the door
was closed. He sat in thought. Since he moved her and otter-girl
and their man into the fort, Jawey had fluttered round him like a
bird; smiling if he looked at her; just softly disappearing if he did
not. He realized that she was trying to express her gratitude.

He was again bent over the map when a sergeant came to say that
the Indian girl wished to see him. He did not know what for. She
had been slipping around in the villages, looking and listening. He
thought she had heard that the British intended to stop the Corps.

"How?"

"By arming the Sioux."

"I don't doubt that," Clark said.

Traders coming down from the north, Sergeant Pryor said, were
telling the Indians that these white long knives were liars and cheats;
that the United States Army itself was puny and cowardly——

"What is that?" Clark roared.

"Captain, I'm just telling you what she tells her man and he tells us."

"Of course. Go on."

"The traders tell them we talk big brag and promise big but will double-cross them when spring comes."

"Better send her and her man in."

When the squawman and his slave came to the door Clark ushered them in and told them to sit on a pile of wood. He then studied them a few moments. When he looked at the girl she gave him a quick little childlike smile but the smile vanished when he looked at her man. Her man was not looking at Clark. He never did.

"Has your squaw learned something from British traders?"

In a halting jargon of English, French and Indian, Old Bean Poop said what Pryor had said. Was he telling the truth, or hoping to win a whisky ration? Clark at first had thought that this man was all French but had heard that a part of him was Indian.

"Have your women go to the villages and learn all they can."

"*Oui*. Zee femme weesh make un bawx."

"A box? For me?"

"*Oui*."

"Well, that's very fine. Now you can go."

The slave-girl passed through the door behind her man and before closing it looked back a moment and smiled. Clark hardly knew what to make of her. She had made for Sergeant Gass a handsome razor box of carved wood, with an adjustable cover. Clark supposed that Gass had shown her some kindness.

The red people had said it would be a cold hard winter and they were right. The night of December 13th the thermometer stood at twenty below zero, and the captains shivered in their beds all night, even though they had a blazing fire. The next morning when Clark opened the door he felt the cold enter and fill him with paralyzing swiftness, and with a grunt of astonishment he slammed it shut. He walked over to the fire, rubbing his hands.

Three days later, with the cold abating only a little, a man named Hugh Heney, together with Larocque and one named George Bunch, came to see the captains, looking frozen and walking so stiffly that their knees bent hardly at all. In the warmth of the cabin Heney proffered a letter from Charles Chaboillez, boss of the North West Company on the Assiniboine. By firelight Lewis and Clark read it. Chaboillez expressed an eagerness to be of any service to them within his power. With neither captain's face revealing a thing, Lewis returned the letter and with it his thanks. He then had a big kettle of hot boiled elk brought in, deep in its rich broth, and with tin cups as tools the five men sat before a roaring cottonwood-log fire and ate. They'll come to it in time, Lewis was thinking—and a vision of the future United States stood in his mind as big as a continent. This was what the slave-girl had been trying to tell them, Clark was thinking, and fed tender dripping elk flesh into his bearded mouth, washing it down with hot broth.

The captains had sensed that Heney was an intelligent man, with more formal education than they had had. They glanced at him now and then, as the five of them ate without speaking. Then at last, with the most extreme politeness, Heney asked why they had come to this country and what their goal was. In the mischievous mind of Lewis the vision enlarged to embrace Canada, and the unknown land called California, and all the land south of the Big River.

He said, "We like this kind of life. We've some knowledge of plants and minerals, and so thought we'd take a little journey in the interest of science."

Clark said, "Captain Lewis is collecting seeds. I expect he has more than a hundred kinds already, and some of them might do for beauty or profit in the United States."

"President Jefferson is interested in plants of all kinds," Lewis said.

Heney nodded, his face revealing nothing. He said he had heard that there had been a change in government. Just what was that?

Lewis said, "The United States bought Louisiana from the French." He stopped there. He wanted to force Heney's hand.

Heney asked in his grave polite way, "Does your President feel that you're in Louisiana now? Is all this a part of what you bought?"

Lewis was trying to formulate a prudent reply when the more tactful Clark said, "As scientists we haven't been thinking about where Louisiana is or isn't. We're here to get specimens of seeds, animals and minerals. We even hope to take a wild goat back."

Heney was nodding and eating. Larocque was just eating and looking from face to face. Heney said he could give them sketches of the country between the Mississippi and the Missouri, if they had use for them, as well as information about Indian tribes farther west, if they were going farther west. *If* they were going farther: how softly he had spoken the word! Lewis said they would like to see the sketches. As for Indians, was not the whole western part of the continent peopled with them? And were not the Blackfeet always on the warpath?

Heney gave no reply. They were all fencing and nobody knew it better than he.

Because it was such bitter cold outside Lewis invited the three men to spend the night in the fort. They accepted, and were assigned to one of the sergeants. With the utmost politeness the five men bade one another goodnight, and the captains were alone.

"I hope the good Lord knows what he's doing," Clark said, opening the door a half-inch to sense the cold's intensity.

Gass, who had been out for wood, said trees were splitting open, and wolves were moving like things poured full of ice. The river here at the fort was now frozen clear across its fifteen hundred feet, and the three boats were stuck fast in the ice.

The next night the mercury dropped to forty-two below zero, and just keeping alive became the primary task of every man in the fort. Charbonneau's slaves heated stones for him and gave him part of their bedding. If the cold did not abate soon the fort would run short of wood, and what man would dare to venture out? When it had been only ten below zero a group of hunters had gone to the prairie and returned badly frostbitten; and since then it had become commonplace to see men sitting dolefully with their naked feet thrust into a pail of water and floating ice. York had crossed the river and wandered toward the Mandan villages, to learn if any young squaws were pining for him. He had come limping back with his feet so badly frozen that he had had to cut his moccasins off. He said it felt as if he had ice instead of marrow in his leg bones.

This night the captains did not go to bed. They sat huddled by the fire, one of them rising now and then to throw wood on. There wasn't much heat in cottonwood, Clark said; it was pulpy and porous and not much good for anything. But it had a wonderful scent when burning, Lewis said. How were the squirrel and the hen doing? He looked over at his dog, sitting on his haunches, shivering. It wasn't the shivering on a man's surface that hurt, Clark had said, but the shivering deep inside him—the cold in his organs and along his veins. The hen and the squirrel? He supposed they were all right. If a hen couldn't stand it in a cabin what would all the hens outside do? The captains were determined to send a few live things to their President and had captured a squirrel and a hen. The squirrel they had brought to the surface by pouring water down its hole. It had come up drenched and gasping and feeble but not too feeble to sink its long sharp chisel-teeth into a Lewis finger when he picked it up.

Clark said he wondered how cold it was on the Assiniboine, and Lewis said he hoped it was cold enough to send the damned British back home.

Clark stood up and walked along the cabin walls, looking at them. The entire wall opposite the fire was gray with hoarfrost. Between the logs the builders had chinked with split pieces and then daubed over the chinking with clay, inside and out; but the clay had cracked and in many places shrunk from the upper log or the chinking, and when Clark put a cheek close to the wall he could feel the cold air coming in from outside. Except that it was not like cold air; it was coldness itself, so pure and intense that it stung like flame. He held a hand up against the roof timbers to see if it was warmer up there. In places the hoarfrost was a lovely filigree of tiny spires that looked like the whiskers of some little ancient man out of the far north.

Lewis came over to the opposite wall for a drink of water. When he saw that the water in the pail was frozen over he stood and looked down at it, as any man might who doubted his senses. "I wonder if it gets this cold all the way up the Missouri." He turned to look at the fire: it was blazing brightly in pale yellow, orange and charcoal dusk. Stooping, he put a finger to the ice and broke it. He then studied the hoarfrost, and looking up at the roof timbers, saw that they were frosted over too. He went over and looked at the logs above the fire and would not have been surprised to have seen frost there. Throwing on more wood, he again sat, hands outstretched, a heavy buffalo robe down over his shoulders and back.

"Why is it women stand cold better than men?"

Clark said he had no idea. He didn't pretend to know much about women.

It occurred to Lewis after a while that he ought to look in on the men to see how they were doing but he shuddered right down the marrow of his bones when he saw himself opening the door and stepping outside. He could feel it now, could feel the cold come in and fill him so swiftly that he just stood there, unable to move. He could feel it over his face like an intense heat; in his mouth like the heavy fumes of some deadly acid; and like a burning down his throat. Yesterday when he was outside, the end of his nose felt as if it had dropped off. He could feel the cold isolate every tooth as it entered him, and numb his gums. Almighty Lord, he had never known such cold as this, nor had Clark or any of the men. The red men had their horses in their big lodges tonight, where the scrawny beasts with raw sores on their backs were chewing cottonwood twigs in a slow weary cynical way, pausing now and then to heave their lean sides up with a long-drawn breath. He wondered why Indians were so brutal with their beasts. It didn't make sense. A horse with a back raw and festering was not a good mount. Recalling Clark's words of a few moments ago, he fell to thinking about Indian women. They stood the cold better than their men. In recent days both men and boys had been to the fort with frozen hands and feet, and already he had amputated about a dozen black toes. But no females had come. Just the same, they were out every day gathering wood. It had been a cold day when one of the chiefs came, his squaw trudging behind him with a hundred pounds of corn on her back. The chief's feet had been half-frozen in his moccasins, but her feet, in moccasins older and thinner, had seemed to be all right. Of course the labor of carrying such a burden had warmed her through. . . .

"I expect I'll be cutting off a lot of toes tomorrow," Lewis said. "Maybe even some feet."

Lewis got up and stood by the fire, with two of his heaviest robes around him. He said he expected he ought to see how the men were doing. At the heavy plank door he stood a few moments before he could believe what he saw: it was entirely covered with frost. He touched the head of an iron spike and found the flesh of his finger stuck to it. "My God!" he said. "What a night!"

As quickly as he could he opened the door, stepped outside and banged it behind him. He was holding his breath but he then made the mistake of sucking in a huge gasping gulp of air, and it was so deadly in its cold that it choked him. For a few moments he seemed unable to move. Then, again holding his breath, he ran to the nearest cabin, a leanto that had been built of leftovers for the squawman and his girls. He rapped only once on the ill-fitting door before plunging inside. Taking a breath, he went over to the fire where the three of them sat huddled, with the man in the warmer and the women in the colder positions. Lewis stood above them, looking down, and the two girls looked up.

"How are you?" he asked, looking into the eyes of Sacajawea.

She was smiling up at him. He wondered what a slave-child owned by a brute could find to smile at. Old Bean Poop, bowed under heavy robes, seemed to be talking to himself. As nearly as Lewis could understand him, he was saying that he had a terrible pain in one side, deep in him, as though a knife had been left there. He needed a drink of wheeskee.

"Are you warm?" Lewis asked, looking at the pregnant girls. Jawey nodded her head yes. She was, he thought, the most cheerful human being he had ever known. Never had he seen her downcast, save for a few moments after her man had slugged her; never touched by that melancholy that lay so heavy upon him. He looked round to see how much wood they had. Then, taking a deep breath and holding it, he bolted outside and for the cabin occupied by the sergeants. He found them sitting by a fire with robes over them.

"Don't get up," he said when they moved. He went over and looked at their upturned faces. "How's everyone?"

"All right, Captain," Pryor said.

"Plenty of wood?"

"We have fifty or sixty cords outside."

"That's a lot of wood," Paddy Gass said.

"Aren't you going to bed tonight?"

"The trouble is," said Ordway, "if we make one bed who gets to sleep in the middle?"

"How are Newman's feet?"

"Frozed bad," Gass said, "but he walks."

Ordway said, "He worries because he can't go next spring."

Lewis looked in turn at the sergeants. "If we let the bars down for one, soon the corral's empty. None of us would come back alive."

"We understand that, Captain," Pryor said.

Ordway said, "That otter-girl, she bawls half the time."

Lewis thought about otter-girl after he returned to his fire. He had seen the poor thing hiding in a thicket and weeping. He had felt deep pity for her. Here she was, a child, a slave-child, a thousand miles or more from her own people; any man's slave to use, to stab, to tomahawk, to shove into a fire. She wanted her own kinsfolk, land, customs, language, but he and Clark had their stern and inexorable duty. They had in their care and would have clear to the ocean and back the lives of twenty or thirty men and it would be cowardly to risk those lives for an Indian girl.

Yes, he had seen her weeping. She had asked Old Bean Poop to tell him that she would be no bother. She would find her own food. She would help row or tow the boats or she would walk. She could carry burdens. Oh, she would be no bother at all! But Lewis knew the gallantry of men—knew that they would risk their lives, might indeed risk the life of the whole party, if the girl needed them. It simply couldn't be. He told Clark what Ordway had said and Clark said he had seen her weeping.

Lewis said, "I can't convince myself we should take her."

Clark was thoughtful a few moments. Then: "We both know that no commander has a right to endanger his men by doing what isn't necessary. It may not be at all necessary to take the other girl."

The princess, Lewis said, might be of great help to them. "But I can't see that otter-girl could help us at all."

"I can't either," Clark said. The captains did not speak of the matter again.

Midnight found them still by the fire, all their robes over them. Lewis thought it might fall to fifty below tonight. The poorer wolves would all freeze to death, and only God knew how many buffalo, elk and deer. Wild chickens would freeze hard sitting on their roosts. . . .

Clark was thinking of their men. On leaving St. Louis they had intended to take only ten or twelve with them beyond the Mandan villages, but if their journey proved half as dangerous as the traders said it would be they'd need more men than that. They'd never get past the Blackfeet with so small a force. Which men they were to take was the problem now. They hadn't seen them under fire. Four of them—Hugh Hall, Silas Goodrich, Richard Windsor and William Werner—were from the First U. S. Infantry and had seemed to be good men. Some of the others seemed to be good men. One trouble was that they had to take some who were skilled men rather than fighting men—like John Shields, the gunsmith; half-blind Cruzatte, the boatman; Paddy Gass, the carpenter.

Some unsuspected virtues had been showing up this winter—such as the phenomenal marksmanship of Drewyer, the sensitive ear of George Shannon, the fiddle playing of Cruzatte and Gibson, the unfailing good humor of John Potts, a fat Dutchman who stuttered to beat the band but could jig almost as well as York. . . .

A wind had risen and was howling in winter madness around the stockade and cabins. It turned Clark's thoughts to the world outside— to the broad river that would freeze still deeper tonight; to the herds of buffalo huddled together out on the prairie, their rumps to the wind. How many of them were there? In October he and Lewis had stood on a hill and counted fifty-two separate herds. Indians said that far up the river—around the Great Falls—they were thicker than stars on a clear night. And the wolves were even thicker. Several times here Clark had seen a herd of buffalo making for a new pasture with wolves trailing; had seen the wolves pounce on any calf that fell a little behind, and watched the enraged mother turn and charge, again and again, but quickly give up and abandon her child and hasten to overtake the herd. How quickly the animal mother forgot! Once he had seen a furious bull dip his horns, throw up his absurd little tail and charge, at the moment when another bull charged the same wolf from another direction. The luckless beast had been caught between two great skulls of bone, with time left for only one anguished yelp. Thinking of wolves reminded him of three of their men who had gone hunting and walked too far to return that night: they had managed to shoot a wolf, an old mangy half-starved thing, and with its pelt had somehow kept from freezing through the long night. The next afternoon they had tottered in more dead than alive. . . .

"I expect we better take about thirty men," Clark said.

Lewis stirred under his robes. "I expect so," he said. He was smoking a strong dry tobacco and looking into the flames. He was thinking of the faraway Rocky Mountains—snowcapped even in August, the Big Bellies said—and wondering what dangers those mountains held for them. "About thirty," he said, after a while. "We better make a list one of these days."

Then there was silence, except for the winds, the two captains sitting with all their bedding draped over them, waiting for the morning.

12

In spite of the cold it was a busy winter for the white men. Some were making cottonwood dugouts; some, ropes of deer, elk and buffalo skin; and some were making battle-axes and spear points of sheet metal, to trade to the Indians. Nearly every day some were out on the hunt.

Lewis spent long hours classifying and arranging his data on Indian tribes; Clark bent over his maps. They had induced Indian chiefs to sketch for them on white tanned hides or in the earth or on the peeled cabin walls the chief landmarks known to them up the river, the distances in sleeps. But Indian knowledge ran out beyond the Great Falls.

After the terrible cold abated, the brave who had been eager to burn his wife brought her and his other wife to the fort. In his sly mind he hoped to do a little business, though he said he had come to apologize. He lamented so and wept so over having stabbed and beaten his woman that he became a nuisance and after a while nobody would listen to him. Clark was bent over a map, Lewis was operating on a big abscess on a child's neck. The lad set his teeth and did not flinch when with a razor blade Lewis cut deep into the swollen mess, and then with both hands squeezed the pus out. Then the mother took the boy home.

The red people were told to stay away December 25th, Old Bean Poop explaining to them that this was a big medicine day. At daylight guns were fired, and then the swivel guns, and a flag was run up. Each man was given a glass of rum. From the precious hoard of food a few delicacies were drawn by the mess-sergeants, such as flour and dried apples, to go with the elk flesh and boiled corn. After the feast most of the men danced the afternoon and evening away. Some of them looked pretty foolish when dancing with one another: only the other day a group of squaws and of men dressed as squaws had come to trade corn and beans for ribbons and beads. The men dressed as women were known as berdashes, and among Indians, Lewis gravely recorded in his Journal, a berdash seemed in no way to be held in low esteem. Some of the white men stared at them with scorn; but not York. Assuming a kingly posture, with folded arms and uptilted head, he had walked around with his haughtiest air, his eyes never once turning to the homosexuals dressed as squaws.

For music Cruzatte played his old fiddle, Potts called the turns, Frazier sang his foolish rimes, and Shannon with the bugle tried to emphasize the high notes. Some of the men danced like creatures possessed. York was by himself, a solo figure, his moccasined feet beating out their own music while his eyes rolled upon the two slave-girls. Potts had a mind that ran to obscene verses, sometimes of his own composing: today he was trying to say amusing things about the berdashes but the rum had thickened his stutter and called forth a strong Dutch accent. "Bird ash oh bird ash!" he called, and some of the men applauded and strained their ears. But Potts got stuck on a word and could only say, "Mup—mup—mup——" his jaws working convulsively. "Mup what?" a voice yelled. "Come, John, say mup the pup or something!" But John couldn't get the mup off his tongue. He staggered over and fell on a robe by the fire, his belly heaving.

From Tabeau the men had heard that the Mandans had a buffalo medicine dance around the first of the year. It was a fertility dance, really. Its purpose was to quiet the buffalo and bring the big herds in close, so that Indians could kill them with arrows. The cows, it was said, were so suspicious that they would never come in until sacrifices had been made to them. What sacrifices? the men had asked. Tabeau had rolled his eyes in imitation of York and said that such medicine was not for boys.

The captains held aloof from such things but let those men go who wished to. Cruzatte preferred to play his fiddle and dream of things known only to him; the Fields brothers and John Colter to take their guns and try for a fresh elk. York had again frozen his feet; Drewyer had seen enough Indian rites to last him a lifetime; a few of the men were sick. But a small group of them went to the village, where in the largest of the lodges the rites would be held, three days and nights running.

They opened with a big feast and the white men decided that they were not hungry. They didn't like the way squaws handled food. It made some of them gag to see the way Indians cut out a buffalo or elk stomach, filled it with water and tipped it up and drank; or ate animal guts without turning them inside out to wash them; or gulped down a hunk of liver with the gall bladder attached. Did the squaws ever wash a kettle? From meat simmering on a fire did they ever dip out the stray insects that came unwarily down? The white man's mess left a lot to be wished for but the cooks did dip the bugs out and they did wash their kettles.

Bob Frazier was watching the Indians eat. He was pretending to eat; he was making the movements of chewing but all the while he was covertly burying a piece of buffalo neck in the earth floor of the lodge. Centrally located was a huge fire, with Indians seated around it. Over at one side were the prettiest wives of the young bucks. Tabeau, the liar, had said they would be naked but these girls were robed.

Across the fire from the young women, so that they all looked at one another through firelight, were their husbands, also seated in a row. At some distance from where the white men sat, over at a far side of the lodge, a number of old men—some so old that they were toothless and tottering and almost blind—were huffing and roaring; pawing at the earth to make the dust fly; bellowing and falling to their hands and butting at the earth with their heads; and in every way possible imitating the bulls out on the prairie. The white men stared at them, fascinated. They had heard Tabeau tell about it but had never dreamed that the old fools would make such a racket and raise so much dust and knock such loud grunts out of themselves. They were all naked. It was John Potts to whom the thought occurred that the old men-bulls were pretending to be warming up to women-cows in heat.

"Mein goat!" he said.

"The old buggers are doing all right," Will Bratton said.

"A fine herd of bulls," said Ordway.

Now one by one the young Indian wives rose from where they sat and, slipping out of their robes, stood for a moment naked and brown.

"Holy grandma!" cried Bratton, his eyes popping out.

"Nice heifers," Bob Frazier said.

One by one the girls advanced to the fire and scented themselves with odorous herbs and woods burning there. The smell of such things as cedar and sage, the white men now realized, filled the whole lodge. The girls picked up hot twigs and boughs and bouquets of plants bound with leather thongs and sprinkled the ash and heat and fragrance over their naked flesh, turning gracefully round and round in the fire-warmth, the hair of each a long braid that almost touched the floor. They looked so lovely and innocent that even Potts was hushed.

When the girls were properly scented and warmed they went one by one in single file to a row of young men, each of whom held in his right hand a stick. A husband had chosen him and given him a stick to mark him, so that his wife would recognize him when she passed down the line. The white men now stared with bugged-out eyes and Potts stuttered in Dutch. "*Süsschen!*" Potts was breathing, having conquered the word. "*O Süsschen!*"

The naked girl passing down the row of young men recognized her stick and, taking hold of it, drew the eager young man to his feet. Together they went away into the lodge-gloom beyond the horses. If it had been warm summertime they would have gone out to the prairie, where, Tabeau said, he had seen them as thick as haycocks. By the time the last of the girls had taken her man and gone all the white men but Frazier were standing.

"You steers, sit down," he said.

Will Bratton sank, murmuring, "Holy grandma!"

"*Gehen wir spazieren!*" breathed Potts. "*Guh-guh-Gott will es!*"

"I can hear the buffalo coming," Frazier said. "The cows leading."

The men now listened to the plaintive bellowing of the naked old bulls. As Tabeau had said, they now seemed to be heaping lamentation and sorrow upon their miserable old bones and their impotence. They kept it up after the men had come back with their girls and gone to the row of husbands, where each in turn gravely offered thanks for the favor. That at least is what Tabeau said they did. Tabeau had told them that the fertility rites would continue till morning, the girls changing partners again and again.

"Why wasn't I born a Mandan?" Ordway said.

Potts was having such trouble with the letter *M* that several of the men turned to look at him. Then he got it out, with a gasp, "Mephistopheles! *Ich bin der Geist der stets verneint!*"

"Is he talking Mandan?" Bratton asked, staring at Potts.

"Only God and Potts know," Frazier said.

The old bulls were now coming forward, shaking the dust from their imaginary horns and flicking their short imaginary tails. They arranged themselves in a circle not far from the fire and in turn took a few whiffs from a long-stemmed pipe which a young brave in clean new buckskin presented to them. After the pipe had been smoked, one of the husbands came forward and in a wheedling voice addressed himself to the first old bull in the line. Ordway reached back in memory.

Tabeau had said that the husband would whine and wheedle, as though begging the highest favor under heaven—begging the old bull to take his beautiful young cow——

"The old bull," Frazier said, "off into the——"

"Buh-buh-bushes!" Potts cut in.

Now one by one, in turn, the other husbands came forward and in shrill wheedling tones begged the old bulls to accept the young cows. One by one the young cows came forward, again slipping out of their robes; and two by two the couples went away into darkness. Some of the bulls were so old and feeble that the cows supported them.

"Tabeau said if the old bull isn't——"

"Holy grandma!" said Bratton in a stricken voice. "Look!"

"He isn't," George Gibson said.

"How many hundred years old is he?"

"Bull," Frazier said.

A couple were returning. The husband went to meet them and again spoke in a high whining voice.

"There they go again!" Bratton said, and Potts began to stutter. He struggled with a word, rested quietly a moment and said, "*Himmel.*"

"I forget how many times," said Frazier in his duellist's voice, "they're allowed to try and fail. Sergeant, was it three?"

"I think it was three," Ordway said.

"What happens then?" asked Bratton.

"Why, you dumb steer, the husband feels insulted. Wouldn't you?"

"You mean would I——"

"Bull," Frazier said.

Sergeant Ordway gave the captains a report of what was done and they wrote it all down for President Jefferson. While Clark wrote, Lewis looked over his shoulder and observed that his spelling today was worse than usual. He supposed that the nature of the subject had disturbed him.

"I just don't understand all of it," Lewis said. "If the old bull fails so many times the husband throws a robe over him and begs him not to despise him and his wife. What sense does that make?"

"A lot of things the red people do don't make much sense to me."

Lewis turned to Ordway. "Sergeant, how many girls did they offer you?"

"Four, sir."

"They offered four to each one of you?"

"Yes, Captain."

"And concluded, I expect, that you must all be pretty old bulls."

"I'm afraid they did, sir."

When the captains were alone Clark said, "You think the buffler will come close this year?"

"If they don't, it's the white bulls will get the blame for it."

"I was thinking that, but Tabeau said the red cows are so attracted to the white bulls that it will be a fine buffalo year."

"Or the black bull."

Clark went on: "I heard someone say these Mandan women want to be faithful to their husbands, and so try to choose a very feeble old man. Doesn't that seem to argue for a monogamous preference in women?"

Lewis looked startled. "Possibly," he said. No question about it, his friend was full of woman-need. Now that the little slave-girl's baby-time was drawing near, Clark was very kind to her. The other day Old Bean Poop had pushed her over and Lewis had seen Clark rush up to the man, his eyes blazing and his hands clenched. He hadn't heard what Clark said but he had guessed close to it by the way the squawman had slunk away.

13

As the long cold winter approached spring Lewis now and then took his dog and went for a walk. The beast was so infested with fleas that day and night it scratched itself, and its master thought a run in the woods would do it good. But the chief reason he liked to be by himself was habit, that went clear back to the lonely childhood time after the death of his father. When alone he could shake off some of his melancholy and he could think more clearly about the problems that lay ahead.

After the turn of the year he went almost daily, when the sun was out and the winds were down. In his mind he would try to number one by one the hazards facing the Corps; to imagine the map of the country upriver, as the Indians had drawn it; to think of all the contradictory reports about it. A man hardly knew what to believe. Confusion had become so triumphant that in 1794 Jean Baptiste Trudeau went forth to discover the geographical facts and publish them to the world. Jefferson had sent him Trudeau's Journal and maps but he and Clark doubted that they had much value. Two years before Trudeau set out, a man by name of Robert Gray, a Boston ship captain, had sailed around Cape Horn in a ship named the *Columbia* and found and named a river for it. But apparently no man in the world yet knew where the head of that river was.

Between the Big Bellies and the Columbia how many tribes of Indians were there who had never seen a white man's face?

How far up the Columbia had white men come?

How long was the portage from the headwaters of the Missouri to the headwaters of the Columbia, or any of its tributaries down which they might go? And would the Shoshone Indians trade them horses to make this portage?

Would the men be able to row or tow or pole the boats up the river, as the Corps drew close to the Rocky Mountains?

Was there any pass over those mountains?

Those were some of the questions that he turned over and over in his mind. He thought often of La Salle, who had claimed for France every river running into the Mississippi. This had given him the idea to claim for the United States every stream running into the Missouri, even if any of its headwaters were up in Canada to hell and gone. What British arrogance to be up there anyway! He supposed Jefferson was right, that there would have to be another war with the damned colonizing English before they would stay home and mind their business. He thought he knew what the William Pitts over in London had in mind—to push down from Canada to Mexico and claim the whole western part of the continent. And if Jefferson had no more brains than the Federalists they'd be allowed to do it. It had been those cynics and braggarts who daily heaped scorn on Jefferson's proposals and did all they could to circumvent his plans. The English were not so stupid. They knew what Jefferson was looking at and they were determined to have it.

Lewis was determined that his country would have it, even if he died for it. If he and Clark could explore it and claim it, and if that claim then stood, though they were killed on this journey they would live a long life—for it would be long in the memory of a grateful country. He liked the thought. It was with him every day when he walked alone—— Our lives will be long in the memory of our people! Well, the British were arming the Sioux for an attack in the spring. Up north they would be arming the Blackfeet and telling them boats were coming up the river with a lot of booty. It didn't look as though he and Clark had one chance in ten to make it but they would make it or leave their bones out there in the unknown. He was eager to be off. He wished spring would come.

One morning he was leaving the fort after a restless night when he caught a glimpse of Charbonneau. He thought there was something queer in the way the squawman was standing by the leanto, as though listening. Lewis paused to observe him. Had the brute killed one of his women? Or had he rented them to some of the soldiers and was he now waiting to collect his fee?

Lewis did not suspect that inside the shack a small Indian girl who was little more than a child was moaning in terrible pain. An hour or two later he was in his cabin when a knock fell on the door. On opening it he found Bean Poop there. The squawman wanted to know if the captains had any big medicine for a woman's pain. Lewis asked what the pain was and Charbonneau said she was trying to have a baby.

He didn't suppose he had anything good for childbirth. His mother ought to be here.

"Don't the Indians here have midwives? You know, old women who can help?"

The squawman shook his dull head no.

"Don't they have any medicine for this?"

Well, yes, Charbonneau said, pulling heavy black brows down to his nose. The rattles of the rattlesnake were good but what man had any?

"Rattlesnake tails?" said Lewis, looking at him. "I've never heard of that."

"*Tres bon,*" said Charbonneau. "*Tres jude maidisan.*"

Lewis told him to go to the villages and find some, but the snow was deep and Old Bean Poop was lazy. Knowing that he'd never walk even a mile for so trivial a thing as a woman's life, Lewis again stood in thought. "Thunderation!" he cried suddenly. Was this the princess who was going to guide them to her people? Charbonneau nodded. Lewis hastened to Ordway and told him to take two or three men and go to the villages for rattlesnake rattles. The princess was in childbirth and her man said rattles were the only thing that would help her.

"I wouldn't judge, Captain, they'd do any more good than a cup of river water."

"Neither would I but it's a world of mysteries. Move fast, for she's in great pain."

Lewis would have gone to Clark but Clark was away hunting. He was waiting by his fire when otter-girl came to him, timid and shrinking but determined to have him go with her. She led him to the hut and he looked down on Sacajawea, lying on robes by the fire. Her face was contorted by pain but when she recognized the captain she forced a smile. Lewis knelt by her and saw the pallor in her face and the sweat over her face and throat. He felt a surge of pity. Gently with a finger he traced the line of one of her brows and patted one of her clenched hands. If Lucy Marks were here she'd know what to do. Surely there were herbs in this area for this sort of thing. Surely there were midwives.

He returned to the cabin and was smoking when the otter-girl came again rapping on his door. Again he went to the leanto and by the door stood and listened. He knew that an Indian, like a horse, made little sound of pain until the pain became unbearable. He could hear her moaning and knew that she must be suffering terribly. Never in his life had he been on the scene when a woman gave birth, or ever thought of the ordeal until this moment. He had supposed that Indian women suffered only a little—but then this one was a child, so young and small. Hearing her moans, he began to feel anger against the child-raping squawman and in an irrational moment considered having him put in irons.

Then his thoughts mellowed: would it be a girl or a boy? Let's see —it would be one-half Snake Indian, and either one-half French or one-quarter French and one-quarter something else. Bean Poop had been hoping for a boy and had already chosen a name for it—Jean Baptiste Charbonneau. Where was the lazy wife-beater, anyway? Lewis wondered, looking round him. Well, he guessed there was nothing he could do. All women suffered in this ordeal, for reasons known only to God.

He returned to his cabin, with otter-girl slinking after him.

In the afternoon he went again to the leanto and entered. There they were, two child-slaves by the fire—two almost friendless creatures far from their own people, one helpless and one dying. That's what he thought when he knelt and looked at the girl's face. She didn't smile at him this time. In the eyes of a dying beast he had seen the same look of glazed-over pain, the same loneliness-in-suffering that he saw in this child's eyes. Her pallor had deepened to ghastliness in her copper-colored skin. The hair across her forehead was matted with sweat.

He hurried outside and sent one of the men to find Juice-um. "In the first village, I think, and see if anyone there has rattlesnake rattles. Hurry!"

"Yes, Captain."

"Or any medicine for childbirth. Our squaw is dying."

While the man was gone Lewis stood by the shed. He was afraid she was dying. If she died he guessed they'd have to take otter-girl, though a princess would suit their purpose better. He wished Clark was here.

Juice-um came in a few minutes. He said the thing to give the squaw was snake rattles. He had brought some with him.

"You really mean that?" asked Lewis, looking into the Frenchman's eyes.

Rattles, he said, never failed. There was a magic property in them that made birth-giving easy.

"How do you give them to her?"

Just powder the rattles, mix the powder with water and pour it down her.

Juice-um broke off two rings and crushed them. Lewis handed him a cup half-filled with water. Juice-um then dropped the crushed rattlebone into the water and stirred it in with a dirty forefinger. Lewis took the cup and hastened to the girl. Kneeling, he reached under her shoulders with a hand to bring her up, saying, "Here, drink this." He gave her the cup and with no hesitation at all she drank it off. Otter-girl was looking at his face and at the cup, back and forth. Sacajawea was lying on her side, her face to the fire. It was cold in here, Lewis said, looking over at the woodpile. He threw wood on the fire and went outside.

In his cabin he took off his heavy coat, sat by the fire and filled his pipe. He had smoked only a few minutes when otter-girl knocked on the door. Lewis followed her to the shed. He took one look at the new wet infant and returned to his cabin, too astonished to speak or think.

When two days later Clark returned from the hunt, half-dead with fatigue and half-frozen, Lewis said, "A child was born."

"In Bethlehem, I think," Clark said.

"At Fort Mandan." Lewis told him about it and said, "You think the rattles did any good?"

"It would be hard to say. Superstitious people get medicine out of queer things."

"She was dying. She drank two rings and ten minutes later the babe is born."

It was a boy. Clark decided to call him Pomp. He thought that meant the firstborn. Lewis said the father had already named him. He was Jean Baptiste.

"I'll call him Pomp," Clark said.

"What if this frail mother gets sick on our hands?—or the baby? And just now it occurs to me that the other girl will follow us. She's pregnant too. Out yonder somewhere in the unknown we'll find ourselves managing a nursery."

"I expect we might," Clark said.

Charbonneau took a fancy to himself after the child was born. He put an eagle feather in his hair. He smeared coaldust and vermilion over the unbearded parts of his face. He then presented himself to the captains and said he was not going west with them on the terms they had offered.

They looked at him and Clark said sternly, "What do you mean?"

The squawman said that for one thing he'd not take turn standing watch. An interpreter was above that. He would do no work that he felt was beneath him, for he was, after all, a special person, and not a cook or wood-chopper or kettle-washer. Furthermore, if for any reason he wished to leave the Corps and return, he was to be provisioned and given a canoe.

"Anything more?" Clark asked.

Charbonneau said he might think of other things.

Clark said to Lewis, "The traders have been talking to him."

"The English. I think the English are the locust plague God dropped on Egypt."

"They probably would love to have all our men desert." Clark turned to the squawman. "So the British have been talking to you."

Charbonneau gave a vigorous denial. Yes, there were some other matters——

"Never mind!" Clark snapped. "Get your bedding and stuff there and get to hell out of this fort! And move fast or I'll have you thrown out."

Old Bean Poop met Clark's eyes a moment, a rare thing for him. He was speechless.

"Go on," Lewis said, "get out."

Clark strode to the shack and a moment later pitched the squawman's things outside.

"Mee vives," Charbonneau was saying to Lewis.

"His vives. He's decided he loves them."

"Go," Clark said, pointing to Charbonneau's things.

Sullen and angry, the squawman picked up his things and left the fort.

Five days later he sent an emissary of good will, a Frenchman who had come upriver with the party, to say that he was deeply sorry. He was ready to go *à toutes jambes;* he would do anything they wanted him to do—wash pots, wade rivers, pull tow-ropes. He'd give them no trouble at all. "À *toutes jambes*," said the Frenchman, grinning.

"Ah toot what?" asked Lewis.

The Frenchman pumped his legs up and down as though running at top speed.

Lewis grinned. "All right, send him over."

The squawman came and this time he had no feather in his hair, no paint, no swagger. The captains asked him if he would abide by their terms all the way to the ocean and back, and with comical politeness Charbonneau said he would. "Oui-suh," he said, and bowed to one captain. "Oui-suh," he said, and bowed to the other.

"All right," Lewis said, "back to your vives."

A day or two later Clark was surprised to find both slave-girls out gathering wood. Going to the shed to have a look at the child, he found it alone, lying on a robe close to the fire. He moved it back a little. It looked to him abnormally small and premature. It looked half-cooked. He doubted that it would live.

But he now had graver worries than that.

14

Some of the best hunters had been sent down the river after elk and had returned unexpectedly to report that a hundred Sioux warriors had surrounded them and cut their horses loose from the meat-sleds. The Indians had made off with two of the horses, and with two knives which they had torn from the grasp of two of the men.

Lewis said, "The British are back in the brush dogging them on. They're getting brave."

"Feeling us out," Clark said.

The captains sent messengers posthaste to the Indian villages to tell the chiefs to come over, with all their fighting men, armed and ready for war. They were told that Captain Lewis and his soldiers would leave at daybreak.

Big White came over with a minor chief and a few old men. He said all the fighting men were out hunting and had taken with them all the weapons.

"Same old story," Lewis said to Clark. "I'll go without them."

And so at sunrise he was off with twenty-four men for Sioux country, accompanied by a few red men with bows and arrows, spears and battle-axes. After the party had gone only a few miles one of the Indians turned back, pleading snowblindness; and the next day another Indian went home, with one of the white men whose feet had frozen. Lewis pushed on for several days but there was no sign of the enemy. Convinced that the Sioux had all fled south or east, he gathered up the flesh that the hunting-party had left—what remained of thirty-six deer and fourteen elk—and returned to the fort.

The Sioux had fled but just the same they were getting bolder every day. The captains decided that they should get the boats out of the ice and be ready to go the moment the river opened. When spring came they had no doubt the Sioux would appear in force— and all the Mandans would be far away hunting! The river ice had frozen to such a depth that Paddy and his men found it impossible to chop through it. They would chop through a foot or more and then come to a sheet of water, with another depth of ice below it. They would stand knee-deep in water and chop through the second layer, and come to another level of water and a third layer of ice. Would it be like this clear to the river's bottom? They supposed it would but they went on chopping day after day.

They were still trying to free the boats when Joseph Gravelines came to the captains with a letter from Tabeau. Lewis read it aloud to Clark. It said that the Ricara Indians were now feeling friendly toward the Mandans and Minnetarees and wondered if these two nations would join them in a common front against the Sioux.

"Good news," Lewis said, looking at Gravelines.

"The rest of it, Captain, isn't so good. The Sissetons and all the upper bands of the Tetons, yes, it is said even the Yanktons, are all coming north against the Mandans. They've sworn by all their manitous to kill every white man here."

"That must mean both of us," Lewis said drily to Clark. To Gravelines: "How many warriors will they have?"

"Well, as nearly as I can figure it, there'll be three bands of the upper Tetons. The Yanktons probably have four or five hundred fighters. I don't know how many the Sisseton Sioux have. You could stand them off in your fort."

"They'd lay siege to us, of course."

"Oh yes."

"And starve us out or burn us out."

"Either."

"Where they getting their arms?"

"Several places but the British chiefly." A man named Cameron, Gravelines said, over on St. Peters River, was arming them. He was mad because three of his men had been killed by the Chippewas. The only friend the white man had down the river was Black Buffalo.

"What could he do?"

"Nothing. He might keep the lower band quiet awhile."

"You say the Rees are on our side?"

"No, just not on the Sioux side." The gang that robbed the white hunters, he said, was a hundred and six Sioux. On their way back down they had stopped at the Ricaras to boast about it. The Ricaras wouldn't give them anything to eat and you couldn't insult an Indian worse than that. The Ricaras had then added insult to insult by giving the Sioux a lecture.

"I expect," Lewis said, remembering Clark's lecture to the wife-stabber, "that did a lot of good."

Clark asked, "Just about when will they be coming?"

"They're watching the ice. They know you can't go before the ice runs."

"How long will it take the river to clear after the ice breaks?"

Gravelines said they could proceed even though ice was running—even though a lot of ice was running—if they had good steersmen. They could keep close to the banks, for the ice was naturally drawn to the center by the swifter current there. It might be possible for them to slip away upriver while the Sioux were still waiting.

"That looks like about our only chance," Lewis said. "We're going to send the big boat back down the river. Will they try to take it?"

"I don't see how they could in high water." They might be fooled, Gravelines said, into thinking the whole party had turned back down.

"They'll have spies up here," Clark said.

The situation again seemed so grave that the captains decided not to tell their men that the Sioux were coming after their scalps. They warned them to be very watchful when out hunting. They put only their most dependable men on guard. The carpenters were busy making crude boxes and crates to hold the materials for Mr. Jefferson, which would be sent down on the keelboat. The blacksmiths were busy making axes, tomahawks and spear points for upriver trade. Not a man except Charbonneau was idle, from the time he rolled out of his robes at daylight until he went to bed. There was an atmosphere of menace and expectancy but the morale of the men was high.

"We'll soon be off," they said to one another, looking into the west.

Morning, noon and night the captains inspected the broad river for signs of ice breakup. When it came, late in March, they were surprised to see so many dead buffalo floating among the ice floes. The stupid herds were crossing the river far upstream and the ice was giving way under them and dropping them in. Thinking of them, Lewis could imagine how the astonished and terrified creatures

swam round and round among the great floes, looking for a channel out; how they weakened little by little and sank; how they came
to the surface and swam again with their last desperate strength;
and sank again and again came up. Or so it was, according to the
squawman. In some years thousands of them drowned when the ice
cracked. In some years the river was almost black with them for
miles and miles.

The captains were even more surprised by what the red people
now did. They preferred putrid to fresh meat. To get the kind they
wanted they risked their lives, venturing far out into the river after
the floating buffalo; leaping with astounding agility from floe to floe,
and sometimes, Clark observed, trusting their weight and their lives
to a piece of ice not two feet square. He watched them one afternoon and marveled—marveled at the dexterity and daring with
which an Indian fetched a beast to the bank, after looping a rope
over its horns or leg; dragging it after him between the ice-islands,
as he himself leapt from one cake to another.

Then he saw that out on the plains on both sides of the river the
old dead grass was afire. Were these fires Indian signals?

He hastened to ask the squawman. Charbonneau merely shrugged.
As the time for the departure drew near he sulked or put on airs.
He wanted the captains to take all his wives along, and in any case
the two girls; and as though to encourage him in his importuning,
the otter-girl wept with hysterical abandon almost day and night.
She saw the men loading the boats after dark. She saw Sacajawea's
radiant face when she looked upriver or across the prairie toward
her home. And one day when her hunger for her people was greater
than her awe of Chief Long Knife she flung herself down before
him and, babbling and weeping, begged to be taken along. Lewis
at the moment was busy with a list of things going to President Jefferson. He ignored her, groveling there on the earth. Clark was sitting
not far from Lewis and she now turned to him. In her primitive
ignorant childlike way she tried to show him how alone and friendless and helpless she was, and how dependent on his mercy.

After a few moments Clark looked down at her. He gazed at her
for perhaps half a minute, observing in his painstaking way that
her braid of hair was not so long as Jawey's; that her throat, convulsed by sobs and grief, seemed thin and undernourished; that her
buckskin garments and moccasins were all old and ragged; that one
hand flung out was clenched, the fingers on the other working in

and out as though to grasp something. It was the movement in the fingers that made him realize how deeply the girl was suffering. Lord, O Lord, he wished he could take her but it was simply out of the question. It was more folly than he liked to think of even to take the other one and her infant.

He clasped the girl's upper arms and brought her to her feet. Then she stood, head down, shrinking and trembling before him. With a hand he moved down over the curve of her belly, forcing her eyes to look down, to see for herself that she was five or six months with child; to understand that they could not take a pregnant woman on a long dangerous journey, where every man would be risking his life, and the first duty of the commanders was the welfare of their men. But she did not understand. Suddenly she slunk back as though he had struck her and went swiftly out of sight. It was then that he felt the most pain and the most pity—and heard his friend Lewis saying quietly:

"Duty, Captain, I've decided is the most unpleasant thing in life."

Clark looked away for a moment to the thicket where the girl had vanished and again bent to his work.

They had drawn up a list of the things that were to be sent to President Jefferson and were looking at it:

1	Box	Skins of the Male and female Antelope, with their Skeletons
"	do	2 horns and ears, of the Blacktail, or Mule Deer
"	"	A Martin Skin containing the Skin of a weasel and three Small squirels of the Rocky Mountains & the tail of a Mule deer fully grown
"	"	Skeletons of the Small, or burrowing wolf of the Prairies, the Skin haveing been lost by accedent.
"	"	2 Skeletons of the White Hair
"	"	A Mandan bow with a quiver of Arrows the quiver containing some Seed of the Mandan tobacco
"	"	A carrot of Ricara tobacco
2	Box	4 Buffalow Robes and an ear of Mandan corn.
3	Box	Skins of the Male and female Antelope, with their Skeletons and the Skin of a brown, or Yellow Bear.

4	Box	Specimens of earths, Salts, and minerals, numbered from 1 to 67.
"	"	Specimens of plants numbered from 1 to 60.
"	"	1 earthen pot, Such as the Mandans manufacture, and use for culinary purposes.
4	Box	1 tin box containing insects, mice &c.
"	"	a Specimen of the fur of the Antilope.
"	"	a Specimen of a plant, and a parsel of its roots, highly prized by the natives as an efficatious remidy in the cure of the bite of the rattle snake, or Mad dog.
"	Large Trunk	Skins of a Male and female Braro, or burrowing Dog of the Praries, with the Skeleton of the female.
" in a large	Trunk	1 Skin of a red fox containing a Magpie.
"	"	2 Cased Skins of the white hare.
"	"	1 Minitaree Buffalow robe, containing Some articles of Indian dress.
"	"	1 Mandan Buffalow robe, containing a dressed Skin of the Lousive and two cased Skins of the burrowing squirels of the praries.
"	"	13 red fox skins.
"	"	4 horns of the mountain ram, or big horn.
"	"	1 Buffalow robe painted by a Mandan man representing a battle which was fought 8 years since, by the Sioux & Ricaras, against the Mandans, Minitarras & Ahwahharways.
6	Cage	Containing 4 liveing Magpies.
7	do.	Containing a liveing burrowing Squirel of the praries.
9	do.	Containing one liveing hen of the Prarie.
10	—	1 large par of Elk's horns connected by the frontal bone.

"I guess that's everything," Lewis said. "You think any ruler in world history ever received such an astounding shipment?"

"Nothing will astound him," Clark said.

"You think the hen will live?"

"She seems in good form. She'll be laying soon."

"He'll probably eat her," Lewis said.

"The hen?"

"He eats anything, at least once. He's what the French call a gourmet. He even brought a French chef from Paris."

"Too bad we don't have a braro for him."

By braro the captains meant the common prairie badger.

"Or a beaver tail. He'd love that."

Clark said nothing. He did not have his friend's catholic taste in foods. He didn't care for the wood-hard fat of the beaver tail.

"Wonder what he'll think of the magpie," Lewis said, still looking at the list. "He'll love the specimens of plants one to sixty."

"And the earth, salts and minerals," Clark said.

"And the big horns. He hoped we'd find monsters out here." Lewis carefully rolled the list inside buckskin. "Think of what we'll have to send him by the time we get back here. As we use up our salt—I see we have over five barrels left—and our twenty-eight bushels of meal and our fifty kegs of pork and our barrels of flour we'll have room for a lot of specimens."

"If we don't have long portages."

"Imagine the things we'll find," said Lewis, looking up. "All the things no white man has ever seen since Adam. Fruits and vegetables they've never tasted; minerals they've never used." He was looking into the west, his imagination filling. "Maybe even women," he said, turning mischievous eyes on his friend. "That reminds me: are all our men in shape?"

"No, not all. About two-thirds of them."

"Well, I hope to God we have no Indians all the way to the Blackfeet. The Blackfeet will be more interested in scalps than renting their wives out. Has Newman been to see you?"

"The other day."

"You know, he stands acquitted in my mind. He's been a fine soldier ever since we flogged him but we can't take a man who was mutinous."

Clark was silent. He was looking at all the parcels which they were sending to the President.

Lewis said, "I suppose he begged you to let him go."

"He promised everything under the sun."

"Don't all the men seem eager to be off?"

"Very."

"Except Shaubonah." In their journals the captains spelled the squawman's name variously and changed their pronunciation with each change of spelling.

"We may be sorry we ever took Shobono."

Privately Lewis was not yet convinced that Sacajawea would not be more bother than she was worth, what with a child that seemed to have been born full of colic and an amazing capacity to make hideous noise all night. For many nights now it had awakened him time and again, and when he slept he dreamed of otter-girl.

That creature was so pitiable, as the time to leave drew near, that she melted the hearts of most of the men. She knew that the boats had been loaded and during the day she sat back from them and wept. George Shannon had looked at her a full minute, his apple-cheeks bunched up and his blue eyes narrowed. This girl made him think of his father. Paddy had given her a few beads, John Colter a moccasin awl. Alex Willard had said, "I never loved my people that much."

When the keelboat was loaded and ready to go down the river it had fifteen men aboard, including Tabeau and Gravelines and four of their men. Among them was John Newman, who refused to look upstream any more. In command was a corporal named Richard Warfington, with whom the captains had entrusted their maps and reports, their letters to friends, and the many things for the President. Two men were sent down the river to light signal fires if they saw the Sioux approaching.

What was holding the Sioux back? Lewis said, "They're not half as brave as they think they are."

As the moment for parting and departure came on them, emotions in some of the men rose to the surface. Not a one but sensed that this was a historic moment. Not a one of those going upstream but had wondered a hundred times if he would ever come back. A few were retracing the sixteen hundred miles back to St. Louis. Thirty-one men, a girl and a child were facing into a vast unknown from which such experienced old hands as Tabeau thought they would never return. On the keelboat when in late afternoon it turned down the river there were faces not hard to read, and hands waving goodbye that were not hard to read either: both said that it was not goodbye but farewell. . . .

The moment the keelboat passed out of sight round a bend, all the members of the Corps, except Lewis himself, climbed into the pirogues and six cottonwood dugouts and headed upstream. Because emotion had been mounting in him Lewis had said he would walk, for he had to be alone now. For fifteen years he had dreamed of this journey—and here it was! The long bitter winter was behind him, the Sioux were behind him; and ahead of him was an adventure of such magnitude and dangers, but also of such promise, that his eyes were a little misty, his throat a little choked. Oh, he was a sentimental man and he knew it, but he had seen the emotion in Will Clark too, and in most of the men!

To try to force some of the emotion down he turned his thoughts to the fleet out there. Well, it was not so imposing as that which Columbus had, or Captain Cook, but it was darned good to look at, moving yonder under its sail and oars. Columbus and Cook must have viewed with pride, he was thinking, but also with anxiety, for the safety and lives of their crew, or the possibility of mutiny. All winter he had carefully watched these twenty-eight men (he did not include Shobono) whom they had picked for the journey and he was sure that there wasn't a coward among them. Nor a whiner. No, nor one who would ever know when he was licked, not even York. They were bold resourceful adventurous men and he was proud of them. He expected that he would be mighty proud before this journey was done.

We are now—so his thoughts were running, as he kept a sharp watch for skulking Indians and warning fires—we are now about to penetrate a country possibly two thousand miles wide, on most of which the foot of civilized man has never trod; and whether for good or evil, the experiment will have to determine. Out there are eight small vessels which contain every article by which we expect to subsist or defend ourselves. The state of a man's mind gives coloring to events, when his imagination wanders into the future; and so now the picture that opens before me is a most pleasing one, entertaining, as I surely do, the most confident hope of succeeding in a voyage which has been my darling project for the last fifteen years. So how certain it is that I must esteem this moment of departure as the happiest of my life. . . .

So his thoughts ran as he walked down the bank, his rifle across his arm, his pistol and dagger and sword at his waist, his dog at his heels. The Sioux had not come. They simply were not half as brave as they pretended to be. He was never to know that whole bands of them were at this moment moving to the river, there to get ready for the massacre of the white party. He would never know what rage and frustration they were to feel on learning that the white men had gone. His dog knew but he was never to know that otter-girl followed him for miles up the bank, always slipping into hiding when he looked back.

His thoughts were soaring far above Sioux Indians and slave-girls. He had written a long letter to his President, saying that he expected to see him at Monticello in September of 1806. It was now April 7th of 1805. He had concluded: "I can see no material or probable obstruction to our progress, and entertain, therefore, the most sanguine hopes of complete success. . . . My inestimable friend and companion, captain Clark, has also enjoyed good health generally. At this moment every individual of the party is in good health and excellent spirits, zealously attached to the enterprise, and anxious to proceed; not a whisper of discontent or murmur is to be heard among them. . . . With such men I have everything to hope for, and but little to fear. . . ."

He had, he well knew, many things to fear but he was not the sort to tell his President that. Besides, when feeling so elated and triumphant, he looked at his enemies and adversaries and found them contemptibly weak. Now and then he smiled when a thought amused him. There was Paddy's Journal, a part of which Lewis had read. He was recalling the words: "We ought to be prepared now, when we are about to renew our voyage, to give some account of the *fair sex* of the Missouri; and entertain them with narratives of feats of love as well as of arms. Though we could furnish a sufficient number of entertaining stories and pleasant anecdotes, we do not think it prudent to swell our Journal with them; as our views are directed to more useful information. Besides, as we are yet ignorant of the dangers which await us, and the difficulty of escape, should certain probable incidents occur, it may not be inconsistent with good policy to keep the Journal of as small and portable a size as circumstances will make practicable. It may be observed generally that chastity is not very highly esteemed by these people. . . ."

That wasn't the way Paddy had written it and least of all the way he had spelled it but that was the sense and rather sententious manner of it; and as the captain recalled how evasive—oh, how prudent! —it had been, his smile spread and twitched at all his features. The other sergeants and the privates who were keeping journals were also *prudent*. It was well to be so, Lewis had decided: their views were directed to more useful information, and the squaws were as incidental in their lives as their meals. Certain probable incidents? What had the sergeant meant? Possibly the monstrous gray bears which, the Indians had said, they would encounter before they had gone far. Perhaps the weird chilling sounds which the Big Bellies said came right out of the Rocky Mountains, as though all the suffering spirits of the doomed were confined there. Or maybe he had in mind the Blackfeet. Thought of the Blackfeet always took the smile off Sacajawea's face.

Well, they would face many dangers. Not a man of them doubted it; not one of them but Shobono was afraid. They would now all forget that for an old tobacco box one of the men had spent a night with the daughter of the head chief of the Mandan nation. They would forget what Paddy in his record had called the old bodd and her punks, who could be found, he had written, not only in Indian villages, but in "the large cities of pollished nations." The captains would forget that the head chief of the Minnetarees had come to them with his handsomest wife and begged them to use her a few nights; that Big White for one tomahawk had offered them the choice of his wives, sisters and daughters; that old Evil Eye had hinted that it would be nothing but a world of berdashes if white men refused to accept the red man's ways. They would forget all these things, for these things were as trivial as last night's bones thrown on the fire, or this morning's ashes left from the breakfast. A vast unknown was about to be entered; half a continent about to be claimed. It was Bob Frazier who had coined the cry, Mister Jefferson, here we go!

It was Frazier out in a pirogue leading the singers now:

> "Mr. Jefferson, here we go,
>   Singing our boat-song sweet and low. . . ."

The problems would be many but during this late afternoon and evening walk he wanted to think of something else. He wanted to forget that the broad turbid river would soon be at its spring flood and running like a thing out of its mind; that the Sioux would be waiting for them when they came back down, if they ever came back down; that the high white Rocky Mountains might be impassable; that they might enter barren areas where there was nothing to eat. A Big Belly chief had said that no man alive could cross the tall frozen mountains that were formed of such jagged stone that they were called the Rockies. He had said that they would come to terrible waterfalls on the Missouri around which they could never portage. He had said that the Blackfeet could advance against them with two thousand men all armed with rifles. He had heard it all during the winter, he had heard it all. He had heard it said so many times that they would all perish that he was sick and tired of hearing it.

To all the men chosen to go, except the squawman and the Negro, the captains had given an account of the hazards and dangers that would face them, according to red man and white; and had said that if any man among them wanted to go back home, or remain with the Mandans—— It was then that Robert Frazier, said to have been a fencing-master in New England, had got to his feet, saluted the captains, and cried, "Mister Jefferson, here we go!"

The men had taken up the cry. They had all shown such zeal and spirit, such eagerness to be off, such contempt for danger, that it had been a carefully considered statement when Lewis told the President that there was no murmur of discontent among them, that they were in excellent spirits and eager to proceed.

Oh, but his mind was filled with light this evening, his heart with joy! This had been his dream for more than ten years, his President's for more than twenty. He and Clark would make that dream come true or somewhere on the broad continental depth of it they would leave their bones. . . .

> "We may not ever return, we know,
> But Mr. Jefferson, here we go . . . !"

The men were still singing out on the river.

15

They did not at once see the last of the Indians. On their second day out hundreds of them swarmed to the riverbank, shrieking, holding up gifts of corn and beans, and then rushing along the bank after them. After they had pitched camp a Mandan brave walked in with an attractive young squaw. He said his wife wanted to go with the party because she had been bewitched by the black white man.

Lewis summoned Charbonneau. "Tell him to get her out of here."

"Walla!" cried the squawman, whose French was almost as bad as his English. He pointed downriver in the direction of the Mandan villages. He waved the squaw back home but she slunk from him, her eyes looking round for York. Almost an hour passed before the camp was free of her, and then for some time the men could see her in brush along the riverbank, peering out.

Reuben Fields said, "That's the nigger's last chance before the Blackfeet scalp him."

By turns one of the captains remained with the boats and the other walked up the bank, or inland to explore; and with unflagging zeal they made notes of everything they saw—not only the daily observations of longitude, latitude, elevations, wind and weather, but of tributary streams, animal and plant life, soils and minerals. Within only a few days Lewis had examined and tasted and smelled a hundred different plants, including sage, wormwood, hyssop, elm, juniper; and many which he could not identify, such as the prairie sagebrush, which he called southernwood, and another that had the smell and taste of camphor, yet was a favorite with the antelope. He noted the appearance of salts, coal, sulphur, pumice stone; and of waters that he called "bitumenous" because they had the color of lye and the flavor of glauber salts. He found stones which, he said in his Journal, "had the appearance of wood first carbonated and then petrefyed by the water of the river, which I have discovered has that effect on many vegitable substances." He found trees twenty inches in diameter which beaver had felled, and concluded that their only food was bark, that their favorite barks were cottonwood and willow. Clark was prowling inland and finding old Assiniboine camps, with their empty whisky kegs; great herds of half-starved buffalo, elk, deer and antelope; tens of thousands of geese feeding on the first green grass of the prairie; the eggs and nests of magpies, the home of the booted owl and the prairie dog.

Lewis often recalled Jefferson's wish, that with great pains and accuracy they would observe all these things, for others as well as for themselves. To guard against possible loss the captains were to make several copies ("He must have thought we'd have nothing to do but write," Lewis had grumbled to Clark), one of which was to be "on the paper of the birch, as less liable to injury from damp than common paper." They were to send to him "at reasonable intervals, a copy of your journal, notes & observations of every kind." They were to encourage all their men to keep journals, and had done so, but only the sergeants, and Privates Whitehouse and Frazier, had written anything down.

The plan was to be off at daybreak, before breakfast. Because the men preferred meat freshly killed usually one of the captains with a couple of the best hunters would go up the river ahead of the boats, looking for game. If they were able to kill meat for breakfast, the boats would then stop at the scene of the kill, and while some of the men built fires the cooks and their assistants would cut off the choicest portions and dig marrow out of the bones, to season the broth or to use as butter on bread, if at the moment they had bread. When the meat was cooked the men would fall to and eat with appetites so ravenous that their captains would have marveled if they too had not been as hungry as wolves in January.

On the third day out the slave-girl endeared herself to the men. With her child standing up her back in its cradle she set off with a sharpened stick in search of wild artichokes, which the desert gophers gathered and stored underground. She would go over the earth looking for signs and probing, and on finding a cache would dig it out. Lewis ate of the boiled roots and thought them a pleasant change from a diet of meat, but he was more interested in describing them for his President: ". . . the flavor of this root resembles that of the Jerusalem Artichoke, and the stalk of the weed which produces it is also similar, tho' both the root and stalk are much smaller than the Jerusalem Artichoke. The root is white and of an ovate form, from one to three inches in length and usually about the size of a man's finger. one stalk produces from two to four, and sometimes six of these roots."

It had been such a hard winter that the game, though abundant, was washboard poor—both captains called it meager and would say in their records, "I killed a bull but it was so meager that I took only the large marrow bones and a little of the flesh." But they were entering beaver land and the beaver were fat. Not all the men liked beaver, and none of them agreed with Lewis that its tail was a rare delicacy, to be preferred to a roast of venison. Paddy Gass had outraged the Mandan Indians by sneering at the weed they called tobacco; he now offended some of the men by heaping contempt upon beaver flesh and its broth. "Even the schmell of the shtuff makes me sick as a widder," he would say, bunching his heavy beard halfway over his nose while fishing in the kettle for a chunk of elk shoulder. A few of the men, including Drewyer, were assigned the task of setting beaver traps each night, for the men needed the pelts for clothing, as well as the flesh for food. One of the trappers was Alexander Hamilton Willard, who as a boy had run away from his home in New Hampshire and had been up to his neck in adventure ever since. A youth with a large powerful body, he had been chosen from a hundred volunteers and was proud of it. He had deep-set eyes and a strong face with an abnormally rugged chin. When Gass inveighed against beaver flesh, Alex would look at him with lidded eyes deep in their caves and restrain a wish to flatten him out. Seeing his sullen gaze, Frazier would wish to chide him, as he once had, "Named for Alexander Hamilton, the biggest rogue and blockhead this side of London." But none of the men had forgotten Newman's lashing and disgrace, and Willard hadn't forgotten the hundred blows he had received for having been found asleep at his post. His back still felt tender from that flogging, and his mind darkened a little when he looked at either captain.

But he kept his mouth shut.

April 13th, only a week after the Corps left the fort, disaster came so perilously close that Lewis was sure afterward that his heart had stopped. Clark at the time was prowling somewhere inland. Lewis was in the white pirogue. With a good wind in his favor he had hoisted two sails and the boat was going at a nice pace, with the squawman steering. Suddenly without warning a downburst of wind struck and swung the boat broadside to the current. This so frightened Charbonneau that the clumsy fellow turned the boat still farther, so that a sail came broadside and the boat almost dipped water. Lewis shouted to Drewyer to take the helm and to other men to pull the sails in, and when the sails were down and the boat righted, Lewis sank back on his heels, his mind filling with a realization of how close the journey had come to its end.

Believing the white pirogue to be the steadiest and safest, the captains had entrusted to it the most indispensable parts of their equipment—the medicines, all the instruments, all their maps and papers and the most precious part of their merchandise. If these were lost they would have to turn back. Furthermore, because this was the safest boat the girl and her baby together with three men who could not swim a stroke had been allowed to ride in it. They would all have drowned. Lewis glanced over at the nearest bank and judged that it was six hundred feet distant. He looked at the high waves breaking around the boat. He looked at Old Bean Poop and decided to order the men not to call him by that name any more. It seemed to unnerve him.

Yes, the six of them would have drowned, all the instruments and medicines would have gone to the bottom, and the expedition into the unknown would have ended right there—all because of a stupid clumsy squawman who didn't seem to be much good for anything. Oh, he could knock his wife down or shake the daylights out of his child but he was no good as a hunter, no good as a steersman or cook, and not much good as a wood-gatherer.

An hour later all members of the party were looking at the hundreds of dead buffalo that had been beached along the river, and at the enormous footprints around some of the carcasses. These had been made by the beast they thought of as the white bear. On both sides of the river here were herds—both captains called them gangs—of buffalo, elk and antelope, together with their enemies, the wolves and the bears. The hunters went out among the herds looking for beasts that still had a little fat on them; and on returning they said they had seen four or five of the white bears, all running away from them. Were these the ferocious monsters the red men had told about? Was this awkward beast, lumbering off into the hills, the one that would charge a hundred men while carrying a full-grown deer in its mouth? Was this the one that ten Indians dared not attack, that twenty sometimes fell before? It all sounded so fantastic and silly that Lewis, who had been waiting to meet this foe, and whose contempt for it had been growing, recorded in his Journal: "Tho' we continue to see many tracks of the bear we have seen but very few of them, and those are at a great distance generally running from us; I thefore presume that they are extreemly wary and shy; the Indian account of them does not corrispond with our experience so far. . . ."

"If," he said to Clark, "the other dangers they told about prove to be no more formidable than this bear we'll all die of what the Frenchmen call honwee."

Most of the men were eager to meet the beast in mortal combat. At least a dozen of them had become rivals in an endeavor to be first to kill the monster.

"They'll have to catch him first," Lewis said.

The men were measuring the footprints and smelling adventure. Old hands in the wilderness like Drewyer said nothing. Pryor and Cruzatte said nothing. Gass said nothing, for he did not fancy himself as a great hunter. The slave-girl tried to warn the men but they laughed and waved her away. They were young and eager, these who wanted to meet the gray monster face to face. Some of them were under twenty-one. Some of those dreaming of renown as hunters were the Fields brothers, John Colter, John Collins, Will Bratton, Hugh McNeal, Joseph Whitehouse. . . . They had heard that when only eight years old Lewis had been famous as a hunter in the area where he lived. They had seen him and Clark shoot and they knew that only Drewyer of all the men in the Corps was a better shot. They dreamed of being greater hunters than their captains.

Meanwhile the party had entered swifter water and the men taking the boats upstream wondered how many hundreds of miles would be like these miles. The water, down from the snow blankets in the Rockies, chilled them to their marrow, yet they had to enter it, either in their leather garments or stripped naked, when they could no longer row or pole, or drag the boats with tow-ropes while struggling along the bank. If the banks were so high that the ropes would not reach down, or were impassable because of dense cover or huge stones, then the men had to plunge into the icy waters and handle the tow-ropes while wading. Day after day some of them could be seen in it all day long, up to their waists most of the time, even to their armpits. Among them was the big black giant, who looked warmer because of his color, yet whose teeth clicked as much as any white man's.

The iciness of the water was not the worst part of it. The worst part of it was the sharp river stones that cut their moccasins to shreds, and then cut their feet open. Some of the men, finding that the stones were destroying their footwear, took their moccasins off and went barefooted, wincing and flinching and bleeding, but never pausing and never complaining. At night they would sit before a fire and drag one foot or the other up to their laps to examine the wounds and to rub into them such salves as the captains gave them. The very worst of all was to rise at daylight and see frost upon everything and have to step with wounded feet into the cold water, knowing that cuts which during the night had started to heal would burst open and bleed again.

"Only a thousand miles of this," one of them would mutter, shivering and wincing and straining on the tow-lines.

"Or two thousand, who knows."

"A thousand miles to the head of the Missouri, the red devils said, and every mile just like this. What man says no?"

"On the Columbia we'll be going down."

"But up it when we come back."

"Yes, but then *down* this, not up it."

One of them was trying to look into the water to see where to place his feet but a man couldn't see a thing. He couldn't see into the turbid muddy depths any more than he could see into the earth. Captain Lewis had said you couldn't look into it even an inch and that was no lie. So your feet were down there out of sight, and sharp stones were there, and you had to put a foot forward and test the next surface; and if it felt dangerous you had to keep probing for a safer footing, but even so you got your flesh torn open. . . .

And all the while you had to watch the bank above you, if it was high, for at any moment it might decide to bury you. The spring melting had softened and loosened it and the higher water had washed under it. When it was possible to walk along the bank and handle the tow-lines, hell, that was even worse because of the prickly pear, which sometimes for half a mile or a mile so completely covered the earth that you had to step on it, for there was no other place to step. The thorns went right through your elkskin moccasins, through a double thickness of deer skin. Captain Clark did not handle tow-lines but walked where he pleased, yet night after night the men had seen him sitting by the fire digging thorns out of his swollen feet. The thorns seemed to carry a poison, for the sores festered and the feet puffed up like sick things. Captain Lewis had tried to solve the problem by putting over his moccasins a covering of thick buffalo hide.

"The Indians never mentioned the prickly pears," one of the men said. "What else didn't they tell us about?"

"Plenty," another said.

Well, anyway, the river was good to smell. It smelled of tall mountains and tall mountain snows; of herds of buffalo and bear and elk, and whole rivers full of beaver and otter and muskrat; of millions of acres of conifers, vines, ferns, berry bushes, pine grasses and leafmold that was older than Adam. You took a handful of water and you thought, Where in the world did this come from?—from what creek or river a thousand or two thousand miles away, there in the west or northwest or southwest, or even straight north or south. Two drops side by side might have come from two snowbanks ten mountain ranges apart. It was good water, for though cold and muddy it was clean, it tasted pure and it smelled of wonderful things.

Of the two captains it was Clark who pushed inland most of the time. The philosophic and meditative Lewis often watched his men laboring in the water, unobserved by them; saw the grimacing of their features; noted how sharply they sucked in their breath when a swollen foot down in the depths struck an enemy; and guessed at their thoughts when they stared across the wide muddy stream or gazed upriver or down. In the evenings he watched them around the campfires. They were failing—it took no sharp observer to see that. All the men on the tow-lines had lost weight and color. Lewis had supposed that when they got away from the squaws they would gain in vigor and mental alertness, but the cold water and sharp stones and prickly pear, and the thought of interminable distances ahead, were taking toll of spirit and stamina, though not a man complained, at least not in camp.

In fact, Lewis thought their spirits remarkably high, for with whoops and yells they daily expressed their contempt for the Blackfeet, to the amazement of the Indian girl and the near-panic of her man.

When not watching the men and worrying about them Lewis liked to stray inland to see what was to be seen. One evening a buffalo calf, separated from its mother, came loping toward him and then followed him as he walked, its nose almost touching his leather jacket. When Lewis paused and turned, the calf's black eyes looked up at him, full of animal-wonder. I expect, Lewis thought, looking at the little fellow, that I don't smell much like his mother. He must be troubled about that, yet seems ready to accept me. The calf's trust in him and the queer wondering way it looked at him filled him with an emotion of tenderness. When he reached out to touch the woolly face the calf backed away, still looking at him, still big with wonder. How strange! Lewis thought, musing. Is he lonely even as men are lonely?—for see, his eyes tell me that he doesn't like my odor; such sense as he has must tell him that I am not his mother; yet here he is, he has followed me clear to the boat; and as I shove off, there he stands on the bank, wondering why I have left him. . . .

Clark told him one evening that he had watched a mother desert her calf when the wolves pressed in. Lewis had seen the same thing. He had more than once seen a herd of buffalo fleeing before a pack of wolves and had observed, with grim humor, that if a mother had to choose between her child and the herd she always chose the herd. She would fall behind a little and show anxiety for her baby, which, though unable to keep up, was doing the best he could. She would let off low bellows of what seemed to be encouragement or alarm. She would even dash at the wolf-pack and scatter it. But, watching her, Lewis sensed how fear overpowered mother-concern, for after a while she dashed forward to rejoin the herd and her child was pounced upon and torn to pieces almost before his last cries ceased.

This sort of experience always went deep into Lewis and left him in a thoughtful mood. He would stroll over to the spot where the calf had been pulled down—the wolves had eaten it and rushed on after the herd—and there would see only bloodstained earth and the wet bones. There was nothing else, not even a piece of hide. Here, the captain would muse, looking down at the bones and blood, here only a few moments ago a baby buffalo was trying desperately to keep up with its mother. She is yonder in the herd somewhere, and though she may look round her and smell of other babies, though she may cry for it a few times, though somewhere in her dark animal soul there may be an emotion akin to pain, an emptiness akin to loss, in three or four days she will have forgotten all about it. The human mother takes only a little longer. . . .

So it was the world over, he supposed. There were those in Washington and elsewhere who wondered about him and Clark and their men—where they were now and if still alive, or if they had all been slaughtered by the Blackfeet or had starved to death in the Rockies. People would say only, "They never came back." People would soon forget them. The mothers might remember longest, and next to them, Tom Jefferson, for if they all perished his dream might perish too. A little buffler calf, Lewis thought, leaning on his gun and looking down at the stains: only a little while ago it was so warm and full of living, so eager, so friendly to all things; and now it was only a smear on the earth, a few bones, a skull with the eyes sucked out, its flesh and most of its blood digesting in wolf bellies. . . .

Such thoughts always made him wonder if he ought to feel shame for himself. Lord, but he was such a melancholy and sentimental fellow, under his mask of stern military discipline! He would not have wanted the men, no, nor his friend Will, no, not even his mother to look into these depths. He took his pipe out and filled it and then thrust it back into a leather pocket. He laid the gun across his left arm and walked again.

It seemed strange to him, a philosopher, but possibly, he thought, not strange to the men, that the wild animals here were not wild at all: while buffalo, elk or antelope were feeding he could walk up and almost touch them, without exciting fear or alarm, so far as he could tell. Indeed, the animals frequently came close to the men, to determine, it seemed, what sort of creatures they were. He was beginning to understand that the beasts called wild were not wild until the loud gun-noise and killing men made them so. He understood that for these gentle peaceable things, the milk-givers that fed only on plant life, men were another and deadlier species of the wolf. Or would be after they discovered what men were like!

When the captains determined by their calculations that they must be close to the Roche Jaune, or Yellow Stone River, Lewis took four men and went on ahead, and soon came to it. An emotion of elation filled him: no white man, so far as he knew, had ever been up the Missouri this far! Climbing to an eminence, he gazed for a few minutes at the huge herds of buffalo, elk, deer and antelope all around him; at hills so fantastically and grotesquely eroded that he found it hard to believe them real; and then at the broad valley. formed by the two rivers. There was more growth on the river bottoms here than downstream, indicating for him that the soil was more fertile.

He decided to go up the Yellow Stone River a couple of miles and camp there for the night. He would explore roundabout while waiting for Clark and his party. Yes, he reflected again, while prowling through thickets of cottonwood, willow and briar, this was a landmark in their journey, an hour of triumph. No white men, not even the boldest trappers, had ever dared come this far. Francis Labiche said he had come almost to this point. When Lewis said, "Did you find any of the yellow stones?" Labiche had been silent. Searching in a stretch of old dry river bed, Lewis muttered, "Roash Shoan, the French call it, meaning yellow stones." The French had never seen yellow stones but had based their name on what Indians had told them. If there were any yellow stones, he supposed they must be on up the river, possibly at some ford where the Big Bellies crossed.

The next morning Lewis decided to send the intrepid and adventurous Joe Fields up the river, ordering him to proceed as far as he could, with time to return to camp before dark. "And watch for yellow stones. If you find any, bring two or three back." About noon Lewis heard the firing of guns, and concluded that Clark and his party had reached the junction. Toward evening he went down the river and found the main party encamped on a point of land where the two rivers came together. All the men seemed to be in gay spirits for having come so far. The captains spoke together privately and decided as a gesture of celebration and thanksgiving to issue a half-cup of spirits to each man.

After the men had drunk their liquor and eaten their supper, Cruzatte played the violin, and upon the bank of the wide rivers the men danced and sang around a big campfire, indifferent alike to the monstrous grizzled bears prowling in the dusk and the Blackfoot Indians who might be watching out in the night. Her child at her breast, the Shoshone girl looked at the men and marveled. She was scared to death, now that the party was so close to Blackfoot country. Why were the captains so unafraid? They were sitting in bright firelight writing in their journals, each a perfect target. Every man was a perfect target as he capered around the fire. She thought the chiefs must have some big medicine that they were keeping hidden.

Joe Fields came in, carrying a horn from a mountain sheep. The captains examined and measured it and then listened to his story: he had gone up the yellow river about eight miles and had found veins of coal, river islands densely covered with timber, and big-horned animals at a great distance in the west.

Lewis said, "But you found no yellow stones?"

"No, sir."

"None that even looked a little yellow?"

"No, sir. They all look just like the ones here."

Lewis turned to Clark. "Well, they call them Blackfeet but it's said they have the whitest feet of all Indians. They call the Minnetarees Big Bellies but they're the slimmest Indians I've ever seen. I expect the yellow stones are probably gray."

"I expect so," Clark said.

"And the mountain of rock salt, Captain," said Frazier, "is a pile of basalt."

"I wouldn't be surprised at all."

The men with wounded feet stopped dancing after a while but eight or nine others danced until almost midnight. Then they rolled into their blankets and fell asleep to the lapping of river waters and the crying of wolves.

"Even if its stones are gray," said Lewis, speaking over to Clark, "it's a mighty handsome river. How wide did you say it is?"

"Eight hundred and fifty-eight yards, including its sandbar."

16

George Shannon, whose ear was the best in the party, called her Sak-a-jaw-we-a and Clark called her Jawey. Jawey was no bigger than a minute: she was under five feet in height and she weighed less than a hundred pounds but before the month of June came in the captains decided that she was worth her weight in blue beads. She was never in the way and she was always busy. She gathered edible roots when she could find them; dressed skins; made or mended garments and moccasins; and day after day pointed out the plants that grew in her homeland. She came to Clark with a branch of a currant bush and made him understand that this was a common fruit where her people lived and hung in clusters like grapes. She was eager to learn English and Clark was teaching her a few words when he had time.

Jawey was astonished night after night to see the men dance around big campfires that threw their light a hundred and fifty feet into the darkness and high into the heavens. Such a great room of light would be visible to the Blackfeet for miles and miles. Were the captains terribly bold or terribly stupid? Day after day she looked back down the river and saw the smoke of the last night's campfire or sometimes the smoke from two or three camps; and she marveled again. It was so foolish not to put the fires out. It was as if these white men were mocking and challenging the Blackfeet by proclaiming their coming. Did Captain Long Knife and Captain Red Hair realize that there were hundreds, yes, thousands of Blackfoot warriors and that they were the most fierce fighters on earth? They seemed not to. Did they not know that if their party was taken captive they would all be tortured in ways more fiendish than they had ever heard of? All day long she cast anxious glances ahead, and all night she dreamed troubled dreams in which she and her child never reached her people at all but were borne away to be slaves in still another nation. She would look at the face of Lewis or Clark when she knew that they were unaware of her and she would wonder about them. Were they as brave as they seemed to be?

She was to decide again and again that they were. One late April morning just after breakfast Lewis was walking upriver with one of the men when suddenly they were face to face with two of the monstrous bears. They were the yellow or gray or white bears—the captains hardly knew what to call them but did not think of them as the grizzly. Lewis said to Drewyer, "Take the one nearest you. . . . Ready?" Almost in the same instant the two men fired. What happened next so astounded Lewis that he was never to forget it. The bear which Drewyer shot made a ferocious roaring but fled nevertheless; the one Lewis shot threw its head up a moment, gave a challenge that shook the earth, and charged. The amazed captain took to his heels, trying to ram powder and ball home as he went and glancing back now and then to see if the monster was gaining. The bear had been mortally wounded, and so was not able to run at its top speed; and after Lewis had gone about a hundred yards he turned and fired again, and a moment later Drewyer fired. The beast went down.

The two men walked over to look at it. It was a male, hardly more than half-grown. Curiously Lewis examined it, observing that its talons and teeth were much larger and stronger than those of the bears he had known; that its color was a yellowish-brown, its eyes black and small, and its fur thicker and finer than that of the black bear. He reflected that the Indians might fear this beast, armed as they were with only bows and arrows or poor guns; but for him it was not a formidable adversary.

"It seems about as easy to kill as any other species of bear," he said to Drewyer. "I can't understand why the Indians are so afraid of it." Leaving Drewyer to dress it, he resumed his walk.

He saw today a great many wolves and concluded that their number was always in proportion to the number of the beasts they stalked. They were craven things. They nearly always hunted in packs, and at this time of year, he had observed, their favorite prey was the pregnant does. But usually not on land: the cowards caught them when they were swimming. His dog had plunged into the river and caught a swimming antelope and drowned it. Sometimes out on the plains the wolves lured a single beast away from the herd or caught one that had strayed off. Because it was fleeter than they the crafty killers tried to maneuver its flight in the form of a circle, so that a divided pack could take turns chasing it and resting. He was a cunning rascal, the wolf.

The wiry Welsh blacksmith, John Shields, had got so filled up with rheumatic pains that he was no good for anything. A number of the men had large painful boils and a few of them had colds. Nightlong May 1st and May 2nd a wind was so violent that the men tossed in their sleep and the baby howled as though covered with mosquitoes and the dog howled; and at daylight the next morning it began to snow and in two hours everything but the river was white. The next morning there was white frost on boats and trees and ice a quarter of an inch thick in the pails. As the men labored with the boats, water froze to their poles and oars. How extraordinary it was, Lewis thought, gazing round him, to see trees in leaf and flowers opening, yet snow an inch deep. Dark against the snow were the huge herds of elk and antelope and buffalo; and everywhere were geese, ducks and swans. By May 4th the cold abated and the insatiably curious Lewis was off to see if three nights of frost had done any damage. Mr. Jefferson would wish to know about such things. The leaves of cottonwood, box elder and willow, it seemed to him, had not been touched, but the leaves of rosebush and honeysuckle had turned dark and curled. Having tucked these facts away in his mind, to be entered in his Journal this evening for Mr. Jefferson, he went out to the prairie and passed close to the feeding herds. The buffalo bulls had so little interest in him that at a distance of fifty paces they would merely look up a moment and then go on feeding. He saw a number of the gray bears but they were too far away for a good shot: he did not like to wound creatures and let them go: both he and Clark had told their men that though hunting was a fine sport they were never to kill more than could be eaten and they were never to kill for the mere fun of it. If they wounded a beast they were always to do their best to bring it down.

But bringing the gray bear down, the captains were to learn the next day, was just about as difficult as the red men had said it would be.

Toward evening Clark, who was with the boats, saw a bear, a huge grizzled monster, on a sand beach; and even while reaching for his gun and before he had got a good look at it he sensed that it was a more dreadful-looking thing than he had ever seen before. He called to Drewyer and the two men went after it. Firing and reloading as rapidly as they could, they shot the beast ten times and it still refused to go down. On the contrary, it set up a roaring that shook the world and then, plunging into the river, swam halfway across it and emerged on a sandbar. It walked around there and continued to roar with the most earth-shaking sounds Clark had ever heard. It gave him gooseflesh just to hear it.

"The Almighty Lord," he said in a tone of awe. "Just listen to it."

The bear, Drewyer said, was pretty mad and no doubt of it.

"Ten times we fired. Ten times I thought I saw the fur part."

"Yes, sir, you did."

"What in thunder is he doing? Digging a hole?"

The wounded bear usually dug a hole, Drewyer said.

But it was only for a few moments that the beast seemed to be digging. Then again it was ambling around and roaring with such thunderous rage and pain that every man in the boats stood up and stared. Hearing the awful sound, Lewis had come in.

He went up to Clark and said, "Why don't you shoot it?"

"Captain, that bear has ten balls in him."

"And still won't die?" asked the astonished Lewis.

The bear refused to die for what Clark calculated to be ten minutes. Then the roaring fell to a kind of whine, to a kind of sad moaning, and at last ceased. The monster was still.

The captains and all their men went to the sandbar and for a few minutes were content merely to stand and look. Clark was to say in his Journal that the beast was tremendous. That is what they all thought. Their astonishment was boundless when after skinning it they discovered that five of the balls had gone through the beast's lungs, two through its guts, one through its neck and two through its lower shoulders. Carefully the captains measured it and proclaimed their findings.

"Eight feet seven and a half inches from the nose to the hind feet. . . . Five feet ten and a half inches around at the breast. . . . One foot eleven inches around the middle of the arm. . . . Three feet eleven inches around the neck. . . . Five talons on each foot each four and three-eighths inches long. . . ." They judged that his maw was ten times the size of the black bear's. They found it filled with flesh and fish.

How did he catch fish? the men wondered.

The beast was cut up in chunks small enough to be put into the kettles. The cooks rendered the oil out of the meat and stored it in a cask for future use. The captains had learned that the fat of the gray bear was as firm as hog lard and of excellent flavor.

Around the campfires this evening the men had little to say. Formerly some of them had been boastful; they had been yearning to meet the monster which Captain Clark now called a grizzly bear. But now they were remembering that two of the best shots in the party had put ten bullets into it. They had been deafened by its hideous roars. They had seen it swim halfway across a wide river. For almost half an hour they had watched it on the sandbar, a monster with ten wounds in it, six or seven of which would have been enough to drop a black bear or a buffalo in its tracks. What kind of creature was this! What man among them would dare to stand up to it? Little wonder that before the red men went forth to attack it they put on their war paint and propitiated their manitous, just as they did before riding away to war.

"Well, this is what I think," said Reuben Fields to his brother Joe, while they sat by a fire. "I think you've got to shoot it through the brain or the heart."

"If you can," said Joe. "You looked at its head? Just go over to the sandbar and look at its head. It's inches deep with tough muscle and thick bone."

"Then through the heart," Reuben said.

"Oh yes, if you can. But what if you miss it?"

Bill Bratton was saying to Bob Frazier, "Would you tackle one alone?"

"Me? Not unless I was crazy."

"I would," Bill said. "I will the first chance I get."

George Shannon and John Colter were listening. George looked at Bill. He bunched his apple-cheeks up and banked the lids against his gentle blue eyes.

"The first chance you get," George said. "I expect you're praying that it will be a small one."

"As big as they come," Bill said.

"God in heaven, I hope I'm watching."

"He's full of brag," Bob Frazier said.

Captain Lewis had been walking among the men. He overheard Shannon's remark and came up.

"Watching what, Private Shannon?"

"Bill Bratton, sir. He's going to tackle the biggest grizzly bear and shoot him through the heart."

Lewis turned to Bill. "You know where his heart is?"

"Yes, sir. I studied that one when they skinned it."

"I suppose you know that this is the mating season and a male bear just doesn't like to be disturbed when he's making love."

George Shannon said, "Sir, no man does."

Lewis grinned. This George youngster had a quick wit.

A few days later these six men in two dugouts had fallen half a mile behind the main party and were rowing hard to catch up when they saw a huge grizzly bear lying out in the open, sunning himself.

"Look," George Shannon said. "Bill, there's your bear."

"Holy grandma!" Bill said. "He's the biggest one yet."

"Can you tell where his heart is?"

"I expect we'd better all do this job," Joe Fields said. "Bill can be brave some other time."

They rowed the canoes to a bank and softly beached them. Because Frazier was the oldest of the six the other five let him act as the leader. The men were now whispering. Frazier said, "I recommend four of us shoot him and two hold their fire."

"Who holds?" asked Joe Fields.

Frazier looked at the men. Still whispering he said, "Joe and John, they're the best shots. Bill wants to shoot, I can see, so he's one of the four. Besides, he'll shoot it through the heart. George and me, we'll hold. Now look, we want to get just as close as we can. How far out is he?"

"Three hundred yards," Joe said.

"Or more," said Bill.

"The wind is that way," said Bob, looking west. "We'll go the other way. See the ridge over there. I think we can crawl up till we're right on top of him."

"Then you'll fence with him," George said.

"Then we'll watch Bill shoot him through the heart. Your guns all in order?"

The men all examined their guns. They then turned to the east, bent over, rifles across their arms; and after going up the river a hundred yards they turned into the wind and headed for the ridge.

The bear was beyond them, over the hill. When they were about halfway up the ridge Bob Frazier, leading, dropped to hands and knees. The men behind him followed suit and they all crept along, as noiseless as the wolf. Now and then Bob would rise a little to peer. At last, after peering over the hilltop, he sank back to his haunches and turned. In a whisper he said, "He's still there. Not more than a hundred and fifty feet."

Whispering, Joe said, "Lying down?"

"Yes. He doesn't know we're here."

Again the men examined their guns. They were not trembling but they were tense and their breathing was labored. Five of them were not yet twenty-one, two were not yet nineteen: they were picked men, every one of them, but they hadn't forgotten the grizzly on the sandbar.

Bob rolled back behind the others and George rolled with him. The other four were side by side, on their knees and crouched down, their guns ready. They were waiting for the signal.

Bob moved forward to whisper, "When you stand up don't be in a hurry to shoot. I don't think he'll see you, so take your time and fire when I give the word."

All six men stood up. Frazier was watching the four men just ahead of him. When he saw that they all had their rifles up and seemed poised and ready he said, "Four seconds now. . . . Fire."

An instant later four guns blazed and the great beast came to his feet with a terrible roar. Lifting his head, he saw the men and roared again, and the men saw the red spumes of his blood. Bob and George had advanced a little and now they both fired.

"You both hit him," Joe Fields said, busy reloading.

That meant six balls in the monster but he was charging now and he came with amazing speed. He came so fast that the six men took to their heels and ran like the wind for the river, never once pausing to look back. They could hear him snorting blood, they could hear the great soft bounce of him. It was two hundred yards to the river: never in their lives had any of them run so fast or moved so swiftly when they reached the bank. Frazier and Shannon plunged headlong into a canoe and their impact shot it out into the river. The other four had dived into a thicket of willow and rose bramble, trying to reload as they ran.

Baffled and frustrated, the monster stood for a moment looking at the two men out in the canoe. He stood so long, his small dull mind trying to determine what to do, that the men in the thicket had time to reload and creep forward. All four of them shot him again. The beast swung and rushed for the thicket and the men there were flushed out like deer from a covert. The four of them separated in pairs, the Fields brothers going together. Still snorting blood and roaring with pain and rage the bear took after the Fields brothers and gained on them so swiftly that they threw away both guns and pouches and from a bank twenty feet high plunged headfirst to the river. The bear was so close to Reuben that he was reaching to seize him when Reuben jumped. Without a moment's hesitation the bear jumped after him and almost landed on top of him. There was a tremendous splash that engulfed Reuben and took him under. The two men in the canoe had reloaded and were maneuvering to get a shot at the beast but they were afraid to fire lest they hit one of the Fields brothers.

Those brothers with all the desperate power they had were trying to swim upstream against the current and the bear was swimming after them. Another monster with ten bullets in him! Reuben thought, and wondered whether to strike across the wide river. What were the other men doing? Why didn't they fire?

John Colter was ready to. Sprawled on his belly on the bank above, he was trying to fix his sight on the beast's head. There was such furious splashing of water by both men and bear that most of the time he was unable to tell where the furred head was; but at last he got his sight on it and fired. With a gurgling roar the great monster rolled over and over in the swift current and the Fields brothers, turning, went after him. The two men in the canoe moved in to help. Reuben and Joe seized talons on a huge paw and towed the dying beast downstream, until they were past the high bank. The six men then beached him and stood looking at him. They were all breathing hard. They were all pale.

Frazier spoke first. "I don't know what we'd a-done if Bill hadn't shot him through the heart."

"Holy grandma," Bill said.

"You still ready to tackle one alone?"

"Sure. This one wasn't turned right."

"Oh, you mean you're going to walk up and turn him around?"

Reuben was examining the leather trousers at the back of his lower legs. "I thought he struck me," he said. "I thought I felt his claws."

Probing with his finger, Frazier was locating the bullet hole in the skull. "It was a mighty fine shot," he said to John Colter. "I think you hit his brains."

Joe Fields said, "Well, we better skin him out. The captains will want the pelt and the lard."

"We'd better get our guns first," Reuben said.

The captains at almost the same time were having troubles of their own. They had both left the pirogues to walk up the bank, a thing they rarely did, for they had agreed that one of them should always be with the party. They had also, contrary to their best judgment, allowed Charbonneau to steer the white pirogue, instead of Drewyer, whose task it was. To this pirogue they still entrusted all their papers and maps, instruments, medicines, as well as a considerable part of their most valuable merchandise.

As formerly, when the squawman almost capsized it, the pirogue was under sail and was moving nicely when a sudden blast of wind turned it broadside to the current. The river was rough, the waves were high. As formerly, Charbonneau yielded to panic and did the wrong thing—and at exactly that moment the two captains happened to be looking at him. Instead of putting the boat before the wind he swung into it. Another gust tore the squaresail from the grasp of the man holding it and the pirogue upset and would have turned completely over but for the fact that the sail canvas acted as a brake against the water.

The two captains went stiff with amazement.

"O my God!" said Lewis. "Look at that damned fool!" With a wild impulsive movement he fired his gun.

Clark then fired his gun and both captains began to shout like men out of their minds. Yelling into the wind, they told the boat crew to haul the sails in but nobody heard them. All but two of those in the boat were so filled with fright and consternation that they had no idea of what they were doing.

"O my God!" cried Lewis. "It will turn topsaturval!"

He began to act like a man demented. He threw down his gun. He hurled his shot pouch aside. He had the thought that he would throw off his clothes and swim the three hundred yards to save the instruments and the medicines. He was unbuttoning his jacket and still yelling furiously when a realization of his folly struck him: the waves were so high they were curling in white water, the water was cold, the distance was nearly a thousand feet and, worst of all, he was a poor swimmer. He would drown. Still, he'd rather be dead than turn back, now that they had come twenty-two hundred miles from St. Louis and were deep in the unknown.

"O my God!" he said, eyes staring, hands fumbling to rebutton his jacket.

The captains could not see clearly what was taking place on the pirogue. They could not hear the frightened and half-paralyzed Charbonneau begging his God for mercy. They did not see Cruzatte seize a gun and threaten to blow the squawman's head off if he did not at once take the rudder and do what he was ordered to do. Cruzatte had two men bailing water. He and two other men rowed the almost-capsized boat to land. Sacajawea all the while had been recovering many of the articles that had been thrown out when the boat turned: from end to end of the pirogue she had dashed and reached out for one floating thing and another, paying no attention to the men and the confusion. . . .

Having shouted themselves hoarse, the captains could only stare and wait.

"That fool!" Lewis muttered. "That damned clumsy fool."

"I think they'll make it to land," Clark said.

The captains entered their canoe and crossed the river. Hastening to the pirogue, which the men and the girl were now unloading, they saw that everything in it had got soaked, except the powder, which was sealed in lead canisters. All the papers and maps were wet. These the captains took gently from clumsy hands and laid out on grass where a breeze could strike them. How much of the merchandise had been lost?

Not much of it, Cruzatte said. The squaw had rushed back and forth along the side of the boat and singlehanded she had recovered most of the things and had then brooded over them like a great hen, to keep them secure. Clark looked over at her, where with her own garments and her hair she was trying to wipe instruments dry. He went over and looked down at the articles she had laid out.

"Jawey, you are a fine woman," he said.

She made a birdlike movement downward, that was both acknowledgment and curtsy, and went on working. But for her, Clark was thinking, our journey would be over—but for this girl who, indifferent to danger, even danger to her son, recovered those things which she knew we must have. He wanted to reward her but could think of no suitable way. . . .

After all the men had come in and the six had told of their close encounter with the grizzled monster, the captains decided to give each man a half-cup of ardent spirits, to cheer and comfort him. Lewis told the squawman that after this he would be a cook and nothing more. Tomorrow could they have another serving of that pudding *boudin blanc,* of which the men seemed to be mighty fond?

In his Journal he had written:

. . . . this white pudding we all esteem one of the greatest delacies of the forrest, it may not be amiss therefore to give it a place. About 6 feet of the lower extremity of the large gut of a Buffaloe is the first mosel that the cook makes love to, this he holds fast at one end with the right hand, while with the forefinger and thumb of the left he gently compresses it, and discharges what he says *is not good to eat* but of which in the squel we get a moderate portion; the mustle lying underneath the shoulder blade next to the back, and fillets are nest saught, these are needed up very fine with a good portion of kidney suit; to this composition is then added a jist proportion of pepper and salt and a small quantity of flour; thus far advanced, our skilfull opporater C——o seizes his recepticle, which has never once touched the water, for that would intirely distroy the regular order of the whole procedure; you will not forget that the side you now see is that covered with a good coat of fat provided the anamal be in good order; the operator seizes the recepticle I say, and tying it fast at one end turns it inward and begins now with repeated evolutions of the hand and arm, and a brisk motion of the finger and thumb to put in what he says is *bon pour manger;* thus by stuffing and compressing he soon distends the recepticle to the utmost limmits of it's power of expansion, and in the course of its longtudinal progress it drives from the other end of the recepticle a much larger portion of the than was prevously discharged by the finger and thumb of the left hand in a former part of the operation; thus when the sides of the recepticle are skilfully exchanged the outer for the iner, and all is compleatly filled with something good to eat, it is tyed at the other end, but not any cut off, for that would make the pattern too scant; it is then baptised in the missouri with two dips and a flirt, and bobbed into the kettle; from whence, after it be well boiled it is taken and fryed with bears oil until it becomes brown, when it is ready to esswage the pangs of a keen appetite or such as travelers in the wilderness are seldom at a loss for.

The men all liked Charbonneau's meat dish but of their other foods they agreed on little. Lewis was fond of marrowbones, beaver tail and of liver from any beast. Some of the men did not like liver at all and a few of them thought that beaver flesh when boiled had a sickening odor. Practically all of them liked marrowbone fat, fat buffalo hump and venison but not all of them liked buffalo tongue, which among Indians was a supreme delicacy. Some of them liked the meal of sunflower seeds made into bread; some liked it to thicken beef broth; but Shannon preferred simply to stir it in water and drink it, and Gass liked it best mixed with marrow grease. For the most part they ate boiled meat morning, noon and night and suffered from boils and abscesses. But not the girl. Clark had seen her a number of times eating berries that still hung on twigs, or roots, bark, cress, moss, or even last year's leaves. Her people, she said, lived chiefly on fruits, roots, tree bark and fish. Though they had many horses they lived in such deadly fear of the Blackfeet that they remained mountainbound, venturing east to the buffalo plains only once in a long while.

After supper the captains sat by their campfire, and Lewis as usual took delight in sniffing the fragrance of burning sage, willow or cottonwood. Soon, he said, they should be able to see the Rocky Mountains.

Clark had Sacajawea sent over and again asked where her people were. Again she looked into the west and said, "There."

"How far?"

As before, she counted on her fingers, adding up the sleeps. Ten more sleeps, she said, but neither captain took her seriously. For one thing, she had been only a small child when she was stolen and taken away. For another thing, the red people found it fascinating to count on their fingers and often did not pause until they had counted off all of them. When the total was ten, Clark told himself, it would be twenty if they had that many fingers.

"Ten sleeps, she says, but how far is that? With horses it might be three hundred miles. You say your people live beyond the Rockies, yet we can't even see them yet." He turned to Lewis. "This western land is bigger than I thought it was."

"It's tall country," Lewis said.

"Tall and broad."

There were so many questions they wished to ask the girl but she had neither the language for reply nor the knowledge. They wanted to know if anywhere near her people there was a river that flowed west into the ocean. Her people must live on a river if they fished a great deal. If there was no river, would they be able to buy horses for a long portage? They had asked her this question and she had said no. If there was no river and they could buy no horses what would they do? As for the girl, she now seemed confused in regard to her people but she recalled vividly her capture and her long journey east; her astonishment at the abundance of food in the lodges of her captors, their handsome houses, their weapons and garments and bedding. Such luxuries her people had never known.

Only the other day she had again warned the captains that they were close to Blackfoot land. She had pointed to the fire, with its great room of light in the darkness; and to the north and the northwest. With the help of her man the captains had got this story from her.

Before she was born her people, literally starving to death, had persuaded two or three other tribes to join them in a foray into buffalo land. There had been six hundred warriors and women and children; it was the biggest hunting-party ever to come out of Snakeland. They pushed ahead as far as the Great Falls on the Missouri and, finding plenty of fat buffalo there, were feasting as they had not feasted in years. The women were drying huge piles of flesh to take home and were dressing skins; the older children were catching fish in the river. They were all happy. Then the enemy came.

They saw two hundred Blackfoot warriors coming afoot and the leaders of her own people laughed. Did they think to oppose four hundred warriors with half that number?—and without horses! "We will go to meet them," the Snake leaders said. "We will go on horses and we will kill them all." And so the Snake warriors, all mounted, set out, the chiefs saying, "Don't let loose your arrows until you can see their eyes." Then suddenly the whole world went wild. Thunder fell from the heavens, lightning broke in vast sheets and the whole sky seemed to be falling; but it was chiefly Snake warriors falling from their horses. Her people's warriors fell by the score but not a Blackfoot warrior was touched by arrow or lance. It was an awful day. The weapons of the enemy, they were the weapons of the sky-gods that gutted trees and broke the rocks of the mountains and knocked men from their horses as easily as knocking an ant from your hand. With the plains covered with dead and wounded Snake warriors, her people who were able had fled back to their own barren home, where the buffalo came never, and rarely the elk and bighorn. . . .

The captains realized that for her people the terror had grown with repeated telling. The Blackfeet could not be that deadly, even with the white man's weapons. Still, they had thought that the grizzled monster was nothing to worry about, yet over there by a fire sat six bold young men whom one bear had put to flight. They didn't look so bold now. They looked quite abashed. During supper, Lewis had observed, not a one of them had met his eyes. He had never seen young men more chastened.

Well, he reflected, the Blackfeet might be as formidable as the Indians said they were but it would get a white man nothing to worry about them. It was time again for sleep and he was tired. He went to the skin-tent and, lifting the mosquito netting, let himself inside.

17

They were all tired, every one of them, including the squawman. The farther up the Missouri they went the swifter they found the water, the higher the waves, the steeper or rockier the banks; and the men rowing or towing the boats became so numbed with fatigue that it was an ordeal when morning came to leave their beds. All those who rowed, poled or towed had cut and swollen feet and torn toenails. Most of the men of the party had boils. William Bratton had such a huge boil on one hand that he was not good for much, and so one morning Lewis told him to take his gun and go up the bank. Walking might ease his pain.

In a few moments Bratton was out of sight.

An hour later one of the men heard an unearthly cry and said, "Listen!" They all listened. They stared at one another, wondering what this sound could be. It came again and again, a kind of agonized shriek or scream torn from a creature mad with fear or pain. It kept coming, and the men gazed up the river but could see no living thing. They had not yet related the sound to the human voice, and did not until about a half a mile distant there suddenly burst from a grove of trees what unmistakably was a man running at full speed. He was running with such speed that he seemed now and then to leave the earth in immense leaps, and touch, only to soar again.

"God in heaven!" said Shannon. "It's Bill."

"It's more than Bill," Bob Frazier said. "Look what's at his heels— and I'll bet any man his next drink that Bill shot it right through the heart."

"God in heaven," said Shannon, "look at them come!"

The thing at Bill Bratton's heels was a monstrous grizzly.

Too fascinated to think of going to the rescue, the men stared and exclaimed. Then, abruptly, the bear gave up the chase and turned and vanished. Apparently Bill did not know that his foe had abandoned him, for he still came at phenomenal speed, flinging his hands as though trying to make wings of them, and screaming with all the power of his voice. Not once did he glance back or break off his infernal sound of terror. A pirogue had been put to a bank to receive him and he hit it with such force that Lewis thought he must have broken his neck. He came in headlong, as if shot from a cannon, and for what Lewis afterward judged to be fifteen minutes he was unable to utter a word. His heart beat so loud that every person in the boat could hear it. He lay sprawled out, white and utterly spent, his breath rasping in his throat and choking him. Lewis stood above him, looking down. He hoped that the big boastful lubber had ruptured the boil in his flight, for then he would not have to lance it, but he saw that the boil looked larger than ever.

When Bratton was able to talk he gasped out this story. He had walked a mile or more up the river and unexpectedly had confronted the largest grizzly he had ever seen. He had time to fire only once. After that it was a race for his life. He gasped the story out, wheezing, sucking air in, choking, moaning.

"You forgot to turn him around," Frazier said.

"I expect you shot it through the heart," George Shannon said. "Of course you did, William."

"Shut up!" Bill cried, wheezing. He had put forth such abnormal exertion that he had ruptured blood vessels in his forehead and nose.

At the head of seven of the best hunters Lewis went up the river. After half a mile they easily followed the beast by its bloody trail and after another half a mile they found it in a thicket, digging itself a hole and licking its wound. They shot it twice in the head and then skinned and examined it. Bratton had shot it in its heart-chamber and it had bled a great deal inside but had seemed to be as strong as ever. It was such an enormous thing that it took two of the strongest men just to carry its hide. From its fat the party took eight gallons of oil.

That evening the captains gave an order: after this, no man was to leave camp alone. They also admonished their men to use more care against rattlesnakes, for these venomous creatures were now to be found in every weed patch and behind every stone. One of the men, lying in camp, had sleepily reached up to a willow limb above him and closed his hand on a rattler's head. He had passed it off as a joke. Lewis had rebuked him, saying, "You won't think it a joke if you fall down in convulsions and begin to pray." Lewis was standing one day when, hearing rattles, he looked down and saw one of the pests upright between his legs, its head ready to strike. With his espontoon, a steel-shod pike, he had killed it. This one and others he had measured and examined: they were about three feet in length and were of yellowish-brown color on their backs and sides, with rows of oval brown spots.

If it wasn't grizzlies or rattlesnakes, Lewis said, it was something else, for danger was now their constant companion. One night in camp the sergeant of the guard let off a fearful yell. On looking out of their skin-tent the captains saw that a huge cottonwood tree, not far from where they stood and leaning toward them, was afire in its entire upper length. Quickly they moved their tent and a moment afterward two or three tons of flaming wood crashed down, striking the exact spot where they had been sleeping.

To Clark, Lewis said, "By just ten minutes we missed being smashed to atoms."

"If the Blackfeet don't get us," Clark said, "something else will."

The thing that seemed most likely to get them along this stretch of the Missouri was the grizzled monster. One day ashore with two of the men Clark met one and shot it. The beast ran at what seemed full speed for a quarter of a mile before it fell. On examining it Clark was amazed to learn that the bullet had gone right through the heart. He stood silent, looking at the monster. He would never have believed that any creature could run four or five hundred yards after a large ball had torn through its heart-chambers. Where in all of creation was there a more formidable adversary than this!

Back in camp he told Lewis that a grizzly had run a good quarter of a mile shot through the heart but at the moment Lewis was too concerned to listen. His dog had plunged into the river to tow in a beaver one of the hunters had wounded and the beaver had sunk his long sharp chisels through the dog's throat. Now the dog was bleeding to death. He had labored over him all afternoon, Lewis said. He was to labor over him all night. Desperately he searched through the list of medicines for something that would stanch the flow of blood.

Now and then some of the men would come over to Lewis and

the dog to learn if the beast was getting better or worse. Lewis didn't know. All dogs in pain, he said, were mute and patient: they would look at you with their eloquent suffering eyes and hope that you could do something. Because they endured without a whimper you never could tell how close to death they were. The blood had stopped flowing from the wound but the dog was too weak to stand. During the night some of the men left their beds and came; and even after midnight, even after three in the morning. The emotional and impulsive Lewis was touched by their concern. The next day, with the beast lying comfortably in a pirogue, the party moved upstream; and that evening the hunters reported that about five miles up the Mussel Shell River there was a handsome stream a hundred and fifty feet wide. Lewis proposed that it should be named for Sacajawea: her concern over the suffering dog had momentarily endeared her to him. Besides, he had observed Clark's tendency to name rivers for women. He suspected that they were for girls whom Clark had once loved or still loved but the captains never spoke to one another about love and women.

Though danger was present every day the captains never turned aside from their principal task, that of discovering new and fascinating things. Their sharp eyes missed little. For a week now they had been curious about a mountain animal with huge horns. Clark called it an ibex. Lewis did not think it was the ibex. Some of the men thought it was a species of goat. One day Drewyer shot one and brought its head and horns to the camp. The captains found that they weighed twenty-seven pounds.

The head and horns, Clark said, were monstrously out of proportion to the remainder of the beast. Moreover, between male and female there was a much greater disparity in size than among deer or goats.

"I had noticed that," Lewis said.

"Their head, nostrils and the split in the upper lip are like the sheep and their legs resemble the sheep's. Like the sheep, they stand forward in the knee."

"Then you don't think it is an ibex. What is an ibex, anyway?"

"A goat with recurved horns," said Clark, who was busy writing a long description of the big-horned animal.

The next day, hoping to get a close view of the ibex-sheep, Lewis climbed to an eminence and looked into the west. He felt a thrill go clear through him. He rubbed at his eyes and looked again. No, this was not an illusion, not a mirage: there they were: he was gazing upon the Rocky Mountains for the first time in his life! His breathing almost stopped. Yes, good Lord, there they were, white with snow and shining in a full sun! He felt deep pleasure at finding himself so near at last to the headwaters of the Missouri; so near, he dared hope, to his ultimate goal. But then, coming to himself, as captain of a Corps and not a romantic dreamer, he realized that this high snowcapped range might be impassable. He had a vision of indescribable sufferings and hardships—of his party marooned in the frozen summits, snowbound and without food; and of its defeat and slow death. But then he chided himself. He told himself (what this evening he was to enter in his Journal) that it was a crime to anticipate evils: he would believe that there was a wide comfortable road across those high cold mountains, until overwhelming misfortune compelled him to believe that there was not! And so, his gaze lingering, he turned away, with the wonder of it all like a great sensuous glow in his thoughts.

On another hill he looked into the north. The captains now knew that Indians were on the river upstream, or recently had been. Were the Blackfeet watching them? They did not, he supposed, remembering the slave-girl's anxieties and fears, worry enough about this ferocious nation. Well, they had many other things to worry about. He and Clark had been asleep in their tent one night when all hell seemed to break loose in their camp. A huge buffalo bull had swum over from the opposite bank and because he was dimwitted and dimsighted, with great shaggy forelocks hanging over his eyes, he had climbed up and over the white pirogue, making an infernal clatter; and then had gone loping straight toward the fires, the sharp chisels of his hooves striking within eighteen inches of the heads of sleeping men. A guard had turned him and, wild with fright, he had gone plunging past other sleepers, his deadly feet striking within three or four inches of the brains of men. Again he had veered and headed for the tent in which the captains lay but the wounded dog had gone mad with rage and had attacked so savagely that the monster changed direction still again and soon was out of camp and out of sight. All the men by this time were in an uproar: they had seized their guns and knives and were shouting at one another, demanding to know who was attacking. Was it the Blackfeet? The next morning it was learned that the rifle belonging to York had been stepped on by the bull and the barrel was now bent in the shape of a quarter moon. In the white pirogue a number of things had been broken or scattered. Looking at the damage, Lewis observed with dry mirth that this boat seemed to be attended by evil genii.

But the threat of danger, the captains decided, was good for their men. Now that they were in swifter waters and between the upper river's higher banks, those with the boats suffered terribly with torn and swollen feet. But instead of complaining they looked out on life for things that might amuse or astonish them. Or they looked at the big Negro. They had forgotten their resentment because of his triumphs with the squaws. They all admitted, at least privately, that he was all man, this big giant, for he never tried to shirk; and though his feet were no tougher than white feet, and his many wounds just as painful, day after day he did the work of two men.

With forked sticks they pinned rattlesnakes to the earth at their necks and then lay prone to study their flicking tongues and cold eyes. They chased wolves and brained the creatures with one blow across their skulls; or while one threw a net over the beast's face another would seize his tail and swing him round and round, at last letting him spill on his head and roll head over heels.

The wolf they hated because of the antelope's innocence. This beast, fleetest by far of all those on the plains, seemed to have the curiosity of both the magpie and the cat. A hunter had only to go into deep prairie grass and push his hat up on a stick or lie on his back and thrust a foot up and the foolish antelope would race round and round it in a steadily narrowing circle, until it was easy to shoot it through the head or neck. This trick the men had learned from the wolf. The wolf would lose himself in deep grass and put a paw up and waggle it or in some other way arouse the antelope's curiosity; and it would begin to race round and round, all the while closing the circle and at last actually coming so close that the wolf could spring and seize it.

The men said they had never heard of a beast so stupid. York said the coon was just as curious. A dozen of the men looked for a few moments at the Negro, wondering about his knowledge of things. Though a slave he was trying to be one of them, and some of the men were willing to accept him as an equal, now that all the women but one were far away and York, like the rest of them, had nothing to do but eat and sleep and work.

Another said the beaver was just as dumb. This busy creature, finding itself in a large grove of cottonwood and willow, the barks of which were its favorite food, was not content to fell only enough trees for its stomach and its dams, but with sleepless energy brought down every tree it could find. Then, having devastated an area, destroyed its food supply and made a shambles of its engineering projects, it had to explore up- or downstream for another site. The beaver or the antelope, George Shannon said, you could take your choice. It was a wonder how either survived.

The day after the buffalo bull plunged through the camp the party came to another tributary and Clark promptly named it Judith's River. He thought Judith was the name of the girl he hoped to marry on his return, having been too busy as a soldier, with so little time for romantic fancies, to have learned that her name was not Judith but Julia. Lewis walked up this river a little way and came to the fire-ashes of a hundred and twenty-six Indian lodges. He thought the fires were about twelve or fifteen days old.

Looking round him, he found a couple of worn-out moccasins and these he took to Sacajawea. She turned them over and over in her small brown hands, studying the leather and the sewing. Looking up at Lewis, she shook her head no and then spoke to her man. Charbonneau said she thought they belonged to Indians who lived east of the Rockies and north of the Missouri. Perhaps the Blackfeet. It was not the sewing of her people.

Were a hundred and twenty-six lodges of Blackfeet up the river from them?

The captains asked the question again when they came to an astonishing sight: a great herd of buffalo—Lewis estimated the number at several hundred—had been stampeded and driven over a precipice with a sheer drop of more than a hundred feet. The stench was overpowering. The scattered mangled carcasses, all of them torn open by wolves and bears, were the most hideous sight any of the men had ever seen. Roundabout were hundreds of wolves and they seemed, Lewis thought, extremely fat and gentle.

Clark at the moment was on the opposite bank. Lewis sent a canoe to fetch him.

"Captain Clark," he said, after Clark had joined him, "I saw you observing this immense number of carcasses. Isn't it the Blackfeet who stampede whole herds over precipices?"

"I've heard that they do."

"Do the Minnetarees?"

"I don't know. You think the camp on Judith's River was Blackfeet?"

"Were we told last winter that the Big Bellies drive whole herds over precipices and leave most of the flesh to rot? I don't remember it."

Clark was looking round him for Indian sign. "I expect," he said, "we're in Blackfoot country all right."

"I expect," said Lewis, "that maybe they're looking at us right now."

The next day and the next they found still other recent Indian encampments and they had the Shoshone girl look at them. They were not her people, she said. Her people had never come this far from home. She thought they were not the Minnetarees; for years she had lived close to them and they did not set up their lodges in this kind of pattern. Besides, they were a small nation: how could so many of them be so far away from home so early?

"That's a good question," Clark said.

"I was thinking the same thing. If a large band had come up the river ahead of us we'd have known it. If so many had been away all last winter we'd have known it."

"It must be the Blackfeet," Clark said.

"Are there any Big Bellies on the Saskatchewan?"

"We've never heard of any."

"The squaw thinks they're the Blackfeet."

"I don't see who else it could be."

"They know we're here," Lewis said. "They've been watching us for days probably. They are going on up the river ahead of us and they surely have some plan in mind."

"I would assume so," Clark said.

Sacajawea was frightened, for she had no doubt that these were Blackfoot warriors. Even more, she was astonished. The captains and their men, without turning a hair, went right on up the river and every night they made their big fires and made their music and danced. She had never heard of such boldness. The Blackfeet were up the river ahead of them, because for days now their fire-ashes had been found along the banks. And day by day the signs had become fresher. Did the captains realize that this might be a huge war-party that was going up and up the river ahead of them only to lead them into an ambush, in some narrow canyon where they could fire from behind rocks?

Her astonishment grew at the incredible boldness of these men. They made their fires just as big as ever and seemed not to care whether their campsite offered any protection. They made their music and danced, and even shouted, appearing not to care at all if a thousand fierce warriors were looking at them from the darkness. She couldn't understand it. She thought them ignorant, for she could not believe that any men were so brave. Furtively she studied the face of Chief Long Knife, of Chief Red Hair—but she might as well have looked at the turbid Missouri waters. The captains were calmly writing in their journals; or while one labored over a map by firelight the other sucked at his pipe. It was true that all night men stood watch but she wished she could leave the skin-tent in which she slept and stand watch herself. That the Blackfeet would strike some morning with overwhelming force she did not doubt at all.

She infected her man with her anxieties and he spoke to Lewis. He said they would be attacked and they would all be massacred.

"Maybe," Lewis said. "Maybe. But the surest way to get the red man after your scalp is to show fear. We are ready for them. Let them come."

During the hours of light Sacajawea did watch, all day long. Time and again she slipped away, her child standing up her back, to climb a tree or a hill and look far up the river. She searched the Indian encampments for some proof that these were Blackfeet, though she had no idea what the proof could be. At last, feeling that the entire party would be destroyed if she did not act, she took her man away and out of sight.

She begged him to speak again to the captains. She told him again what terrible warriors the Blackfeet were and with what triumphant shrieks they tortured their captives. Some morning five hundred or a thousand of them—she indicated the numbers by the leaves on trees —would dash in and some of them would die and some of them would be taken away to the torture-places. Her man told her that the white chiefs said they were not afraid. They had powerful medicine. Most of them were deadshots. They had big boom-guns——

"Warn them!" she begged him in French. "Warn them!"

He shrugged. He was scared but he had to pretend to be as brave as any man here. He had also been pretending that he was a mighty hunter, and two days later when he saw Drewyer, the best shot of them all, take his gun and set off he asked to go along. Drewyer, a man of few words, said neither yes nor no, and so the squawman went with him. The Bear of the Forest, Drewyer was thinking. The Bear of the Forest. That's what the Mandans called him.

An hour later they jumped a big grizzly and for a few moments Drewyer tried to get a bead on its head. Unable to, he shot it through its chest, aiming for its heart. At once the monster swung and charged. With a shout of warning to the squawman Drewyer took to his heels, trying to reload as he ran. He was not so nimble as younger men and he had been stiffened by rheumatism: his speed was too slow, the beast steadily gained on him and was soon almost close enough to seize him with jaws so powerful that they could crush a buffalo calf. Drewyer was despairing of his life, for there was no tree in sight, no river, no stone ledge, when on a most unaccountable impulse the monster turned and charged the squawman. With a shriek that was heard by men two miles away he aimed his gun straight at the sky and fired it. Drewyer saw him do it. He saw the fool just poke his gun up at the sky and pull the trigger, then throw it away with another horrible yell and plunge headlong into a dense thicket of rose brambles. In that thicket Charbonneau with frenzied power rushed away on hands and knees, deeper and deeper into the mess of briars; and the bear, seeing that his foe had vanished, swung and headed for Drewyer. Drewyer had had time to reload. He was determined not to shoot again into the chest. All the men had learned that shots anywhere but in the tiny brain were wasted. And so he waited, as cool as a man could be, as the beast rushed him. There was such a deep ridge of frontal bone and muscle on the grizzly that a bullet straight into the forehead was a bullet thrown away. It had to be a little to one side or from the top down. A man had to hit an area no larger than a dollar on a bear in fast motion but this man was the best shot in the Corps and there was none cooler; and a few moments later he stood looking at the dead monster at his feet. He called to the squawman and he came crawling to the edge of the thicket, his face covered with blood, for he had gouged and torn his flesh in his panic. For a few minutes Charbonneau remained there on hands and knees, looking over.

Drewyer told Lewis of the incident—told him in only a few words and in only a few words Lewis recorded it, concluding: ". . . finally killed it by a shot in the head; the shot indeed that will conquer the farocity of those tremendious anamals." Then, before completing the day's entry, he filled his pipe and sat a little while thinking of the man whose name the captains spelled as Drewyer but whose name was Drouillard: it had been a lucky day for the Corps when this man was chosen, for he killed twice the game of anyone else with half the fuss.

If I were to go on a really dangerous journey, Lewis was thinking (as though he were not on a really dangerous journey now), and were to choose of all the men I know only three or four to go with me, Drewyer would surely be one of them, even if he is a Frenchman. . . .

He dipped his pen in ink and wrote again.

18

On the 3rd of June, fifty-six days and nearly a thousand miles from Fort Mandan, the captains knew that they were lost. Deep in this unknown land where no white man had ever been, with the tall snowcapped Rockies now only a hundred miles to the west, they were at the junction of two great rivers; but which was the Missouri and which was its affluent? A wrong choice, the captains realized, could be disastrous.

It had been wearisome and often dangerous toil for the boatmen the past six hundred miles, struggling barefooted over the sharp and slippery stones, often in water to their armpits, always in water so cold that it chilled them; and now none of them could stand without pain or walk without limping. In his Journal, Lewis had written, ". . . it is with great pain that they do either. for some days past they were unable to wear their mockersons . . . they have fallen off considerably, but notwithstanding the difficulties past, or those which seem now to menace us, they still remain perfectly cheerful." They were, the captains agreed, remarkable men but they were men who could stand so much and no more. They were men with feet scarred and calloused; men who had lost twenty or thirty pounds wading deep in icy water ten or twelve hours a day; yet men not one of whom had ever whimpered or given any but a cheerful response when asked how he was. They were men who could reach the last extremity of endurance and blow up in mutinous rage if the captains were to choose the wrong river and punish them with needless miles. How easy it would be for them to say they had had enough and to seize the pirogues and go back home!

One of the rivers came out of the northwest, the other out of the southwest. One of them, the Mandan Indians had said, had its headwaters close to the Columbia. But which one? Hoping to find an answer, the captains climbed a hill overlooking the junction. While climbing the hill Lewis was thinking, Two months of our traveling season have already gone: if we mistake the river and ascend the wrong one, and then have to return and take the other, we'll probably have to accept defeat and turn back. . . . Clark had much the same thought. Together without speaking they climbed to the summit and then looked at the vast level countryside around them, black in spots with its herds of buffalo, with here and there a pack of wolves, a herd of elk or the solitary mother antelope and her child. Far in the south they saw a lofty range, a part of it snowcapped. They could mark the courses of the two rivers only a short distance, and so could not be sure of their direction. They descended and took the width of the rivers, finding that the one on the south was over eleven hundred feet wide, the one on the north about six hundred. The north river was deeper but not so swift; its waters had the whitish-brown color of the Missouri. The south river was as transparent as glass, its bottom covered with round pebbles like those to be found in any stream that came down from mountains.

Lewis said, "I asked our riverman Cruzatte, which is the main river? He says the north one."

"Most of the men think that. They judge by the color."

"But the north one would color the whole Missouri."

"They don't seem to realize that."

"If the south one clarified the Missouri they'd think it the main stream. What does the squaw say?"

"She's as lost as we are."

"She doesn't know which way her people are from us?"

"An Indian," Clark said, "has only four directions."

The captains decided to send a small exploring party up each river. They chose Gass to lead two men up the south river, Pryor to lead two men up the north river; and they sent still other parties out to look for an eminence from which they could gaze far into the southwest, west and northwest. When those exploring the rivers came back with sketchy and wholly unsatisfactory reports the captains knew that they would have to go and see for themselves. Lewis chose six men, with Drewyer among them; Clark chose five, including the Fields brothers and his servant York. They chose men whose feet would allow them to walk rapidly and far, because they intended in a couple of days to push up these rivers fifty or sixty miles. They would go until there was no doubt left in their minds.

The evening before their departure they gave each man a drink of whisky, as a kind of good luck token, or possibly as a kind of farewell. They were in Blackfoot country. They knew that Indians would not hesitate at all to attack a party of six or seven men. As he prepared his pack this evening Lewis was thinking, with wry humor, that during all his years as a soldier he had never carried his own pack. Because he hoped to walk thirty or forty miles a day he took only one blanket, powder and ball, a pair of field glasses and his weapons. Telling the men in camp to get busy dressing hides and making moccasins and garments, and to keep an alert watch day and night, the captains at daylight filled their bellies with boiled elk and corn and set off with their squads.

Two days later, Clark, who had a geographer's intuitions, had made up his mind. Lewis had to go farther before he could be sure. His party ran into a terrific rainstorm. It poured all night without letup and because they had no shelter they were soon soaked and before daylight left what Lewis called their watery beds and set off as drenched as if they had been pulled out of a river. While walking along a precipice Lewis slipped on the wet earth and came within a hair of pitching headlong over the ledge and into the river below. He had hardly recovered his poise when he heard an agonized cry.

"Good God, Captain, what shall I do?"

It was Dick Windsor. Lewis looked at him and was horrified. Dick had slipped and fallen and now lay on his belly, his right leg and his right arm hanging over the precipice. Lewis took a moment to consider before he spoke. He was thinking fast. He was saying to himself, "I must speak quietly and with complete assurance, because without confidence he is doomed." Still looking at the terrified man he saw that his left foot and hand had dug into soaked earth that threatened at any moment to give way.

In a voice perfectly calm Lewis said, "You're all right, you're in no particular danger at all. Just do as I tell you. Slip your knife out of your belt with your right hand and dig a hole in the bank for your right foot. . . . Careful, now. Easy. . . . That's it. Now, slowly— very slowly and carefully, hugging the earth as tight as you can, pull yourself up to your knees. Dig your left fingers in deeper, if you can That's it: just dig deep—and up. That's it—deep and up. . . . Now

—now with your right hand slip off your mockersons, if you can . . . dig your left toes in . . . that's it, dig them in. . . . Do you see your knife? Reach around a little and you'll feel it—it's just a few inches above your right hand. . . . There. Now take your gun in your other hand—that's it—and crawl forward on your knees . . . slowly, chest and head down, hug the earth. . . . Slowly . . . that's it. . . ."

Lewis was amazed to see the man do it. When he first saw him, half over the precipice and barely clinging to wet earth, he had not given him one chance in a thousand to save his life. Yet here he was, standing before him, white and shaken.

Lewis said, "It wasn't so difficult, was it?"

Windsor took a deep breath and grinned. "No, sir," he said.

The other five men had stood back and watched. They were not looking at Dick Windsor. They were looking at Meriwether Lewis, and in the eyes of every one the admiration was bright and plain. Lewis was not aware of them. He was not aware that five of his men were thinking, This is a leader we can be proud of, or that Dick Windsor was telling himself, "He saved my life."

"I almost fell," he said to Dick. "I would have gone over but for my espontoon."

Toward evening they killed six fat deer and over a fire roasted the choicest of the meat. They ate like gluttons, for this was their first meal this day. A sun had warmed and dried the earth. After making a mattress of willow boughs Lewis stretched out, hoping for a good night's rest, reflecting meanwhile in his dry way that a good meal and a dry bed could revive the spirits of the weariest traveler. Over by the fire the six men sat in silence and looked at him.

When his party arrived at the main camp he found that Clark had been back two days and was worried about him. He was afraid that Lewis and his men had fallen before the Blackfeet.

The captains went off by themselves and Lewis said, "Captain Clark, which is our river?"

"The south one. What do you think?"

"The same."

This evening they called the men before them and Lewis then spoke to them, saying, "Captain Clark and I are convinced that the south river is the main river, but we expect that some of you have another opinion. We have examined our old maps; we have consulted all the information we have, viewing the matter from every possible angle; and though we've no doubt which river we should take, for the well-being of our party it will be best if none of you doubt either. We're sure that some of you do doubt. We therefore invite you to speak up."

George Shannon spoke. He had little awe of Army rank or of these two captains. Besides, it was his way to speak his mind. He puckered his apple-cheeks and opened his blue eyes wide.

"Captain Lewis, it's this way: Cruzatte here is an old riverman. He spent half his life on rivers. He's sure it's the north fork."

The captains turned to look at Cruzatte but he sat with his head down. Lewis said to Shannon, "Private Shannon, on what evidence does he reach that opinion?"

"The color of the water, sir. The north fork looks exactly like the main river."

"But it would color the whole river, wouldn't it? If you run a muddy river and a clear river into the same stream do you get a clear river or a muddy river?"

"Well, he says the Columbia is away up north, as he understands it. I was with Captain Clark down the clear river. It goes into the southwest. How could a river coming out of the southwest be close to a river away up north?"

"Do you think this north fork penetrates the Rockies?"

Whitehouse spoke up. "St. Peter thinks so."

Lewis turned to Sergeant Pryor, who had gone with him up the north fork. "Sergeant Pryor, what do you think?"

"I agree with Cruzatte, Captain."

Sergeant Gass had gone with Clark. "Sergeant Gass?"

"I feel the same, Captain."

"Sergeant Ordway?"

"I agree with them, Captain Lewis, but we're all ready to follow you and Captain Clark, no matter where you go."

Lewis looked at him a moment. Then he said, "Captain Clark and I know that, Sergeant. We know we have a corps of fine brave men and we certainly want to make no mistake in the choice. Are we to understand, then, that you all agree with Cruzatte?"

Shannon said, "Yes, Captain."

"All right, we won't talk about it any more this evening."

The two captains entered their tent to discuss the matter and in a few minutes heard the sound of Cruzatte's fiddle. Some of the men were dancing and those with good voices were singing. The captains could hear York's feet.

Lewis said, "Since all our men feel that way about it I guess I'd better go up the south fork and see if the falls are there. If they're there, that's our river."

Clark did not speak at once. He was recalling what he had heard about the two rivers—that one had its headwaters up north, that the other rose in the southwest. He was trying to shape in his mind an image of this vast country, with its ranges of mountains, its many rivers, its two watersheds. If only they knew the latitude of the Columbia's source!

"That might be best," Clark said at last. "While you're gone we can cache some of the things and dress out a lot of skins."

"The falls can't be too far from here."

"I shouldn't think so. They have to be this side of the mountains."

"They must be there. All the Indians mentioned them."

"Some of them said they'd seen them. And besides the falls there's the sound the mountains make. We haven't heard that."

For a little while the captains were silent. Lewis had named the north fork Maria's River, for a Maria Wood, whom he had known in childhood. In his impish way he had written in his Journal, "it is true that the hue of the waters of this turbulent and troubled stream but illy comport with the pure celestial virtues and amiable qualifications of that lovely fair one; but on the other hand it is a noble river; one destined to become in my opinion an object of contention between the two great powers of America and Great Britin with rispect to the adjustment of the Northwestwardly boundary of the former . . ."

He was cherishing the idea that the United States could lay claim to all land adjacent to all the rivers that he and Clark discovered, even clear to their headwaters, even clear across Canada. He hoped that some way could be found to claim all of Canada. He wished he had the time to go up Miss Maria's river all the way to its source but he had to go on now, because great mountains stood ahead of him and the summer was well along.

"The north fork," he said at last—he had not dared to call it Maria's River out loud—"is so full of mud and silt that it must drain a large fertile land. I wish we had time to explore it."

"I wished back yonder that we had time to explore the Yellow Stone."

"If we only could! If only we could take a map of this whole western country to the President!"

"And the Federalists," Clark said.

"Oh yes, the Federalists."

In one of his rare moments of levity Clark said, "We've just got to
find that mountain of salt."

"And the eagle."

The next morning when the captains left their beds they became
aware that the Shoshone girl was ill. Clark knelt to look at her and
saw that the blood was drained from the copper skin of her face and
that her lips were trembling. He found that her pulse was feeble.
After breakfast he opened a vein in her arm to bleed her and massaged along the vein until he had forced out a pint of blood. She refused breakfast, even broth. She was too weak to stand. After mixing
a little meal in elk broth Clark took the babe to his lap and fed it. He
called it Pomp because pomp, he had heard, was the Shoshone word
for the oldest boy in a family. Pomp looked at him with round
black eyes. Most of the time he had been a good baby: all day long
he stood in the harness on his mother's back, showing a curious bright
interest in what the adults were doing. Clark liked to hold the child.
This stern military man even talked a little baby-talk to it, but not
so that anybody else could hear. "Pomp," he said, moving his face
close and looking into the sober black eyes, "Pompey boy, you know
your mama is ill?" He touched his long sunbaked nose to the tiny
neb on Pomp's face and rubbed it gently. Pomp drew back and
turned his lips out and opened his eyes wide. The eyes now reminded
Clark of an owl brought from dark into daylight. "Pompey boy, tell
your mama to get well fast. Will you?" When he was dead-sure that
no eyes were watching him he took the child close to his chest and
gave it a little hug. The next moment he returned it to its mother,
and when he came out of the tent his long irregular face was again
stern—was the face of Captain William Clark of the United States
Army and the Corps of Discovery, and not the face of the man deep
inside who wanted a wife and children and a home back in
Kentucky. . . .

Captain Lewis meanwhile was getting ready to go up the south
fork. He went among the men, casually looking at their feet; observing how they walked; studying their faces for signs of discouragement or homesickness—and chose at last to go with him George
Drewyer, the deadshot; George Gibson, Joe Fields and Silas Good-

rich. They were four men of unquestioned courage. He had seen them all tried. In an encounter with the Sioux, Silas had recovered his tomahawk from a brave who had taken it from him.

Lewis was not feeling well this morning. He swung his pack up and set off with his four men and after only a mile or two realized that he was sick. His sleep for several nights had been restless, filled with a recurring nightmare of men trapped in deep snows while he tried vainly to sail up a swift river to their rescue. He now had violent gut-cramps that bent him double. Clasping his ears, he knew that he had fever. He seemed to be cold, for he had chills. He helped the men dress out four elk and hang the hides and flesh within sight of the river. He had looked forward to a feast of marrowbones, but when the meal was cooked he was unable to eat a thing. The three young men looked at him with concern when they saw him grimace with pain, for he was tortured by sharp thrusts in his bowels.

Pushing the pain down in him and trying to ignore it, Lewis forced himself to march mile after mile at the head of his party but toward evening he could endure no more. He had a high fever. He had such convulsions of agony in his lower body that he thought he would faint. He told the men they would camp at once and he asked them to gather for him a bed of willow boughs; and on this he stretched out and closed his eyes, shuddering the whole length of him with each seizure. He was furious at his weakness in a time of crisis: the hours were passing, back at Maria's River the Corps was waiting for his return, yet here he lay, barely able to move and so savagely and furiously frustrated that he wanted to die. What, he asked himself, could he do about it? Was he to let the men make a stretcher and carry him back in shameful defeat? No, great thunder, he would not: he would go on if it killed him; he would get well and he would get well fast. What would his mother, the famous yarb doctor, do for him if she were here? She would dose him with some of her yarb simples. Thinking of this, he saw no reason why he should not do it, and so called to his men. They came over and looked down at the sweat on his face. He told them to gather an armful of the smaller limbs of the chokecherry; to strip off the leaves and cut the limbs into short pieces, and then boil them until they had a decoction as thick as molasses.

An hour and a half later they brought the kettle to him and a tin cup and he dipped the cup into the thick black stuff and drank it. It was bitter—O God, it was even more bitter than aloes! It was simply the most bitter stuff he had ever tasted and the most sickening. But he drank about a pint of it and lay back to study the sensations within him. Everything inside him now seemed to be gurgling and rumbling but he sensed that the rumbles turned something free and eased the pain; and an hour later he felt so much better that he drank another pint. He had burst into heavy sweat and he felt horribly weak but steadily he felt better. Two hours later he drank still another pint, for Captain Meriwether Lewis was a man who believed that if a little was good for you, a lot was a certain cure. Before midnight he felt so fully recovered that he walked around to test himself and the miracle. Silas Goodrich, a youngster who would rather fish than eat, had caught dozens of fine fat trout and Lewis now roasted and ate one. Then he had a good night's sleep and awoke a new man.

The next morning he pushed on with his party and late in the forenoon felt a thrill go through him that left him tingling all over. He stopped, breathless, and listened. Yes, there it was! There in the distance was the unmistakable sound of falling waters. He hastened forward and after a mile or so stopped again: in the southwestern sky he could see spray rising like broken columns of smoke, and in his ears now was a tremendous roaring. It could come only from the Great Falls on the Missouri.

Again he hastened forward and about noon came to the first falls: he had only to look at the churning white water and the boiling fury with which it plunged over a precipice to put all doubts away: this was the falls the Indians had told about, this was the right river. He would send a man to tell Captain Clark and while waiting for the main party to come up he would explore the other falls, for he had known and now could see that there was a whole series of them. In his Journal he wrote that his supper this evening was really sumptuous: he feasted on buffalo hump, tongue and marrowbones; on roasted trout and parched meal, all of it seasoned with pepper and salt.

The next morning he set off alone to have a look at the other falls and to determine if he could how difficult the portage would be. Soon he was gazing upon a thousand head of buffalo and it occurred to him that it would be sensible to kill one and hang up the choicer parts of the meat, so that if he went so far during the day that he could not return to camp he could spend the night here. Approaching close to the herd, he chose a fat young heifer and, resting his rifle

over the upturned end of his espontoon, he took careful aim and
fired. The beast did not fall or move but red blood poured in streams
from its mouth and nostrils, and so Lewis waited, looking at it and
expecting it to fall. He had not bothered to reload his gun.

He had no sense of the presence of an enemy and so was completely astounded when, glancing behind him, he saw a monstrous
grizzly creeping up, at a distance of no more than sixty feet. Gooseflesh covered his neck and back. His hair almost rose when he saw
that the monster had abandoned his stealthy advance and was ready
to charge. In the fraction of a second Lewis had looked round him
and had seen that there was not a bush or tree, neither precipice nor
neb of stone, within a distance of four hundred yards. In that same
fraction of a second he felt a stinging sensation up the back of his
neck and heard a queer rumble in his belly. His thoughts in this
instant were racing like lightning: among them stood one, larger
than all others: it said, Sometimes if you back away slowly you confuse a wild beast and he will retreat. . . . But the moment he
started to back away the monster gave off a roar that shook the earth,
and came at full speed, his enormous mouth wide open. Holding on
to both his gun and espontoon, Lewis took to his heels, and later,
when telling the men (who laughed till they thought they would
die), he said that for eighty yards he broke all known records. He
had never dreamed that he could run so fast. William Bratton's race,
he said, had been the crawl of the tortoise compared to his own. But
even so, the bear gained on him: he thought he could feel the creature's breath; he was sure that he could hear the soft muffled blows
of its feet. . . .

Knowing that in another moment or two he would be seized and
that his organs would be gutted out of him with one sweep of the
huge talons, Lewis swung sharply to the right, where, though he
doubted his senses, he saw the river. He plunged in. His thought was
to get into water deep enough that while he could stand the bear
would have to swim. And so he plunged in and forward until the
water was almost to his chin, when, turning, he raised his espontoon
in his right hand, intending to strike the beast an awful blow across
his tender nose. But the bear, to Lewis's amazement, wanted none
of it: he stood a moment at the water's edge, his small stupid eyes
looking, but when he saw the espontoon rise and flash in the sun and
heard his foe's wild screaming cry of challenge he turned as if in
great fright and hastened away at full speed.

His amazement growing, Lewis waded to the bank and while re-loading his gun watched the monster rush away. The most astonishing thing for Lewis was that though the bear ran as fast as he could go he kept looking back, as if imagining that he was pursued. When the bear vanished from sight Lewis looked carefully round him to see if another beast was sneaking up on him. Then with a short queer laugh he said, "Well, I'll be damned!" His emotions were badly mixed. He knew that again he had come within a hair of losing his life but the thing that disturbed him most was that he felt like an utter greenhorn. He had told his men never to go alone into grizzly land and always to reload as quickly as possible, yet he had broken both rules. He felt a kind of weakness all through him, as though he were recovering from a fever.

He went on up the river and presently was gazing with astonishment at another beast. At first he thought it was a wolf but on approaching within fifty yards he saw that it was of brownish color and was standing at the entrance of what seemed to be a burrow. What on earth could this be? As he continued to approach, the beast crouched like a cat and seemed ready to spring. He took careful aim and fired. The creature vanished. After reloading his gun he went forward to examine the spot. He saw around the hole the footprints of some member of the cat family. Dropping to his knees, he peered into the burrow and would not have been surprised if he had seen yellow eyes looking out at him. He sniffed the scent: it was unfamiliar, and wild and strong. Standing again and looking round him, he reflected that today for some mysterious reason the whole animal-world seemed bent on his death.

His whimsy took on a sober coloring when, three hundred yards from the hole of the tiger-cat, three buffalo bulls suddenly left the herd and charged full speed toward him. Instead of running, he advanced swiftly to meet them, aware that he was foolhardy but piqued by the way wild beasts seemed to be singling him out for destruction. The bulls came on a tail-flirting dead-run until they were a hundred yards from him. They then stopped and looked him over. As suddenly as they had charged they swung and, tails flirting, rushed away.

"I'll be damned!" Lewis said again.

All these experiences had unnerved him a little. He thought it prudent to give up the idea of spending the night alone, and so headed back toward his own small camp. Darkness overtook him.

He heard again and again the rattles of rattlesnakes. He flinched when he felt the thorns of prickly pear go through his moccasins. He saw huge shadowy forms out in the dusk and sometimes whole herds of shadow; and once he was sure he saw a grizzly. What a wild world it was! He saw the firelight an hour before he was to reach it and fling himself down on his bed of willow boughs, a wry humor playing over all his emotions as he looked back on the strange adventures of this day.

19

Captain Clark meanwhile had been having troubles of a different kind. He was afraid that the Shoshone girl was going to die, now that they were drawing near to her people and would most need her. Two of his men had aching teeth; two had large tumors; one had a tumor and fever; but it was Jawey to whom he gave his time and skill. About four o'clock in the afternoon of the day Lewis ran from the bear, Joe Fields walked in from the southwest with a note saying that the Great Falls had been found on the south fork, twenty miles in advance of the main party.

Early the next morning Clark set forth with his group and all day long he had nothing but trouble. The river was swifter than it had been; the boatmen toiled with a fatigue in their bones and muscles that the captain in his Journal was to call "incretiatable." The Indian girl was so sick that she had no wish to live: Clark dosed her with steeped barks and applied various poultices to her and thought she felt a little better. He wondered if her sickness was related to her menses. The men towing the canoes repeatedly cut their feet on the sharp stones, or slipped on wet stones and fell; or if towing from the bank they had to look for cactus and rattlesnake at literally every step.

Jawey was so sick that she had been wild with delirium. Clark suspected that two or three days ago, after she had got to feeling better, she had slipped away and eaten ravenously of fish and what her man called white apples. Clark had then tried poultices of bark and laudanum and had confided to his Journal that if she died, her stupid husband would be the fault of it. He had told Charbonneau not to let her eat more than meat broth. As the party moved slowly up the river she lay back in a canoe, her eyes closed, her hands pressing on the pain in her belly. Three or four times a day Clark had held the babe to her breasts and then had fed him a little corn meal in warm meat soup. After Lewis rejoined the main party and saw how sick the girl was he felt pity for her, as well as concern for the success of his adventure. When one of the men reported the presence of a hot sulphur spring he told Ordway to bring a quart of the water, and with the squawman's help he persuaded her to drink it. Perceiving that this did her no good, he gave her a pint of the bitter chokecherry concoction and a big dose of opium. He asked her man where her pain was. Charbonneau put his hands to his lower abdomen and pressed in. After studying his list of medicines Lewis decided to apply to her belly a cataplasm of bark and laudanum.

To Clark he said, "I expect she suffers from an obstruction of the menses."

"That has been my opinion."

"Or is she pregnant again?"

"Her man says she is not."

"If she dies, what'll we do with a baby four months old?" When Clark gave no reply, Lewis said with dry whimsy, "Shoot a buffalo mother every day?"

"Soon there'll be no more buffalo," Clark said.

"I expect, though, it could live on meal and meat broth."

Lewis covered the girl's belly with a large hot bark poultice, tucked warm buffalo robes snugly around her and put a flat heated stone under her lower back. The next day she was much better; her fever was gone and her pulse was normal. Lewis told himself that he was not a bad physician after all. His mother might be proud of him. When the girl said she was hungry he gave her sparingly of boiled flesh and hot rich broth.

Meanwhile he had other problems. Clark had gone ahead with a small party to discover the length and difficulties of the portage. The next day Alex Willard was rushed by a grizzly bear that pursued him almost into the camp and came within only a few feet of catching him. When he saw the man coming and heard his wild cries for help Lewis realized that John Colter, out looking for axle timber, was somewhere in the area from which the bear had come and to which it was now returning. Lewis called three of the best hunters and gave chase. The bear had indeed found and pursued Colter:

Lewis and his party found the youth out in the river almost to his
chin, with the bear facing him from the bank. The beast then fled,
and because night had come Lewis returned with his men to the
camp. It was no less than a miracle, he was thinking, that so many
of the men had been pursued by this monster and almost overtaken,
yet none had been seized.

He had heard a sound now and then which he took to be thunder
but Joe Fields, who had been farther up the river, said it was not
thunder but a weird unearthly noise that came from the mountains.
Lewis spent an hour listening to it and at last decided that it was
like the sound of a piece of ordnance of six pounds, at a distance of
five or six miles. He went for a walk to the higher hills and spent
an hour or two listening; and then wrote in his Journal: "I heard
this *nois* very distinctly, it was perfectly calm clear and not a cloud
to be seen. . . . I have no doubt but if I had leasure I could find
from whence it issued. I have thought it probable that it might be
caused by running water in some of the caverns of those emence
mountains . . . but in such a case the sounds would be periodical
and regular, which is not the case with this, being sometimes heard
once only and at other times several discharges in quick succession.
it is heard also at different times of the day and night. I am at a
great loss to account for this Phenomenon. I well recollect hearing
the Minitarees say that those Rocky mountains made a great noise,
but they could not tell me the cause. . . ."

The other men of the party also listened to the strange sounds
and gazed wonderingly at each other. One suggested that high up
there was a river falling into an echoing cavern, the irregularity of
the sound being determined by the wind. Another thought it was
some kind of volcanic eruptions from a fissure, like steam blowing
from a tea kettle. For the more superstitious men it was an infernal
noise right out of hell and speculation about it was impious. It gave
all the men a feeling of chills and apprehension: what kind of unknown world were they about to enter and what marvels would they
find there?

"If we don't find out what it is," John Colter said, "I'd like to come
back someday and run it down."

"All alone, I suppose," Bob Frazier said.

The sound and the thought of back-breaking labor over a sixteen-
mile portage were too much for the squawman: he began to sulk, to
snarl at his wife, to whine to his sergeant. He had had enough of

this voyage; he wanted to go back. Deep down in him the man was afraid. He had come about a thousand miles from the Minnetaree villages and he asked himself day and night how many more thousands of miles the captains expected to cover. He stared at the stupendous mountains before him, blanketed by snows and shrouded by mists; he remembered that there would be no buffalo there or beyond them and probably no friends either; he looked at the men and saw that they had lost weight and were now haggard and older-looking; he observed that the river had become swifter, the stones thicker and sharper; like the others, he now fought mosquitoes day and night and small black fleas, and he decided that he had had enough of it. He told his wife they were going back. She looked at him and shook her head no. He ordered her to put the matter up to Captain Lewis, for he was afraid of both captains. She said no. Then, feeling desperate, he resolved to tell the captain himself—not Clark, whose sternness paralyzed him, but Lewis, who seemed more indulgent.

Incredulous, Lewis looked at the man. "What did you say?" he asked, his slate-gray eyes turning hard.

"Aye va-wee pore," said the squawman, grimacing with his hands, shoulders and face. "Oh, aye wret-ched mann! Mee pore vives, me ba-bees!"

"O God yes, your poor wives and babies! You mean you want to go back down the Missouri?"

"Oui, Cap-n."

"And take this wife and child with you?"

"Oui, Cap-n."

"And you want Captain Clark and me to give you a canoe, a gun and powder and ball, bedding, a keg of pork, some corn meal?"

"Oui—oui," said Charbonneau, nodding his head.

Lewis stepped close to him and tried to look into the half-lidded shifting eyes. "Shobono, listen to me: your wife is going with us, no matter what you do. If you want to go back, go; and yonder in grizzly land always shoot straight up at the sky. If the Blackfeet take after you, shoot at the sky or dive into a bramble thicket. You may have a gun, some powder and ball, one blanket, enough food for two days."

"Laissez-moi passer!"

Lewis did not understand the words but he understood the tone. His temper burst. "Look, Shobono!" he cried, turning to a group of men fifty yards distant who were laboring to build a cart. "Get over there and get to work!" He called over to Gass, "Sergeant, put this man to work and work him hard!"

Surly and angry, the squawman shuffled away.

Lewis followed him over to see how the work was going, for of all the wood available none was hard enough for axles, none of it better than the wild cherry. The men, working under Gass and Shields, were trying to build a large two-wheel cart, on which to transport the baggage seventeen or eighteen miles over hills and gullies. The terrain that hugged the river was what Lewis thought of as a mess of badlands—of stone barriers, steep hills and ravines, washouts, ledges, all of it impassable to men with burdens; and so it had been necessary to find a route at a considerable distance back from the river. This lay over gentler hills and through narrow valleys. Even if they successfully built a cart the Corps would be delayed two or three weeks, when summertime, the thing it needed most of, would be running out.

During these days Lewis was a worried man. How many and how long would the portages be on other rivers? How far would they have to traipse overland from headwaters to headwaters? Would the Shoshones let them have horses? He had to face these questions because before leaving Mandan he had written his President that on reaching the Great Falls he would send a part of the men back, with a report on the journey to this point. He now felt that they would need every man they had.

He put the matter to Clark and Clark said, "I expect we will."

"But has it occurred to you what will happen if we send none of the men back?"

Clark looked away at the sky, thinking. He turned at last to Lewis. "What?" he said.

"Everybody will figure we've all been wiped out. They'll think the Blackfeet got us. Around Fort Mandan nobody will doubt it."

"Nobody at all," Clark said.

"Word will go down the river by traders that it's the end of us. Will the President send a ship in that case?"

"Well, I expect he wouldn't. If all such people as the traders figure we're all dead the President could hardly think anything else."

"But we'll need that ship," Lewis said. "Would our men face the prospect of fighting these rivers all the way home? And then there's that. If we let two or three go back how would the others feel?"

The captains named them over one by one and decided that most of them would feel all right but some of them, perhaps a third of them, possibly even half of them, would not. They were a bold and gallant crew but this clawing their way up icy rivers and over cactus thorns was more than some of them had bargained for. It was easy to spot those who would go on in the face of hell—Colter, Shannon, the Fields brothers, Collins, Willard, Drewyer, Bratton, Whitehouse, the sergeants and a few others; but in the faces of some of the men the captains had seen an emotion that looked like homesickness. It was a good thing, Lewis said, that the men knew nothing about the promise to Jefferson. For two overpowering reasons, the captains decided, they would send nobody back: they would need all the men through the vast unknown that still lay ahead of them; and they would risk mutiny, or if not mutiny, then at least a lowering of morale and a division in the ranks, if they let any of the men return.

The prospect tickled Lewis's sardonic sense of humor. Grinning at Clark, he said, "Well, now that it's decided, we are all dead men— and one dead woman and child. From Mandan clear to Washington will go the news, They are all dead! The Blackfeet got them!" Then thought of his mother's grief occurred to him and he sobered. "The grief in the relatives of all of us," he said, "that's the worst part of it." He was about to propose that they send Charbonneau back with a message but thought better of it: the clumsy squawman would be killed by Indians or grizzlies before he got to the Yellow Stone; and besides, it was a rule with the captains that once they had agreed on a thing, there was to be no reconsideration. Clark felt especially strongly in this, for there was no Hamlet in him.

"Yes," Clark said, "that's a bad thing about it but they'll all get over it."

"Except for that," said the whimsical Lewis, "I sort of enjoy the prospect. If we do return, how astonished everyone will be—including your Judith. Especially," said Lewis slyly, "if she should be married."

Clark said nothing. He had no taste for such jests.

"Come to think of it," Lewis went on, "I expect a ship will be there. Mr. Jefferson has a wonderful imagination. He'll think of all the possibilities. One will be that we're all dead. Another will be that the messengers were killed on their way back."

"That surely will occur to him," Clark said.

"That may seem more likely to him than the other. A third possibility is that the message went astray somewhere on its long journey to Washington. A fourth . . ."

Clark was looking rather sharply at his friend. He thought Lewis was working pretty hard to put a cheerful face on the thing.

A few of the men were laboring on a bullboat. All the way from St. Louis, Lewis had brought a heavy iron frame over which he dreamed of spreading and sewing hides, to make a round boat that would carry four tons. He was, Clark reflected, the sort of man given to such fancies. Clark had never taken the plan seriously but had masked his feelings, as he always did when he thought his romantic and impulsive friend a little ridiculous. He granted him the right nevertheless to emulate Mr. Jefferson, who was everlastingly trying to invent something.

The day he was chased by the white bear Lewis had wondered in his whimsical way if the whole animal-world had entered a league for his destruction. When the long and arduous portage began he suspected that all the elements of nature had conspired to dishearten his men, wear them out and delay the journey, for there was one minor disaster after another. Gass and Shields had built an ungainly absurd-looking cart of native timbers, all of them soft wood, with fat thick twenty-two-inch wheels and a frail axle; and to the cart they attached sails, for Lewis believed that a wind against the sails would equal the power of three or four men on a rope. But not the power of three or four Yorks, he admitted, watching the herculean labors of the huge Negro. York, it seemed to him, had lost thirty or forty pounds but he was still a giant, and stripped to his waist with sweat running off him in small rivers he pulled with the power of a horse.

But the wood was so soft and brittle that one axle after another shattered and collapsed. After a new axle was put in, the whole preposterous thing creaked and swayed from side to side as a dozen men on elkskin traces, pulling like oxen in yokes, clawed and stumbled and fought their way up the stony or grassy slopes, seizing anything they could lay a hand on to anchor themselves while they dragged the load forward. They were nearly naked but none of them told himself any more that a woman was present. Never in their lives had the captains seen men toil with such unflagging and dauntless will, without a word of complaint, even when they fell fainting from exhaustion or dying of thirst. The slave-girl lugged forward burdens that no man would have believed she could move.

It was a dreadful ordeal under a sun that was like a furnace. The first day of the portage every man thought he would fall from thirst and rise no more. They were far from the river and had only a few light vessels to bring water in. All day in the awful heat they labored, falling only to rise and struggle forward and fall again; and the Indian girl, sitting a few moments to rest, looked at them and marveled and looked at their captains. Why did they want to take boats over the hills and valleys this way? Why didn't they go find her people and borrow horses if they could not buy them . . . ?

When evening of the first day came, the dog led the choked men to a small pool of brackish water and they drank; and then with no wood anywhere around them with which to make fires, and no water in which to boil meat even if they had wood, they lay down and slept. But they were cheerful. There were so many things on earth, Bob Frazier said, whose lot was worse than their own.

There were the buffalo, the stupid beasts: on the riverbanks as the men came up had been hundreds of dead animals that had drowned: above the falls a herd would go to the river to drink, and those drinking would be shoved in by those pushing forward from behind. The beasts shoved in would swim with wild energy but the boiling down-sucking current was too much for them and over the falls they would go, a score, a hundred, all in a few minutes. Captain Clark and the men with him who had gone upriver to explore said they had never seen a one of them come up, after going over the plunge. They were borne down and under in the deep maelstroms, and over the next fall; and there was no sign of them in the next inferno of raging waters. They were borne over another fall and still another, until beached at last and left to the wolves and bears.

The second portage day the men had to rest more frequently, and most of them, on halting, immediately flung themselves down. With arms and legs stretched out and eyes closed they rested, breathing deep. Now and then in the heat one would faint and fall and some of the others would fan him and chafe his wrists; but like the good adventurer he was he would rise and toil again. They had two camps, an upper and a lower, with Clark at the lower and Lewis at the upper camp. Each day they portaged between the camps and moved the camps each night.

As though the conspiring elements had given up the thought of destroying the men with heat, hunger, thirst and toil, and had decided to bring forth deadlier resources, one day hail struck and it was such hail as no man among them had ever seen. At that moment the men were stripped to their waists. They were bareheaded. The hailstones struck their skulls and one after another among the men went down, knocked senseless. Clark later reported to Lewis from the lower camp that he had expected a number of the men to be killed. It took more than gigantic hailstones to take the whimsy out of Meriwether Lewis: with a gay gesture he picked up one of the largest stones and after measuring and weighing it announced to the men that it was seven inches in circumference and weighed three ounces. He poured water into a tin pail, dropped the huge white stone into the water and said the men could now look upon the finest punch in the world.

Will Bratton, lying back and breathing hard, saw nothing funny in what the captain was saying. He had been knocked down three times and was bleeding from three wounds. Three times, he was thinking with horror, he had been struck on his skull as by an iron fist and had gone down. Twice he had struggled to his feet. On being felled a third time he had decided to stay down and think it over. With fingers he explored the wounds in his skull and the blood that had spilled down over his face.

The sudden squall lifted as suddenly as it had come and again a hot June sun was blazing on the men.

Those who came closest to death during the weeks at the Great Falls were Clark and the squawman and his family. Clark had made and then lost some notes on the falls and was again writing down his observations when in the west he saw a black cloud rising. It seemed so deadly with menace that he began to look for shelter, suspecting that a violent wind might soon be upon him. The storms here were unpredictable. As Lewis had said in his Journal, the same cloud would discharge hail in one area, hail and rain in another and nothing but rain in a third, all within the space of a few miles. A sudden gale would chill every man to his marrow or blow him down.

With Charbonneau and his wife and child Clark hastened into a deep ravine, where a stone ledge lay out in a large flat shelf. Under this shelf the four of them waited for the wind and rain to strike. The two men laid their guns aside. Back under the stone ledge Clark put his compass and, on second thought, his powder horn, shot pouch and tomahawk. Then he peered out to see if a storm was coming. He was thinking that if the hail had been as severe on the portage path

as on either side of it, most of the members and possibly all the
members of the Corps would have been killed.

There came first a gust of rain driven by a violent wind. Sacajawea
carried her child in what Clark called a bier and Ordway called a
net: she now set this at her feet and put into it the blanket in which
her babe had been wrapped. She laid the babe on the blanket. Clark
was watching her and reflecting that her habits were quite clean for
a squaw; that the child—— At that moment he heard a dreadful
sound. He was to conclude later that it had been a cloudburst up
the hillside. Almost at once a roaring deluge came down upon them,
driving and tumbling and rolling enormous stones before it; and with
amazement Clark perceived that the water was up to his knees almost before he knew that water had come. An instant later it was
up to his waist. There were horrible sounds above him and in the
sky overhead; and there were sounds of great boulders plunging into
the water of the ravine. It had all been so sudden and overwhelming
that his senses had been dulled. With one hand he seized his gun;
with the other, the Indian girl, who at that moment snatched up
her child but had no time to take the blanket and basket. Thrusting
her before him, he frantically clawed his way up over the shelving
and sought desperately to find something to cling to. Charbonneau
had made a queer sound of terror and had clambered part way out
of the hole, when, pausing and reaching back down, he made foolish
and futile movements, as though to rescue his wife and child. Not
more than two seconds later he turned rigid with fright. He just
stood there, stooped, his black eyes bugged out in horror at the overpowering torrent of water and mud and stones that came roaring
down the hill. Clark shouted to him to move and save himself, and
after another two or three seconds the stupid fellow did utter a shriek
of terror and begin to scramble upward. Clark was still sheltering
and assisting the woman and child; trying to watch the avalanches
above him, the rising water below him; hugging the girl to him to
keep her from falling and shouting in her ear to clutch the babe
close to her; digging with his feet to try to find toeholds; yelling to
the paralyzed and gawking squawman to clamber up before he was
drowned or crushed; and never pausing in his superhuman efforts
until the four of them were safe on top of the hill. He then looked
back down into the hole. The water, he judged, was fifteen feet deep
and was boiling round and round in a frenzied mud-bath. The In-

dian girl was looking at him. She was looking as a woman will look at a man who has just saved her own and her child's life.

She was thinking, Chief Red Hair saved my son and me from death! Chief Red Hair was thinking, O Lord God, I've lost my shot pouch, my powder horn and my compass!

York, the huge black man, had come rushing up, crying, "Masta, is you safe?"

"Safe," Clark said calmly, "but wet."

He was wet to his waist, the Indian girl to her chin. The child had been drenched. Seeing that both mother and babe were shivering, he took her arm and hastened with her back to the camp and there he poured down her throat a half a cup of whisky. Her child he wrapped in a small buffalo robe, the hair side in. He felt so shattered by the loss of the compass—for the Corps had no other large one—that he was hardly aware of what he was doing, and not at all aware of the way an Indian girl's black eyes were looking at him. She had drunk the whisky. She had slipped out of her wet leather garments and now sat with a robe around her, with the child on her lap under the robe. She still trembled from the cold but she was happier than she had ever been in her life. She had not known that there were men in the world who would risk their own lives to save the lives of women and children. She had known none among the red people, not even among her own people. But this white man had lost his compass and had got his watch wet just to save her: he could so easily have leapt out, leaving her and Pomp, but he had taken them both with him, ahead of him, his strong arm around her all the while. . . .

If anyone seemed to look her way she cast her gaze down but the moment she felt that she could do so unobserved she again looked at Red Hair, knowing that alone and without help she could never have got out of that dreadful hole. It had all come down as if a sky of water and stones had fallen: she would have been knocked senseless and drowned before she knew it, and her son with her, but for the swiftness of this strange man who had put their lives before his own. Under the robe she patted her child, thinking, remembering—her shy Indian eyes watching a man with red hair who was coaxing a wet fire to life. After the fire was blazing he beckoned her over to it and she went over, marveling: not only had he saved her life and given her whisky when he had so little left, but now he wanted her and her son to be warm! She, captured as a child, and after that the slave mistress of any man who won her—a mere thing for a man's bed—a beast of burden at other times—a slave, an enemy, a woman—a creature to be knocked senseless at her master's pleasure, or killed—these things but no more she had been until this day, but now she was more. A man had been tender to her—had lost big medicine for her and risked his life for her! It was all so incredible that she had to tell herself the wonder of it over and over. . . .

She patted her child, thinking, If we'd been alone with your father we'd both be dead now, little Pomp! This was the first time she had thought of her child as Pomp: an obedient wife, she had thought of him as Jean Baptiste, but he would be Pomp now, for that was the name Chief Red Hair had given him. Red Hair had named a river for her and she had been so moved that she had wept. She thought he intended to name a river or mountain for her child. She understood many English words but she could not always understand what the captain said, though she could always tell what his eyes said. She had known what they said one day after her man had struck her. Until then, she had not known that any man in the world cared about what a man did to a woman. For a while on this journey she had wondered if he might want her in the way men wanted women but had decided that he did not. Even more incredible, for her, was the fact that this white man had decided that no other man would have her either, except the man who owned her. At first she had thought she would be the woman of all the men in the Corps but she had been only Charbonneau's woman and she could not understand why this was so. She was not sure that she understood why both captains were kind to her. With a woman's intuitions she could read the eyes of some of the men when they looked at her but not a one of them had ever tried to lure her into the thickets or catch her alone. Not a one had ever come to her when, alone with her child, she was looking for roots or berries. For weeks this had puzzled her. Then little by little she had come to understand that Red Hair was her protector and guardian and that dreadful things might happen to any man who tried to take her in love. She was afraid that dreadful things might happen to her man before this journey was done, for she knew that he lived in fear of both captains and that the captains detested him. She knew that her man was a coward. She had not known at first that he was jealous.

This she had discovered one day when he struck her.

Chief Long Knife, she had been quick to learn, preferred certain morsels in a meat dish and with a long spoon tried to find them. Chief Red Hair ate what he first came to and seemed never to be aware of what he was eating. He ate like a man sunk in thought. One day she had found a certain root and a cook had prepared a whole kettleful. Watching Red Hair eat the roots, she had realized that he liked them and the next day she had gone looking for roots, just for him. She had given them to him in her shy way and had not known that her man was spying on her.

When alone with her that evening he had struck her. He had struck her a hard blow with the back of his hand right across her mouth and when she ducked her head and shrank away from him she felt the blood on her lips. That night he had taken her, but with more than his usual savagery: he had dug deep into her flesh with his fingers, into the soft part of her just above her hips. When he was done with her he had shoved her away and given her a blow of contempt across her rump. She would have thought nothing of it if she had not known these white men. Now she spent a lot of time thinking about these things. . . .

The morning after her man struck her she tried to hide her bruised lips but she knew that Red Hair had seen them. He did not have the way of a man who saw everything but he saw everything. She knew that he had seen her lips when she saw him look at her man. . . .

After learning that her man was jealous she knew that he would strike her if he saw her do little things for Chief Red Hair. Just the same, she intended to do things for him. He was the only friend she had ever had since she was taken from her people. He had been kind to her in so many ways—and today he had saved her life and her child's life, and had given her a drink of the precious firewater, and had built a fire for her. . . .

Shyly she raised her eyes to look at him again.

20

When the last of the portaging was done the men sank to the earth, where they stood and slept all night and most of the next day without stirring. Lewis meanwhile was preparing a treat for them—a feast of the choicest parts of buffalo, roasted, and suet dumplings of meat, flour and sugar. Some of the men observed that he gave the Indian girl an extra helping.

This evening the men danced and sang, and York jigged and capered with such wanton eye-rolling abandon that in his Journal his master said that he "carried on turribel." The dog barked in a frenzied way during the hours of dancing and then barked all night. Until his bedtime Lewis gazed thoughtfully at the men, or at the mountains in the west, his mind teeming with problems and questions. His bullboat had been a ludicrous failure. There was no good canoe timber in this area. The Corps had spent a full month here at the falls and soon it would be autumn, snow would be falling again. Upon both captains had come a sense of urgency, and as their anxiety sharpened they looked more frequently at the sky and the west.

They looked at their men. Their friends and relatives would never have recognized them now, for they were bearded and long-haired and ragged. Clark was still wearing his tattered artillerist's outfit but most of the men were in hand-sewn skins that were torn and scuffed, and frayed open at elbows and knees. Some of them braided their snarled and uncombed hair because when braided it was less of a bother; but some of them just let it hang loose and wind-blown down over their ears and shoulders. They were a tough-looking lot and they were tougher than they looked, Lewis reflected, watching them caper in square dances, while Cruzatte sawed on his fiddle and Potts called the turns.

Yes, it was a tough crew. In boldness and resourcefulness Lewis would have matched most of them against men anywhere. None but the squawman had yet complained. The Indian girl had confided to Clark that Whitehouse had been ill when she was ill and had almost died. This had astonished the captain: Whitehouse had labored every day, without complaint. In his own Journal he had confessed that he was terribly sick. Well, one of the Fields brothers had been as sick as a dog, yet had hidden his illness from nearly everyone. There was an esprit de corps here that looked with contempt on signs of weakness and made the squawman a symbol of what the other men would rather have died than be.

Yes, good Lord, they were tough but would they endure to the end? No man could know what lay ahead of them now; what starvation when they left buffalo land; what cold and snows; what hostile Indians; what interminable distances. The middle of July they packed their canoes and went on: they had passed clear through Blackfoot land and had not seen an Indian; they should be in Snakeland soon, though the girl did not yet recognize any landmarks or know where they were. The buffalo were now the thickest they had ever seen—vast herds darkened the prairies for miles and miles. There were ripening wild fruits now—yellow and black currants, gooseberries, serviceberries, chokecherries: the men wolfed them down, especially the black currants and serviceberries, for Lewis told them that fruit would help to clear up their boils. Sacajawea daily slipped away to gather fruit by the pailful, and to find some choicer berries for Chief Red Hair.

Feeling hard-pressed for time, Lewis decided to take two or three men and push on. To Clark he said, "If I can find the pass through the mountains we might save a few days."

"It should be where the river leaves them," Clark said, looking at the Rockies. He could see no sign of a pass anywhere.

"I'd better take a couple of invalids. Potts is no good for anything now."

"Better take Drewyer. We'll need a lot of dried meat."

Lewis took Drewyer and two very tired men but he did not push far. The very next day Clark and his river-party overtook them and it was then decided that Clark should take two or three men and go on ahead, until he came to the Shoshone Indians. The truth was that Lewis was so fascinated by all flora and fauna that his insatiable curiosity was repeatedly engaged. The big-horned animals left him popeyed because of the amazing agility with which they bounded from stone to stone, where one misstep would have been certain death. Clark, when he set out for a goal, pushed steadily on, allowing nothing to divert him.

Every day the party's hunters were firing their guns and Clark was afraid that gunfire would alarm the Shoshones and send them deep into the mountains. If he were to go at top speed ahead of the main party he might reach the Indians before they were alarmed, and convince them that these men approaching with thunder-weapons were not Blackfeet but their friends.

"You're absolutely right," Lewis said. "If they go back into the mountains we'll never get horses. What on earth would we do then?"

"We'd have to winter here."

"What does the squaw say?"

"She says we'll scare her people clear out of the country. Somewhere in the southwest there are caves they'll hide in, caves with ice in them, she says."

"Caves with ice in July?"

"According to her. She says her people won't wait to see what we are. When they hear the guns they'll think we're Blackfeet and they'll go."

"Maybe they've already gone."

"That's what I'm afraid of."

"Well, you'd better take good men and leave the invalids with me."

"One good man," Clark said.

The river had become swifter, the work with the boats was man-killing: Clark chose Joe Fields as his good man, together with Potts, who looked sick, and his black servant. He intended to lose no time but at once ran into difficulties. Potts was so feeble that he was unable to keep up and every mile or so Clark had to halt and wait for him. The prickly pear so completely covered the earth that most of the time it was impossible to find a safe place for a moccasined foot. The mosquitoes were huge and ravenous, and so numerous that they filled and darkened the sky. The four men were all suffering from fatigue, and even Joe Fields, even the giant York, walked like old men. At night without mosquito nets they got little sleep and arose at daylight, bone-tired and depressed, to fight their way again across pathless country over the dreadful thorns.

The evening of their second day out they sat by a small fire of buffalo dung, each man drawing a foot up to look at the cuts and bruises and imbedded thorns, all the while swatting angrily at the mosquitoes that swarmed in clouds around him. Not a one of them said a word. They all bent to the task of killing mosquitoes and pulling thorns out of torn feet. From his two feet Clark drew seventeen, some of them half an inch long; and when he stood up his feet felt so tender and throbbed so with pain that he wondered if he would be able to walk the next day. He felt half-sick and quite discouraged, but the face his men saw showed only the indomitable will of one who had set out to do or die.

Lewis and his party were having a dreadful time. The river had become violent in most of its channel, and so filled with enormous stones over which the water boiled that it was impossible to use oars. The men had to use poles, or tow-ropes; most of the time they had to drag the canoes close to a bank, and they slipped and fell on the wet stones or disappeared momentarily in the plunging rapids. They had to seize anything on the bank that they could cling to with one hand, while with all their strength they pulled a canoe up abreast of them, and stood breathing hard a few moments before making the next move. Along the bank the rattlesnakes were so thick that the men had to look at every stone before they touched it. They were drenched from head to feet in water which in the dim sunless canyon was like winter water. Some had sprained shoulders or backs; some had boils; some had fevers and loss of appetite; and all of them had bruised and swollen feet. How long, O Lord, they wondered, would they have to claw their way up this river between these high sheer walls that shut out the sun? How many miles would it be? Nobody knew. The Indian girl didn't know where they were. Her people were yonder, she said, pointing; it was always yonder, always somewhere off in the west.

The morning after Clark pulled the thorns from his feet Lewis looked up the river and saw smoke. He saw great billows of smoke, whole clouds of it, and wondered if the Indians had seen the white men and set signal fires, or if Clark and his men had accidentally fired the mountains. Sacajawea thought the fires had been set by her people to call the hunters home. If this was so, would they all flee beyond the mountains, far into the west, even to the ice caves?—or would they hide and wait? She did not know. Her man said they would hide but he had proved himself to be an ignoramus in practically all things.

This evening the prickly pears so completely covered the earth where the party camped that the men couldn't find room for a bed. They had to take hatchets and clear the ground. But there was one great blessing, Sergeant Ordway said, looking round him cheerfully: though the dog was unable to catch the adult geese that were so plentiful along the river he caught and fetched to the camp enough of the young fat goslings to make a feast. The cooks steamed a big kettleful of wild cucumbers and onions, and Sacajawea came in with a pail of large blue serviceberries, her child standing up her back with mosquitoes so thick over his face that it was almost hidden. The men ate geese and elk, vegetables and fruit; slapped at the hordes of mosquitoes; examined their aching feet, their shredded moccasins, their boils; and jested when they rolled into bed. They would jest, Lewis thought, but not forever: there was the point at which they would reach mutiny. It was drawing toward the end of July, there was already a hint of autumn in the mountain air. He felt desperate and wondered what Clark was doing.

Clark at the moment was so bruised and cut and had such a swollen and painful ankle that he decided to wait for the canoes. He also felt dispirited. He added only a few sentences to his Journal, then pulled his robe over him, seeking sleep. But his ankle throbbed so with pain that he spent a restless and miserable night.

The next day was July 22nd. About noon the Indian girl went shyly to Lewis and made him understand that she now recognized this country, that this was one of the rivers on which her people lived. Lewis told the sergeants and they told the men and there were loud whoops of joy. Some of them behaved as they might have if they had reached the ocean.

"The three forks!" one of them was yelling. "You dumb scunners realize we're close to the three forks?"

"Close to the Columbia!"

"Almighty Moses!"

"We'll just sit on our butts and float downstream! Holy grandma!"

They stared into the west as though by looking hard they might see the three forks but they all knew that between them and the Columbia stood a stupendous mountain range. Still, they could not be far from the Snake Indians, not far from the headwaters of the

Missouri, upon which no white man had yet looked. They were eager to be off.

Just at dusk the main party saw Clark and his men waiting for them on a riverbank. They put over with the canoes and took on board the men and what remained of an elk and a deer and went over to an island to camp. Clark, Lewis thought, looked ill and exhausted. His feet were so covered with infected sores and his ankle so swollen that he moved only in great pain; but nevertheless he planned to push on again in the morning.

"You'd better stay with the boats and let me go," Lewis said.

"I'm all right," Clark said.

"You don't look all right. Look at that ankle."

Lewis knew what the trouble was. It was pride. For a week now Clark had been trying to discover the Indians and had failed; he had got himself sick, he had worn out his men; and now he was in a bad mood with himself. A man who had fought Indians and the wilderness since boyhood did not give up easily.

Understanding the chagrin and frustration inside Clark, Lewis said tactfully, "Better choose good men this time. We'll make out all right with the boats."

Clark knew that Lewis was putting the best face on the thing. They weren't making out all right at all. Half the boatmen were sick, the others were in constant pain from boils, cuts and infected sores. The men expected any day now to find impassable stone slides in these awful canyons, or waterfalls that they couldn't go over or portage around. The next morning they watched Clark limp away with his men, and then turned to what Lewis called three curses worse than any that ever fell upon Egypt: billions of huge mosquitoes whose hunger made them indifferent to danger; billions of huge gnats that got into the men's nostrils and ears and the corners of their eyes and down their throats; and the millions of prickly pears.

Two days later Clark and the four men with him reached the three forks of the Missouri. Without even pausing to rest, the captain trudged back and forth from stream to stream, trying to determine which was the largest and therefore the main current. But the north and middle forks were of almost exactly the same size, with the same kind of bed and stones and water. Because the north fork went in a more westerly direction the harassed and exhausted explorer decided to follow it, and after leaving a note for Lewis pushed on with his men.

With rarely a pause to rest, Clark led them on and upward for twenty miles. Bob Frazier then called to him, saying, "Captain, our squawman says he's tuckered out."

Clark turned to look back at Charbonneau. He had not wanted the squawman but Charbonneau had begged to be taken and Clark had yielded, not from bad judgment but from weariness.

"Can't he walk at all?" Clark asked, observing that the squawman was sitting.

"Captain, he says his ankle has plumb give out."

"Tell him to rest a little while," Clark said, and at once left his men to make observations. He had come at last to mountains that were rocky and steep. The river here was channeled by a number of small islands and, looking over at them, Clark saw deer and elk and what he took to be a grizzly bear. All around him hung ripened masses of red, black, yellow and purple currants, as well as choke-cherries, and a red berry which neither captain could identify. Clark gathered berries and ate, meanwhile studying the mountains west of him. He was nearly twenty-five hundred miles from the mouth of the Missouri and the Columbia seemed as far away as ever.

A few days earlier, when the two captains had stood together looking at the white Rockies, Lewis had said, "It's tall country."

"It's damned big country," Clark had said.

"Bigger than I ever dreamed of, bigger than what Mr. Jefferson has in mind."

"He thought we'd be back in a year."

"It will be two."

"Or three," Clark said.

The next morning Clark told Charbonneau to stay with Joe Fields, who had swollen feet; and with Frazier and Reuben Fields he climbed to the top of a mountain, the three of them struggling upward over stones and through brambles, until at last they could look over the meandering north fork, and the valleys that flanked it. This river, Clark decided, was the one the boats should go up. Searching round him and finding no Indian sign, he turned back down the mountain and presently came to a spring of extremely cold water. Before drinking he splashed water over his head, hands and feet, and advised the two men to do likewise. They all drank as men half-dead with thirst.

A little later Clark felt severe cramps across his upper abdomen and down his left side, and by the time he came to Joe Fields and

Charbonneau, his feet filled with pear thorns and bursting with blisters, he wanted to sit down somewhere alone and not move for a week. Never in his life had he felt so utterly feeble and discouraged. With the pain in his feet and ankles running up the bone to his hip joints and with cramps so convulsing his belly that he could straighten only with an effort of will he led his men across to the middle fork, determined to have a look at it before Lewis could take the boats up the wrong stream. He waded the north fork and found it waist-deep and swift. The clumsy squawman while trying to climb up a slippery bank fell headlong in. Knowing that the simpleton could not swim a stroke, Clark dived in after him, risking his life, and seizing the man's long black hair, towed him to shore.

Drenched, exhausted and sick, Clark wanted to go off alone with his misery but he kept marching, for in his mind was a picture of men with swollen feet dragging boats up the wrong river.

Lewis and his party meanwhile had come to the first fork, the south or left one; and leaving his men on the bank he went a half-mile upstream and climbed to the summit of a limestone cliff, for a view of the area. What he saw so impressed him that for ten seconds he did not breathe. Then, sucking air in, he turned again to the east.

A great blue range of mountains, snow-topped, was there, running north and south. The range—the same range, as far as he could make out in the blue haze—swung around in the southwest and then ran east and west. They looked like magnificent mountains, even at so great a distance. Off to his right, in the west, were barren hills sloping downward from mountains that stood much closer. His gaze then came down.

He could see the three forks. At his feet was the south one, a clear beautiful river flowing past the precipice on which he stood. To the right and a few hundred yards south two other rivers, the middle and north forks, formed a junction, and these with the south fork formed the Missouri. It was a wide valley that lay at his feet. In the southeast a wide valley disappeared into blue haze, running far away to the mountains; and in the northwest was a valley just like it, its twin, with an abutment of high hills between them. So far as he could tell, the north river came out of the south by southwest for ten or fifteen miles and then out of the west, for he thought he could see the dim line of a mountain passage. Clark, he supposed, was somewhere in the mountains on his right, looking over this vast area and trying to determine which of the three rivers headed closest to the Columbia. In regard to that, Lewis now had no doubt: the river on his left came down from the southeast and the middle river came down from the south: only the river on his right could come out of the west. And, so far as he could tell, it seemed to be the largest river of the three.

Carefully descending over dangerous slide rock, he returned to his men. All eyes were on his face.

"I had a fine view of the three forks and the mountains beyond," he said. "I'd say the one on the right is the one we'll go up."

"Does it run fast, Captain?"

"It comes down out of mountains."

"And the mountains get higher and higher," someone said. "Soon the river'll be standing on its end and we'll be climbing straight up waterfalls."

Lewis decided that his men would have to rest a day or two, and so he pitched camp and waited for Clark's return. Clark staggered in the day after saving the squawman's life, his ankle horribly swollen, his face red with a high fever. The previous night he had slept hardly at all because of chills, and the pains in all his muscles and bones. He had found no Indian sign, he told Lewis, no sign at all. It was pretty barren country as far as he had gone.

Lewis was looking at him with alarm. He knew a sick man when he saw one. He knew that Will Clark was a pretty sick man.

But Clark tried to wave him away, saying, "I'm just a little bilious." He stared down at his ankle a moment and added, "To tell the truth, I haven't had a passage for several days. I expect that's about all that's wrong with me."

"For several days!" cried Lewis. "Good God, man!"

"Four days," Clark said.

"Holy Jerusalem! No wonder you're sick."

One of the first laws of health with his mother, the yarb doctor, was open bowels. That was a law with Lewis. He had brought an ample supply of Dr. Rush's pills, having found them, in his own words, a sovereign remedy for such things as constipation. He took them frequently. He now told Clark that he should take a big dose of them and then soak his feet in hot water.

When Clark had four of Dr. Rush's pills in his stomach and his feet in a kettle of hot water Lewis sat by him and filled his pipe. He looked at his friend, studying his pale face. Both captains knew that if they did not find the Shoshone Indians or some other tribe with horses their journey would end in failure: when they left St. Louis they had thought it would be a portage of only a few miles from the headwaters of one river to the source of the other but now their knowledge of rivers and mountains told them that the distance would be far greater than they had imagined. They had only to look up at these Rockies to realize that.

Looking at the pain in his friend's eyes and the pallor in his face, Lewis decided that he would leave Clark with the boats and go on. He would find the Indians, even if he had to go a hundred miles, even if it took him a month. He would find them or never come back.

The next day Clark felt much better and the two captains turned to a pleasant subject: they had three rivers to name and they loved to name rivers. They agreed that it would be highly improper to call either fork the Missouri: that noble river they had followed for twenty-five hundred miles and they would terminate it right here at the forks. For whom should they name these three streams?

"The north one is probably the longest one," Lewis said. "I propose that we name it in honor of that illustrious person, Thomas Jefferson, who sent us on this great enterprise."

Gravely Clark gave his approval.

"All right, that's the Jefferson River. The middle fork——"

"I propose," said Clark, knowing that he had to speak up or Lewis would name all of them, "I propose that it be named to honor another illustrious person. Shall we call it the Madison River?"

"Why, of course!" said Lewis. He was delighted. "The Jefferson and the Madison. Now the south fork is the smallest one. We named a river for our Secretary of the Navy. We also named one——" Lewis stopped abruptly. A few days ago *he* had named one for the Secretary of War, having forgotten for the moment that the stupid rascal had forced on Clark the humiliation of a lieutenancy instead of a captaincy, a rank he had formerly occupied. Recalling the way Clark's face had reddened and his eyes turned cold, Lewis broke off, tried to hide his confusion, and then said lamely, "There's the Secretary of the Treasury, Albert Gallatin. Is he worth a river?"

Clark said, "Doesn't he rank next after the Secretary of State?"

Was there a barb in the question? Lewis did not know. He said, "I think he does. So if you approve——"

"I think it'll be appropriate," Clark said.

And so the south fork was named the Gallatin.

Lewis had some of the men build a bower for Clark, to shelter him from sun and wind. In the shelter, though too sick to sit up without feeling nausea, Clark worked over his maps. All around him the men were dressing skins or making moccasins and leggings, trousers and jackets. When the watchful Sacajawea saw Clark resting and looking off at the mountains she slipped up to him with a quart of large luscious berries.

He smiled at her and said, "Jawey, are you feeling well?"

"*Oui*," she said.

He knew by the way she looked at him that she wanted to speak. He waited. After a few moments she said, "*Ici*," and pointed to the earth. "*Ici*," she said.

"Oh? There, yonder?" He pointed to the west.

She shook her head no and pointed to the east.

"They took you that way, yes. But your people, where are they from here?" When she seemed not to understand he asked the question in sign language.

She pointed west and southwest and said, haltingly, "Allay too d-d—wa. *Voila*," she said brightly, and pointed again.

"How far?" he said.

"Far?" She looked off at the sky. She seemed to be thinking. With a finger and thumb she made a circle and on the other hand held up two fingers.

"Two moons? Two sleeps? You must mean two sleeps."

She nodded.

"Forty miles," he said. "Thank you, Jawey." He turned back to his maps.

The next morning Lewis decided to scout ahead of the main party and took with him two limping half-sick men, whom in his Journal he called invalids, and Jawey and her man. They crossed river bottoms, and after three or four miles the girl made Lewis understand that on the spot where she stood she had been captured, or in the river. He could not tell which she meant. Looking round him, he wondered by what stones or trees she recognized the place. The squawman began to complain loudly of his feet and in fact made such a clamor that Lewis decided to wait till the boats came up. He then told the three men and the woman to join the main party.

"I'll go on alone," he said.

He was glad to be alone. He would rather be alone than listen day after day to the lamentations of Charbonneau. Going on up the river, he came to such a welter of beaver dams and ponds that again and again he had to wade waist-deep in muck and cold water. The river here had been channeled into a half-dozen streams. He walked until sunset, when, coming to a small island, he searched it for footprints. The boats had not passed, at least not here, but they might have gone up one of the other channels. He fired his gun and then listened. He shouted at the top of his voice but no answer came. A lone duck flew down from the sky and stood very still, looking at him. He shot it, reflecting that it would do for his supper. He swatted at mosquitoes and again listened. A little later he made a fire, stripped the feathers and skin off the duck, pulled the guts out and roasted it, impaled on a green stick. It was a fat duck and it roasted nicely, giving off appetizing odors from its sizzling juices.

While eating the duck he fell to thinking of the Indian girl. Little by little the captains had put together her story, or thought they had: as a child she had come with her people over the mountains and down into the three forks area, to hunt game, to gather berries and roots and the tender inner bark of certain trees. Her people starved most of the time but feasted once in a while, she said. Now and then they had feasted on buffalo before the dreadful Blackfeet came with their sky-weapons but after that massacre they had done well to get a few elk or deer. They had killed a few elk and were preparing to feast when out of the river thickets came the Big Bellies, sounding their horrible war cries. All the Snake Indians had fled up one of the rivers but the enemy overtook and killed some of the men, women and children, and had taken a number of the children away into the east.

Somewhere between the three forks and the Minnetaree village there had been a dramatic, even a miraculous, escape. The children —there had been seven or eight of them—had gone to sleep or had pretended to, lying among their captors. Sacajawea had seen one of the Snake boys move. She had known that he would. She had lain awake almost breathless waiting for him to. That afternoon the warparty with their captives had passed a huge quantity of driftwood that had lodged in a river eddy, and the boldest of the Snake lads had whispered to one of the other children, who had whispered to another, and the third to a fourth, that this night they would all escape and flee to the driftwood. They would each find a log to use as a buoy across the wide swift river and on the far side they would be safe, for their enemy would never believe that they could cross the river. He, the resourceful and daring one, who had conceived this plan, would steal a gun, powder and ball and a knife from one of the sleeping warriors and take these things out of the camp. Then the others would softly crawl out after him. . . .

Thinking of the story, Lewis always felt a thrill when remembering the almost insupportable anxieties in Sacajawea for one of the children, the stupid otter-girl, who had gone to sleep and was snoring! He could imagine how Sacajawea lay there, an Indian child eight or nine years old, her black half-lidded eyes watching the daring lad as he crawled, soft and noiseless as a serpent, toward a sleeping warrior . . . crawled so slowly, she said, that she thought he covered only the span of two arms in an hour; as one by one he drew toward him a rifle, shot pouch, powder horn and knife; as, clutching all these, he then crawled backward like a crab, noiseless, oh so noiseless and so slow . . . so slow that she thought she must scream, for she could not endure the awful suspense, yet somehow did endure it, all the while hating the stupid girl at her side, snoring like an exhausted warrior, her mouth wide open. Should she leave her or awaken her? She knew that she could not leave her. She could not possibly leave one to be tortured after the others had fled. She had thought that she might gently prod the girl, pinch her a little, bring her slowly and soundlessly into consciousness. . . .

Dwelling on the drama of that moment and sucking juices from a leg bone, Lewis decided that otter-girl had been dreaming. That was the only possible explanation. The bold lad had got out of the camp with the weapons and one by one all the others had followed him but the two girls. Sacajawea had been trying with gentle methods to arouse her companion. Unable to, and falling into panic, as in fancy she saw the other children bobbing across the river, she had taken otter-girl's hand and drawn the girl toward her. At that moment the stupid thing screamed!

It showed character in the Indian girl, Lewis thought, that she had gone on loving her friend: that scream, which brought a score of warriors to their feet, clutching their guns, had cost Sacajawea so much —an unmerciful beating by an aroused camp after the furious warriors failed to find the other children (had they tortured the girls to try to drag information from them? Sacajawea had not said). And not only the beating but the long lonely years away from her people . . and the degradation of being any lecher's child, for she had been used as a child before she was a woman. . . .

At the side of a big fire the captain had dozed and fallen asleep. He was aroused by the sound of animal feet and on sitting up heard what he took to be elk hooves striking the island stones. It certainly was not a grizzly, for that beast's sheathed talons made no sound. It was an elk or deer, or a bighorn crossing from bluff to bluff. Sleepily he thought he should rise and pursue it, because fresh meat was getting scarce among men who wasted it as though there could never be an end of it. He and Clark had chided them but they went on wasting. When the Corps came to Snake country, he was thinking, while building up the fire, where an elk or a deer was as rare as wisdom in a young man; when they starved the meat off their ribs and the marrow out of their bones, then perhaps they would show some sense. Still, he had never seen sense in a young person.

He pulled the blanket over his face to shut out the mosquitoes and went back to sleep.

21

The next morning the main party came up and Clark reported that the labor with the boats was more than human flesh could stand: the river was now one series of rapids after another, over which the boats would not float and so had to be dragged, the men falling on the sharp stones and bruising themselves terribly. Lewis walked among them and saw their ailments—two of them had a half-dozen boils each, ripe and inflamed and ready to burst; a third had had an arm thrown out and only with great pain replaced; a fourth had a back so badly wrenched that it was torture to pull on tow-ropes; a fifth had the nails torn off two fingers; a sixth had feet that nobody would have dreamed a man could walk on. . . . Was there, Lewis wondered, a whole man among them? There was not. He saw that it was absolutely necessary for him to push on and find the Snake Indians, and horses, no matter how far he had to go, or at what risk. He chose Gass to go with him: the sergeant had a sprained back but he could walk. He chose Drewyer, the mighty hunter, and Charbonneau. The squawman had a bad ankle but was able to limp along. And so on August 1st Lewis set out with his three men, two of them limping. He himself had felt so ill that he had taken a huge dose of glauber salts and now, climbing a rough steep mountain, had to excuse himself again and again and disappear. By midforenoon he felt too weak to walk. Then Drewyer killed two elk and after Lewis had dined on roasted flesh he felt his spirits much revived and went on. He was saying to himself, "If we are all spent and half-dead even before we cross the mountains, how under heaven shall we ever reach the ocean!"

The days were hot, the nights so cold that the men slept under two blankets. On the fifth day out, still climbing steep and pathless mountains, Drewyer miscalculated a mountain goat step and slipped and fell, spraining a finger and so badly wrenching a leg that for twenty minutes he seemed unable to move. Looking down at him, Lewis asked him how he was. Receiving no reply, he wondered if he would have to send this man to the boats by stretcher and he looked off to the east and south, scanning the formidable series of ridges and valleys that the stretcher-bearers would have to cross.

"Where are you hurt?" Lewis asked. The man must be badly hurt, he reflected, for Drewyer was no whiner. Drewyer pointed to a leg and Lewis knelt to examine it. He pulled the leather trousers down and felt over the thigh with firm powerful fingers, trying to reach in to the bone. Was the leg broken? Had he paralyzed a kneecap? Had he numbed the principal nerve?

For a few minutes Lewis rubbed and massaged the thigh. Then he said, "See if you can move it now." To his astonishment Drewyer moved and then struggled to his feet.

"I can go now," he said.

"You sure it isn't broken?"

Drewyer picked up his rifle. "I can go now," he said.

Not knowing whether the man was badly hurt, Lewis headed for the river. At the fork of two streams he had left a note for Clark, telling him which channel to take, and had tied the note to a green sapling, which he had sharpened and thrust into the riverbank. He never dreamed that a beaver would come along and cut the sapling down and take it away. Learning that Clark had gone up the wrong river, Lewis sent Drewyer to find him. Drewyer found Clark almost beside himself with discouragement: most of the boatmen had such swollen feet that they could barely walk. A canoe had overturned and a number of valuable articles had been lost, including a box of medicines. Whitehouse had been thrown from a canoe into swift water and the boat had then passed over him and missed crushing him to death by only an inch. Two other canoes had got filled with water and everything in them was soaked, including the parched meal, the corn and most of the presents for Indians. Shannon had been sent out to hunt and was lost again.

Lewis with Gass and the squawman came down to the river and after one look around him Lewis decided that he had never seen the morale of the men so low. For nine miles they had fought their way up the wrong river, over the worst rapids they had yet encountered. Now they had to go back down! Their spirits were so low that for the first time on this journey they questioned their captains: couldn't they leave the canoes and go overland, carrying the essential things on their backs? Would it not be shorter that way, and a lot quicker?—for, see, these mountain rivers meandered ten miles to cover one as the crow flew. Why not all go ahead and find the Indians and get horses? The men first asked the questions of one another, then sent Ordway to Clark.

"Captain, the men wonder if it would be best to go by land. They say they can carry all the essential stuff."

"A lot of the stuff is soaked," Clark said. "Our first job is to dry it."

"Yes, sir, Captain."

No more was said. Ordway went over to Whitehouse, who lay under a tree by himself, writhing in pain. In passing over him the big heavy canoe had caught one of his legs at the knee and crushed it a little. Seeing Ordway approach, Whitehouse stopped grimacing and lay back with eyes shut, as though asleep. Ordway looked down at him a few moments and then went to the wet baggage.

By early afternoon the men had dried most of the things and repacked and reloaded them. The party then proceeded up the Jefferson River, with the grim Clark at its head, his ankle so swollen that he walked in obvious pain. Whitehouse lay stretched out in a canoe. Lewis remained behind to make readings of longitude, latitude and elevation but overtook the party before dark. Around the campfires this evening the question was, What in hell has happened to Shannon? Had a grizzly bear eaten him? Early this morning Reuben Fields had been sent to look for him. Reuben had not come back.

Bob Frazier said, "I'll bet anyone half my future glory that he's living on more than grapes this time."

"Venison," said Joe Fields, "and apple pie."

Bill Bratton said, "I figger he just likes to get away from us. He eats and sleeps and takes it easy."

Another said, "He's too darned smart to get lost, even if his pa did."

The next day at noon Reuben returned. He had found no trace of Shannon. This evening the huge boil on Clark's leg burst open, discharging its pus and relieving the pain. An hour later news was abroad in the camp. The slave-girl had slipped up to speak to Clark, and from him had come the news that yonder was the Beaver Head, that high point in the north; and not far from it, just over the mountains, lived her people, on a river that ran to the west. Some of the men felt elated, some felt cynical.

"Just over the mountains," said Frazier. "It can't be more than two thousand miles."

"I can see it," Bill Bratton said, stretched out on his back, his belly instead of his chest rising when he breathed. "I can see us go up this river until we're looking down on the snowbanks, and the bighorns are ten miles below, looking up at us. I can see this river standing plumb on its end before we reach the head of it."

Some of the men thought that was funny. They laughed.

"And all the while," Joe Fields said, "George Shannon will be in the shade somewheres munching venison."

Meriwether Lewis was one of those who felt elated. He again resolved to choose two or three men and set out to find the Shoshones but for a day or two would remain with the party, to see if Clark's ankle would heal. With unflagging curiosity he noted that what he called buffalo clover was in bloom on the river bottoms. He knelt to have a better view of sunflower, flax, thistle and several species of grass, one of which bore its seeds much like the timothy but which would not be, he suspected, any good for meadows, though he gathered some of it for Mr. Jefferson. He observed that the river here teemed with beaver, otter and muskrat. In his Journal he said that this day the Corps covered eight miles.

The next day, feeling even more ebullient, he made a long entry, "which I conceived from the nature of my instructions necessary lest any accedent should befall me on the long and raether hazardous rout I was now about to take." His feeling that he would soon encounter Indians, and that they might kill him and the men with him, he confided to no one, but he had the thought in mind when he looked over the men and chose three. When he slung his pack and set off with Drewyer, Shields and McNeal his gaze lingered a few moments on the face of his friend Clark, for whom on this difficult journey his respect and affection had steadily grown; and in his mind he had Jefferson's words, "to your own discretion therefore must be left the degree of danger you may risk." This time he did *not* intend to turn back. He had three good men with him—the best shot in the Corps; the wiry and tireless John Shields; and Hugh McNeal, who had shown himself to be cool in the face of danger. McNeal and Shields he had chosen because they looked able to walk long and far.

It was August 9th when they set out, following an old Indian trail. The next day they came to a fork in the river and Lewis perceived that not even small boats could be taken beyond it. The canoes would have to be buried here. He left a note for Clark, tied to a dry and not a green sapling, suggesting that the main party should wait here for his return. He then went up one of the forks and came presently to a large handsome cove which he took to be fifteen or eighteen miles across, its uplands covered with prickly pear and bearded grasses. Once the beards of the grass got inside the leather leggings they were a worse torment than thorns.

The next morning he was off at daylight, sensing that he would see Indians this day. He told Drewyer to go up the stream, sent Shields a hundred yards to his left, and with McNeal headed across the valley. After an hour and a half he felt his chest thicken and his breath stop, for there, a mile or two distant, was an Indian approaching on a horse. Looking at him through his glasses, Lewis decided that he was a Snake all right: he could see the bow and quiver of arrows, the saddle, and fancied that he could see the throatlatch. He walked again until he thought about a mile separated him from the Indian and was wondering whether to advance or pause when the horse stopped. At once Lewis jerked a blanket from his pack and made the signal of friendship which he had been told was universal among the mountain Indians: seizing the blanket by the corners, he threw it above his head and brought it downward with a movement of spreading it. Sacajawea had told him and Clark that in her language tab-ba-bone meant white men, though the captains wondered why the Shoshones should have such a word, if they had never seen white men, or what use they had for it. Lewis now cried, "Tabbabone!" but knew that he was too far away to be heard. It seemed to him that the red man was looking with apprehension at Drewyer and Shields, both of whom still moved forward, but at a distance from Lewis too great to hear him, even if he had thought it prudent to shout. Wondering desperately how he could keep the Indian from fleeing—for if he fled in alarm his people might all vanish far into the west—he handed his gun and pouch to McNeal and advanced unarmed, holding up a mirror and a few trinkets for the Indian to see. The red man sat stiffly on his horse, staring in turn at Drewyer and Shields, until Lewis was within two hundred yards of him. Lewis now shouted the word tabbabone over and over but what he wanted to shout was curses on the head of Shields, for though

Drewyer had halted, Shields still advanced. Having no doubt that
the Indian would allow him to come up, if only Shields had the
gumption to see the situation and sense enough to turn back, Lewis
again advanced, drawing a leather sleeve high on an arm and holding
the arm up to show that it was white. At that moment the Indian
smote his horse, dug his heels in and fled.

Lewis was as angry as he had been in a long time. He wanted to
march over and cuff Shields on his thick skull and cry, "You damned
stupid Welshman, now see what you've done!" He called the man
over, and while Shields was coming he tried to quiet his emotions.
He tried to speak calmly when he said, "Why did you keep advancing? Why did you scare him away?"

"Me, sir?" said Shields, his astonishment unfeigned. "I thought we
were all advancing."

"Didn't you hear me order you to halt?"

"No, sir."

"Didn't you observe that the rest of us had halted?"

"No, sir."

"Do you realize that he'll give the alarm and that they'll all flee
to hell and gone and we'll never get horses now?"

"I'm very sorry, sir."

Lewis shrugged. He felt positively ill with frustration.

Well, there was nothing to do now but follow the tracks of the
beast and hope that instead of fleeing to ice caves the Indians would
be curious and bold enough to hide and spy on him. He wanted to
advance swiftly but he knew that that was the surest way to frighten
them off. He therefore climbed a hill and had his men build a fire.
To the end of a pole set in the earth he attached a few trinkets—a
mirror, some beads, a moccasin awl. With his men he was eating a
late breakfast and scanning the distant hilltops when a sudden
shower of rain and hail smote them, drenching them to their skins.
There, he thought, went the last of his hope! The rain would obliterate the tracks of the horse. At once he set off again and after
camping for the night he felt so utterly depressed that he lay awake
almost till daylight, turning one plan and another over and over in
his mind. He knew that he and Clark had again come to a crisis in
their journey and he was afraid that it would be too much for their
pitiable resources; but before falling asleep at last he forced his mind
to more pleasant thoughts, and awoke from dreams of friendly Indians all around him.

He sent Drewyer ahead to see if he could find any fresh trails. After an hour the scout returned to report that there were none. Lewis then sent Drewyer over to his right, Shields to his left, saying that they would look for an Indian road over the mountains. McNeal walked with Lewis. When they came to a swift mountain stream confined between stone walls McNeal spanned it, with one foot on either bank.

Grinning at Lewis, he said, "Captain, I thank God I've lived to find the mighty Missouri so small I can straddle it!" Up against the base of a mountain they came to cold springs and, lying on his belly to drink, Lewis reflected that this water was a part of the source of that great river, in search of whose remote end he had spent so many fatiguing days and restless nights. He drank deep and on rising said to McNeal, "I expect we might drink of the waters of the Columbia before we sleep tonight."

"The Columbia?" said McNeal, in a voice that seemed awed. He gazed round him.

They now climbed to the top of what Lewis took to be a dividing crest and he then looked upon stupendous mountains, running north and south, most of their summits white with snow. He descended a little way and found a creek flowing west.

To McNeal he said, "This is it. This is Columbia water." The men stretched out and drank again. Filling his pipe, Lewis looked at the immense mountains before him.

"Captain, do we have to cross those?"

"Somewhere, through some pass."

McNeal stared but could see no sign of a pass. He said, "If this is Columbia water it must be a river pass."

"I hope so."

"About how far is it from here to the ocean?"

"No man knows."

"Captain, do you think it's as far as we've come?"

Lewis knocked his pipe out and said, "It may be farther."

They now descended, following a wide Indian road into deep ravines and up steep hills until, toward night, they came to a patch of dry willows. Here Lewis decided to camp for the night. During the day they had killed nothing and had seen nothing to kill. When Drewyer came in he said he had not seen a bird even, not even a sparrow or finch. The men ate the remainder of their salt pork, about six ounces to each, hoarding against greater hunger their few pounds of flour and parched meal. Lewis felt even more dispirited than on the previous evening, for they had traveled by his estimate twenty miles this day and for all they had accomplished they might as well have gone berry-picking. They had found the serviceberries large and ripe and abundant but they disturbed rather than settled a man's stomach and put no strength in his legs. But the willow smoke close by his mosquito net was fragrant and all of heaven's stars were shining tonight. He took this as a good augury and snuggled down in his blankets and slept.

The next morning the four men again walked into the west and about ten o'clock Lewis saw two squaws, a buck and four or five dogs on a hilltop immediately before him. When two of the Indians sat as if to wait for him he said to his men, "We'll proceed but keep your ears open for orders and make no gestures that they can interpret as hostile." When he judged that he was about half a mile from them he told his men to wait. Leaving his pack and rifle, he unfurled a small flag and advanced. The women vanished behind the hill but the man stood and stared until Lewis had gone a hundred yards, when he too vanished. Lewis had been calling the word tabbabone and he now wondered if this had frightened them.

He ran as fast as he could to the top of the hill but found only the dogs there—four mangy shaggy half-starved beasts that came sniffing toward him, tails down. He thought that perhaps he could tie a handkerchief round the neck of one of them, with some beads and other trinkets in it, but when he approached the dogs they slunk away, tails dragging and lips curling. Waving to his men to come on, Lewis waited for them, and again the four of them marched westward, observing that the road they now traveled was literally covered with the prints of dogpads, moccasins and naked human feet. After about a mile they rounded a hill and came face to face with two Indian women and a girl. The younger of the two women dropped the roots she held and fled so precipitately that she fell and rolled and leapt up to run again. The other woman, who was old, and the girl remained, their eyes on the white men. When Lewis laid his gun down and advanced toward them they both sank to the earth and bowed their heads forward, as though expecting the tomahawk. With a gallant gesture Lewis sank to a knee and, taking one of the squaw's dirty hands in his own, he said, "Tabbabone . . tabbabone. . . ." Releasing her hand, he drew his shirt sleeve up to show his white skin and forced her to look up. He met her eyes moment and thought them exactly like the eyes of a wild thing in the woods.

He then gave the woman and child some beads, a few awls, a mirror, a half-ounce of vermilion. He summoned Drewyer forward and said, "Talk to them in sign language and in God's name don't alarm them. First, have her call back the one who fled, or she'll empty the village."

The old woman seemed at once to understand what Drewyer was saying with signs. Suddenly she stood up and in a high piercing voice that rang from hill to hill she uttered a cry. The one who had fled came running, breathless, her black eyes opening with amazement when she saw the wonderful gifts which the old woman was holding up for her to see. Lewis now gave similar presents to the younger woman and he painted the copper-cheeks of all three with vermilion, having learned from Sacajawea that with these Indians this meant peace.

"Make them understand that we're their friends and want to go to their village."

When the old woman understood what these strange pale men wanted she set off at a trot and after following her about a mile Lewis saw a group of mounted warriors coming at full speed. He felt gooseflesh. Convinced that they were a war-party, he handed his gun to Drewyer and then ran forward, waving a flag; and right at his side was the old woman, running too, and calling to her people. The war-party, sixty strong, dashed up in a cloud of dust, and the old woman was almost knocked down and trampled, so eager was she to meet her people first and speak to them. Lewis stood back. The red men seemed to be questioning the old woman. She was replying but chiefly she was holding her presents up for them to see.

The next moment Lewis almost died of astonishment. Sixty Indian men tumbled from their horses and came rushing toward him, their voices shrill with exultant cries, their arms eagerly reaching for him; and while he was still wondering what they intended to do they began to embrace him with an embarrassing excess of good will. Their method of embrace was to throw their left arm across the person's shoulder and at the same moment hug him fiercely to them, their left cheek to his left cheek, their deep voice crying, "Ah-hi-e! Ah-hi-e . . . !" Lewis's three men had come up and they were being embraced too. Because all sixty warriors had their faces covered with grease and paint, and because all sixty had to embrace all four of the strangers, Lewis soon found himself smeared from his forehead to his beard-tip. And still they pressed in, still uttering their cry of joy; and the two women and the girl were uttering shrill cries and fairly dancing with delight, or holding up their gifts as though foolish enough to think that painted warriors had time to look at them when there were four pale strangers to hug up against their greasy cheeks.

McNeal was muttering, "Great God, Captain! You were afraid they'd shoot us but they're going to love us to death!"

"I do confess," Lewis muttered in return, "that I'm getting heartily tired of this national hug."

"I've counted them, Captain. I have twenty-six to go."

"Be careful not to give offense," Lewis said, and accepted the embrace of his thirty-fourth warrior. He turned, half-fainting from the smell of rancid grease and sweating bodies, and said to Drewyer, "Make them understand that we're delighted too. Let's all make cries of joy."

The moment the embracing was done it occurred to him that the best way to show delight was to offer his pipe; and so he filled and kindled it, miserably conscious all the while of the terrible stink in his beard and eyebrows and all over his face—he could even taste it on his lips. The Indians seated themselves in a circle around the white men and after pulling off their moccasins accepted the pipe, each taking two or three whiffs and passing it to the man at his left. Lewis had to fill the pipe a number of times. Never had he seen Indians smoke with such relish.

After the smoking he gave them a few small things, including blue beads and vermilion. He told Drewyer to explain the object of the visit and when this was made clear, to say that they were hot and weary and thirsty and wished to be going. They all put on their moccasins, and of the Indians one rose who was, Lewis supposed the chief—a short man with fierce eagle-eyes, sunken cheeks, and the look of starvation and hunger all over him. He made a short speech to his warriors and then they all insisted that the white men should mount four of the finest horses; and when this was done the sixt warriors with their chief at their head acted as a bodyguard and escort. They were so proud and happy they were foolish. Lewis was not impressed by these Indians: around him, he supposed, were the tribe's ablest warriors, for they had ridden out to meet the enemy yet they were short and scrawny, indeed, almost frail; their legs were so bowed that with heels together most of them could have admitted a dog between their knees; all of them seemed to have thick flat feet and all of them had the sunken bleak eyes of starved men. No wonder they were scared to death of the Blackfeet!

At a willow lodge the chief again removed his moccasins and asked the white men to do likewise. He then brought forth a crude clay pipe and for two or three minutes harangued his warriors, who sat in a semicircle around him, staring with popping black eyes at the white men. Filling the pipe with the Shoshone tobacco and kindling it, the chief offered it to Lewis, but the moment Lewis reached to take it the red chief withdrew it and twice repeated the movement, when he then pointed the stem at the sky and at the fire, took three whiffs himself and presented the pipe to Lewis. Sucking smoke through the stem, Lewis thought he detected the odor of burning kinnikinick bark. He puffed three times. After his men had each taken three puffs Lewis told Drewyer to explain the object of their journey.

This Drewyer did in sign language and with drawings on the earth. Perceiving that the chief understood, Lewis had Drewyer tell him that the white men were hungry and would eat; and presently the Indians were offering to him and his three companions round black cakes of a dried fruit which they recognized as serviceberry. Lewis bit into one and told himself with unflagging optimism that he was dining heartily but he knew that the cake was as flavorless as dead tree bark and he saw his men making polite faces over their portions. Through Drewyer the chief explained that this dried fruit was all they had to eat at this time of year, save occasionally when they managed to kill a deer or an antelope, or catch salmon.

"Ask if there is timber anywhere big enough to make canoes. Ask if there is a river anywhere around here that we can go down in boats."

Drewyer talked in sign language and drawings with the chief and turning to Lewis said, "No. He say no."

"No river?"

"He say the river, it big; big mountains, rocky, high, steep. He say no canoe could go."

That, Lewis told himself, was terrible news, if true. While eating the tasteless berry cakes he had been looking round him at horses feeding in all directions. If he could buy horses his party could go overland.

"Ask how far to Salt-Water-Everywhere."

Again Drewyer and the chief talked in signs and Lewis closely studied their signs. Even before Drewyer spoke he understood that the distance was great, and the mountains in places almost impassable. It was tall country, all right. God in heaven but it was big! It was bigger than anything Mr. Jefferson had dreamed of.

This evening an Indian brought to Lewis in dirty hands a morsel of boiled flesh and a small piece of salmon. Lewis stared at the fish, thinking, Even if I doubted before I know now that I stand on the watershed of the western ocean. Curiously he tasted the salmon. He liked it. After the red man had gone he turned over and over in his palm the morsel of boiled meat and at last plopped it into his mouth, telling himself that if he was squeamish over an Indian's filth he would eat serviceberries and die.

As night drew on, the red men built up a big fire and some of them danced round it while others yelled or beat on skins. Squaws clapped their hands and uttered cries so shrill and wild that they set Lewis's nerves on edge. He could see no difference between the dancing and music here and those of Indians on the Missouri. He was weak and hungry and tired; he wanted to sleep. About midnight he withdrew to his blankets but from time to time the loud Indian yells awakened him and he would sit up, muttering with vexation.

Lying back again, he would look at the stars and say, "I am deep in the unknown. With three companions I am the first white man ever to look upon these Indians, or at the face of these white-topped mountains and the source of the long Missouri. . . ." Here he was; and yonder a thousand or two thousand miles was the western ocean, which he must reach before winter, no matter what impassable barriers stood in the way or what hostile tribes lined his path. He hoped that Clark's ankle was healing. He hoped that all the men with Clark were in good spirits, for he sensed that the most difficult part of the journey, the part that would demand most in courage and stamina, was still ahead of them. If only they had a broad river gently flowing across the vast distance to the ocean! If only they had decent canoes! If only at this moment he had a feast of cornbread, beavertail and marrowbones, with some of Jefferson's vintage wine!

An aroma of burning willow came to him on the breeze. He loved it. He loved the smoked smell of the skin-blanket where his cheek pressed; the fragrance inside a palm through which he had drawn a cedar bough. He turned to ease the hunger pains in his stomach and slept again.

22

To give Clark and his weary men time to catch up, Lewis decided to spend a day making observations. Because he and his men had only the flour and parched meal, and the unnourishing fruit cakes, he sent Drewyer and Shields out hunting, keeping McNeal with him as a kind of bodyguard. The Indian braves decided to go hunting too; they gave Drewyer and Shields two good mounts and the party set off and from a hilltop Lewis watched the hunt. With ear-splitting shrieks the Indians rode pellmell after a small herd of antelope and two hours later returned, their horses drenched with sweat and white with foam.

What senseless hunters they were!

After eating a little flour paste mixed with berry cake Lewis made a few notes on mineral, plant and seed life of the region and on Indian dress. Both men and women here wore the same kind of robe, a sort of blanket hanging loosely from the shoulders; and this robe, he had observed the night before, was their only bedding. It was made of deer, bighorn or antelope skins, dressed with the hair on. The men wore a skin shirt, on which, as on their leggings, they left the animal's leg, tail and neck pieces, and added for decoration fringes and quills. He thought the Shoshone tippet, made of otter skin, was the most elegant article of Indian dress he had ever seen, especially when they attached to it many tiny pieces of ermine. Both men and women wore their hair loosely over shoulders and face but the chief had shorn his as a sign of mourning. When Lewis perceived—for one of the squaws approached him, eager to take it off—that the women under their robes wore a kind of skin chemise, he fell to wondering about the condition of their health. Young men, he well knew, could be nothing but young men: his men for almost four months and fifteen hundred miles had seen no woman but the slave-girl and had known no woman: he supposed that he and Clark would have to turn them loose, if these squaws expressed a desire for them, as they certainly would, for they had already tried to entice him and his three companions into the thickets. Did they have venereal disease? He would have to find out. Weakened men could not face still greater hazards and labors with the white man's sickness in them.

But first he had to persuade the chief to go with some of his men to the forks of the Jefferson River, to fetch the baggage. The chief's name as he made it out and wrote it down was Cameahwait. He had Drewyer explain his problem to Cameahwait and found him most agreeable: the chief said that in the morning his men would go with horses to bring the baggage. Incurably optimistic, Captain Meriwether Lewis fell into a deep sleep, little dreaming of what the morning would bring.

At daylight he arose with a ravening appetite and asked McNeal how much flour was left. Two pounds, McNeal said. Lewis told him to cook half of it with berries and keep the other half for evening. The four men ate for their breakfast a small helping of what looked like a kind of pudding and tasted like unsalted half-cooked flour slightly sweetened. It was enough to turn even a hungry stomach but the men gulped it down and licked out their tin cups. Lewis gave a pinch of flour to the curious chief, who prodded at it with a finger, tasted it, and then wanted to know if it was made of roots. Drewyer explained to him how it was grown. While eating his tiny portion by wetting a fingertip and dipping into it and then licking the flour off his finger, Cameahwait said, through Drewyer, that his men had refused to go after the baggage. His men thought the white men were in league with an Indian nation on the Missouri and had come to ambush and massacre Cameahwait and his people.

In the chief's eyes Lewis saw suspicion and he sensed that his position was critical: in the minds of these ignorant savages, who had never seen white men nor heard any good of them, suspicion could easily and swiftly turn to alarm and alarm to panic. If this were to happen the hotbloods would first kill Lewis and his three men and then go to the river to see if other white men were there.

He watched the chief eating the flour and quickly considered this new and terrible menace. At last he turned to Drewyer.

"Our lives are in danger. You must know that. So make him understand these things—that with our people it is a shame and a disgrace to lie, or to deceive and ambush an enemy with lies. Tell him if they think of us this way, no white men will ever come to trade with them, nor ever bring them guns, powder and ball; nor knives, tomahawks, blue beads and all the things they want. Drewyer, do you understand everything I say?"

"Yes, Captain."

"Be very sure that he understands."

With all the signs he knew, Drewyer labored to communicate these thoughts, and Lewis closely observed the Indian face. In one moment he saw that the chief understood, in the next, that he was puzzled; saw his eyes open in friendliness, saw them darken; and concluded at last that he would have to be bolder. He would have to risk the chief's anger and their own lives.

"Drewyer?"

"Yes, Captain."

"Tell him this, that we are not afraid to die. Tell him we hope he has some braves who aren't afraid to die. Tell him he can keep our guns until he knows whether we're telling the truth. Then tell him that if he has any men brave enough to go, then let them go with us to learn if we have lied."

After Drewyer had communicated to the chief these plain slanders upon the courage of his braves, Lewis said: "Now tell him that our boats are loaded with supplies, that I'll give him many presents. Make him understand that our men are down there, on the river, waiting."

Cameahwait seemed to understand a great part, at least, of what Drewyer was trying to tell him, for suddenly he swung, anger glowing in his face, and mounting his horse, addressed his men. That he was scourging them with savage words was plain to Lewis when he saw the warriors slink back, looking abashed and shamed. Even so, only eight of them were bold enough to volunteer. With these eight and the chief Lewis now smoked a pipe and on looking round him saw that a number of the squaws were weeping. Their tears meant that they expected their chief and eight braves to be killed. When with packs on their backs Lewis and his three men moved off, followed by the chief and his eight warriors, the squaws set up an infernal wailing, like women whose men were being led to their death. After a mile or so a dozen other braves came forward on their beasts, and then more men and a number of squaws with them. Lewis judged that most of the village had decided to go along. Looking full of surliness, suspicions and treachery an hour ago, the red men were now gay and cheerful, as though on a march to buffalo country. What a capricious people they were! Lewis thought, looking round at their happy faces. What children acting on impulse!

Because he felt weak and miserable for lack of food he sent Drewyer ahead to hunt but he found nothing. The country seemed to have been stripped clean, even of birds. The white men prepared a supper of a pound of flour stirred in boiling water and asked the chief to join them. The chief's eyes said that he liked the thin gruel— or were his eyes mirroring a mind that anticipated another smoke? He was greedy for the white man's tobacco, his own being nothing but bark. Lewis and his men drank their supper from tin cups and after smoking with the chief tried to sleep but all night their bowels rumbled and hunger pains convulsed them. Before daylight the next morning Lewis sent Drewyer and Shields out to hunt, after begging the chief to keep his own men quiet in the camp; but when the warriors saw the two white men slip away into morning dusk they formed two armed parties and went slinking after them. "O my God!" Lewis muttered. About thirty warriors had gone, three of whom had small crude guns, the others with bow and arrow: in his mind Lewis saw Drewyer and Shields lying dead, as full of arrows as a porcupine with quills. He knew that if he said a word or made a move the suspicions of the red men in camp would be confirmed.

With both hunger and anxieties consuming him he waited, his ears strained for sound of a shot. In a low voice he said to McNeal, "Be sure you have everything in order. If we have to die here we'll take a lot of Indians with us." Then he was sorry that he had spoken and wondered if privation was affecting his mind. After a restless two hours he decided that those in camp might as well be on their way.

They had gone less than a mile when they heard a man yelling at the top of his voice. Looking off to the north, Lewis saw a rider coming at full speed, his whip smiting his beast at every jump. Glancing at the chief, he saw alarm in his face. To McNeal he said, "It would be just our damned luck for a whole war-party of their enemies to be arriving at this moment."

"That's what they seem to think," McNeal said.

"If that's what it is, then this is where we die. Hold yourself in readiness."

But the onrushing rider brought no news of a war-party. Drewyer had killed a deer! A few moments later Lewis was on a horse, sitting without stirrups, with an Indian on the horse behind him. The instant the Indians roundabout understood the good news they swung their mounts north, and the horse Lewis sat on swung, almost throwing him. With thunderous whoops of joy the Indians headed north. Feeling that his insides were being jolted out of him; feeling around his waist the arms of the red man hugging him and hanging on and shouting rapturous cries against his neck, Lewis began to rein his horse in, and to jab the Indian with an elbow to force him to stop flogging the horse. Fearing that he would lose his part of the feast, the Indian leapt to the earth and sprinted on ahead and for a mile or more easily outdistanced Lewis and his horse. Never had he seen a man run so fast, not even Bratton.

By the time the captain arrived on the scene of slaughter Drewyer and Shields were throwing the guts out, and like starved dogs the Indians were tumbling over one another to seize any part they could lay a hand on and tear it away and gulp it down. Such ravenous hunger made Lewis feel well-fed: the scene was so revolting that his own hunger died and he swore to himself that he would never be able to touch any part of this meat. He had seen famished wolves at a carcass, and jackals, but they had not been so savage in their blood- and hunger-lust as these creatures before him, tearing the spleen apart with their two filthy hands, the liver, kidneys, the lungs, the guts, while blood gushed from the corners of their mouths and their eyes rolled in rapture as, choking and gasping, they wolfed it down. The one who fascinated Lewis most was a scrawny bowlegged brave who had managed to possess nine or ten feet of the small intestine and now fed it into his mouth and down his throat, his cheeks and tongue sucking it in, his throat muscles rising in blood-filled rolls, as his two hands squeezed down the tube, forcing the contents out at the other end. In what seemed to Lewis only a few moments the long piece of gut disappeared.

He looked round at these Indians with what in his Journal he was to call pity and compassion. He was to confess that he had not known that human nature could be indistinguishable from brute nature. It was compassion that forced him to give three-fourths of the deer to the chief, keeping only one hind quarter for himself and his men. To the chief he also gave the hide. The Indians right here on the spot devoured their flesh raw, sucked the marrow out of the bones, ate the tongue, brains and eyes out of the skull and nibbled all over the hide and licked it dry.

A little later Drewyer killed another deer and Lewis saw the disgusting scene all over again. McNeal made a fire and roasted two hind quarters of venison, and after Lewis and his men had eaten he gave what was left to the Indians—for he had seen them eating the soft part of the hooves, sucking the moisture out of the eye sockets, and pounding and eating the bones. The three men with him were thinking that their captain behaved with great plenty, for they had almost starved and might starve yet before they found more game. Their resentment ran still deeper when Drewyer killed a third deer and Lewis gave most of that to the red people. But Lewis knew what he was doing: it was more than pity or much besides pity: if he could fill their bellies they might feel braver, they might go on with him. But when again he sent his hunters out, most of the Indians fled back to their village, leaving with him only twenty-eight men and three squaws.

On learning exactly where Lewis expected to meet the other white men Cameahwait insisted on halting. So they all dismounted, and the chief with solemn gestures to indicate that he was performing a very special ceremony put round the necks of the white men adorned tippets of the kind the Shoshones wore. Perceiving that this was to disguise the white men, in case they intended an ambush of the red men, Lewis beamed upon the chief and set on his head his cocked hat with a feather, and then held his hand side by side with the chief's hand, to show that one skin was about as red as the other. He told his three men to disguise themselves as well as they could, meanwhile muttering, "But if Captain Clark and his men are not yet there, our friends here are going to be ten times as suspicious and our lives not worth a dead serviceberry. We're in mortal danger."

Shields grumbled, "Captain, our lives has been in danger ever since we met the Sioux."

"But not in mortal danger," Lewis said. "That's a special kind."

Whether he was spoofing, Shields did not know. None of the men, not even Clark, could tell when Meriwether Lewis was serious.

McNeal said, "Captain, we can stand them all off. Drewyer himself is a match for any thirty."

"I expect he is," Lewis said. "Well, let's be going."

He gave his flag to one of the Indians to carry and then they all mounted and set off for the forks, Lewis praying with all his heart and soul that Clark would be there. Bravado was all right. Drewyer might be a match for thirty. They might in a showdown kill fifty of them before they fell but in the end they would fall.

Clark was not there. Lewis sensed that he was not there long before he arrived at the forks and for a few minutes all the sunshine went out of him. When Cameahwait learned that the white men were not where he had been told they would be, would he then turn with his men and vanish, or would he come against the white men with his entire force? In either case it would mean failure of the expedition. Without horses they could never go on. He racked his brains to know what to do and decided to risk everything on another gamble.

"Drewyer," he said, "pay attention." He reined his horse in and dismounted. An instant later the red chief dismounted, his suspicious eyes on Lewis. To Drewyer, Lewis said, "Tell him that I will now let him take my gun." Drewyer talked in signs, and Lewis saw that the chief understood. Promptly he advanced and presented his rifle. "Tell him that if enemies are hidden down there, he can shoot me. Tell him I'm not afraid to die. Tell him that if he thinks I lied to him he can use my own gun against me. Be sure you make him understand all that."

Cameahwait's warriors drew up behind their chief, their eyes on the white men, their hands grasping their weapons. The chief had accepted Lewis's gun fearfully, and now held it as if he expected it to explode in his hands. Drewyer was talking to him in signs.

Lewis now spoke to his men. "The three of you will each choose a warrior and offer him your gun. Drewyer, you will tell the chief to tell his three men that if I have lied, they will keep the guns. If I have told the truth, they will give the guns back. Be sure he understands it. Tell him twice."

The three warriors accepted the rifles, and four white men stood unarmed and defenseless.

After Drewyer had finished talking in signs, Lewis said, "I can tell by his face that he understood. Now tell him to send spies on ahead to learn for himself if enemies are down there."

Cameahwait also understood that. At once he looked round him and, choosing four men, sent them on ahead. Not until the four spies had disappeared did the main party advance, the four white men walking, Shields and McNeal now and then glancing at their cap-

tain. They thought he had done a very queer thing but they had almost boundless confidence in his judgment.

When he thought he was only two or three miles from the forks
Lewis remembered the note he had left there for Clark: he now told
Drewyer to take an Indian and go ahead with him and show him
the note. When in an hour or so Drewyer and the Indian returned,
the note in Drewyer's hand, Lewis read it aloud to the chief and his
solemn warriors, though keeping his own face straight was almost
more than he could manage. He told Drewyer to explain to the chief
that his brother, the white chief, Clark, had only this day left a note
at the forks, saying that he and his bone-tired men were coming as
fast as they could. He was then to tell him that he would choose a
man and Lewis would choose a man and they would send the two
of them to find Chief Clark, while Chief Lewis and the other two
white men remained, unarmed, with him and his warriors. If he had
a man brave enough to go, Lewis would give to this man, on his return, a knife and a string of beads.

While Drewyer was trying to explain all this, a few of the braves
began to harangue their chief. They spoke in such loud angry tones
that Lewis said to Drewyer, "Now what in hell do they want?"

Drewyer said he thought they were afraid. They were telling their
chief that if they did not go at once they would all be killed. They
had no doubt any longer that this was an ambush.

Disgusted, Lewis said, "I can't imagine how the story got abroad
that Indian warriors are brave men. Like the wolf, they're brave only
in packs."

"Captain," McNeal said gravely, "that's true of most men."

"I expect maybe you're right."

It was dark by this time. A fire was built and by the light of the
fire Lewis wrote a note to Clark, telling him in a few words of the
extreme danger he and his men were in and suggesting that he hasten. He gave the note to Drewyer, with Cameahwait looking on, and
told him that as soon as there was enough daylight to guide him he
was to take it at top speed to Clark.

Then, pretending that all was well, and grimly amused in the deep
sardonic part of him, Lewis lay down by the fire. His watchful half-
lidded eyes saw most of the warriors slip away to hide in the willow brush. Cameahwait and six of his braves, clutching the four rifles
of the white men, took positions at some distance from the fire and
in such a way that they surrounded Lewis and his men. Seven pairs

of black eyes were fixed upon them. Four copper-colored hands grasped trigger-guards.

In a low voice Lewis said to his men, "The longer I live the more I realize that hunger is a more powerful force than fear. All I want right now is buffalo hump and marrowbones."

"A saddle of fat elk," Shields said, and sighed.

The four men were so nearly dead from hunger and exhaustion that in only a few minutes they were sound asleep.

23

One of William Clark's friends had said that if perseverance could be isolated, like the elements, in pure form, it would be discovered that in regard to this one virtue Clark was twenty-four-carat pure. Only perseverance that never for a moment considered alternatives brought him and his men up the river, in water so swift that often the men could not stand in it, and so cold that they almost froze in full sunlight. Day after day, mile after mile, they struggled upriver with the boats, their sufferings so pitiable that again and again Clark stripped his leather off and plunged in with them. Day after day they searched the banks for a message from Lewis but found only a few deer skins.

One evening around their one small fire—wood became steadily scarcer as they climbed upward—the men were eating when Clark heard a strange sound of pain and distress and, looking over, saw the squawman strike his slave again. That he had already struck her Clark knew instantly, for blood was gushing from her nose. She had shrunk back from him and he had lunged forward and struck again, just as Clark and most of his men looked over. Clark shouted, "Charbonnie!" and Charbonneau, clenched fist upraised, looked over at the captain. All the men were watching to see what would be done. Joe Fields muttered, "If only he'd turn him over to me!"

Clark stood up. He was angry. He knew that in a land without laws he had no right to interfere in this situation: after all, he had a slave too, a big black Negro, and though he never struck or abused him he had the right to. He knew, besides, that she might not have brought her man's wrath on her head if she had not persisted in find ing choice roots and berries for the captain—and berries especially, for here in the higher mountains whole hillsides were berry orchards.

These thoughts were in Clark's mind as he walked over to the squawman. He looked first at the girl, who with one arm was clutching her child against her and with the other was shielding her face. So much blood had poured from her nose that her leather jacket and skirt were red with it. Then Clark looked at Charbonneau, who stood silent, sullen, hostile, waiting.

"Why did you strike your wife?" There was no reply. Clark had expected none. He now looked over at the other men and at last at Shannon, in whose blue eyes there was something that caught his attention. He was a strange one, this George: after having been lost for days, after having been given up as dead, he had walked into camp with a hundred and fifty pounds of deer flesh over his shoulders. When asked where he had been, he said hunting, and that was all any man was ever to get out of him.

Looking at Shannon, Clark said, "Do you know why he struck her?"

"Not for sure, Captain Clark. I think it was because she was feeding the baby a morsel that he wanted."

"Was that the reason?" Clark asked the squawman.

Charbonneau now growled and said something in French. Clark looked again at Shannon. "Do you know what he said?"

"It's a French phrase he uses more and more. It means to keep your hands off."

Shannon now saw the red coming up Clark's throat. He couldn't see it in the red beard but he saw it in the nose and forehead and he knew that his captain was terribly angry. Neither he nor the other men were at all surprised when one of Clark's big powerful hands seized the squawman's shoulder and spun him, and an enraged voice cried, "Look at me, you wife-beater!" Charbonneau refused to look up. "Charbonnie, listen. Are you listening?"

"*Oui.*"

"Don't ever strike this girl again, or your child. Never. Do you understand me?" When the squawman said nothing but only hung his head, sullen, mute, Clark raised his voice. "I asked you, do you understand me?"

"*Oui, Cap-n.*"

Clark removed his hand and turned away, feeling far more put out with himself than with the squawman: in his code there was no for-

giveness for that officer who showed anger before his men. He had
lost his temper and now he was sorry.

But none of his men were sorry. In low voices they talked among
themselves, now and then glancing over at the girl, who had gone
away from her man and now sat alone with her child, her face hidden. Some of the men thought Charbonneau should be punished. He
should be dismissed from the Corps and sent back.

"What in hell did they bring him for?" Joe Fields asked. "If he's
the interpreter why did Captain Lewis take Drewyer?"

"What I wonder," said Alex Willard, "is why Captain Clark got so
mad about it. You reckon he gets any of her?"

Frazier shook his head. "Our captains don't like squaws. Not that
way."

"Clark seems to like her," Willard said.

"It's the kid. He's crazy about kids."

The squawman struck his wife on a Wednesday evening. The following Friday, Lewis gave up his gun and lay by a fire, surrounded
by Indians. Early Saturday morning Clark set out to walk up
the river, taking with him Charbonneau and his wife and child.
Sacajawea with her babe went on ahead, and presently Clark saw
her dancing like a woman bereft of her senses. She was dancing like
mad and uttering shrill cries. Again and again she turned to look at
Clark and to point up the river, all the while furiously sucking the
four fingers of one hand. A few moments later Clark saw several Indians advancing on horseback and hastened forward. The girl continued to cry and dance, jouncing the babe up and down in its
cradle, and to suck at her fingers to indicate that these were her people. She was home again!

Looking closer, Clark saw Drewyer, dressed like an Indian, and
went over to him. Drewyer gave him the note. The mounted Indians
turned back up the river and all of them began to sing a high wild
song of joy, with Sacajawea running after them, and Clark and
Drewyer running after her. In the night-camp the Indians guarding
Lewis and his two men had received the good news and all those in
hiding had come rushing out, so overjoyed that in turn they threw
their arms around Lewis and his men and hugged them. "Will this
never end!" Lewis muttered, submitting to one greasy hug after another and trying to keep the rancid fat out of his beard. Because he
was taller than the Indians some of them reached up with both hands
to pull his head down, determined to press their cheeks against his.

He was so weak from hunger and fatigue that he could barely stand.

McNeal was saying, "I tell you, Captain, they'll kill us yet."

"With kindness," Lewis said, and groaned.

Down the hill there was wild yelling, and soon the other Indians came in sight, then the girl and then Clark and Drewyer. The red men now insisted on embracing all the white men and some of the white men thought they would die. Their feet were so wounded and swollen that it was torture to stand, their stomachs were empty, yet the hugging went on and on as though it would never end, and smiting their ears was the fierce wild yell, "Ah-hi-e . . . ! Ah-hi-e . . . !" Lewis looked over at his friend Clark and made a face. "Captain Clark——" he began, but was silenced by a piercing shriek in his ear and two hands grasping his long hair to pull his head down. "Captain Clark, only last night I expected to be tomahawked, yet see me now! Who ever dreamed there was so much love on top of the Rockies?"

"Ah-hi-e!" the red men cried, and hugged the white men, smearing their beards and faces and elkskin, their dancing black eyes all the while looking round for the hundreds of rifles which they thought would be theirs. There was no wilder voice among them than Sacajawea's. Lewis was submitting with stoic grace, though Clark heard him mutter, "I swear to God this is the same guy who hugged me an hour ago!" From the red throng an Indian girl flung herself and rushed forward and a moment later was hugging Sacajawea and crying with such shrill joy that Lewis thought his eardrums would break. He stared at the two girls as they wept and cried and kissed one another with the most extravagant joy he had ever beheld. "I think I must be losing my mind," he said, speaking to no one; and again bowed his tall form so that a red cheek could press against his own. Sacajawea, leading the other girl, rushed over to Clark and talked to him in her own tongue, in French and in a few words of English all mixed together.

Clark, gracefully submitting, said to Lewis, "This is the girl that escaped that night when the otter-woman screamed."

"I'll be darned," Lewis said.

Like the child she was, Sacajawea beamed innocently up at Clark to see if he was happy too; and when he smiled at her she turned impulsively and again hugged the girl.

York had become the center of a gathering and was again happy and proud, after months of river labor and neglect. The red people, both men and women, had crowded round him and were doing their best to wash the black off his skin. Failing with fingers moistened at their lips, some of them ran away to fetch water. They gave him a more thorough scrubbing than the Sioux or Mandans had given him; and while some rubbed and shrieked, others were gasping over his kinky black hair or staring bug-eyed at his two rows of strong white teeth, which he gladly revealed to them by drawing his big lips far back. The boldest of the girls were examining other parts of him to learn if they were black also. What puzzled the Snake Indians, Drewyer told Lewis, was the fact that only one member of the invading party was painted black for war. They were speechless when at last convinced that he had not been painted black at all but was actually black. Greater medicine than this they had never heard of. After they had given up trying to wash the black off and had examined him from his torn feet to his kinky skull York began to show off his powers. He astounded them with the nimbleness of his dancing, the incredible way he could roll his big eyes, the strength in his great shoulders. With what seemed to be no effort at all he seized two of the scrawny undersized half-starved Shoshone warriors and hoisted them above his head, holding them there a few moments belly to belly and gently setting them down.

"I think the love-feast is over," Lewis said to Clark. "Now we'll see how much we have to pay for it."

Cameahwait now had Clark seated on a white robe and to his red hair attached a half-dozen small sea shells, his most precious possession, for these from trader to trader had come all the way from the western ocean. All the Indians took off their moccasins and the chief indicated that all the white men were to do so; and when this was done the pipe of peace went round and round. Lewis decided that both red men and white could understand more clearly if instead of sign language he used all his interpreters; and so he summoned them, saying that Sacajawea would translate from Shoshone into Minnetaree; the squawman from Minnetaree into French; and Francis Labiche from French into English.

When the translators were all seated Lewis said to Labiche, "You know what to tell them—the same old thing: that we come as friends from the Great White Father, to trade with them, to open routes, to protect them against their enemies. Tell them that for pelts we'll give them weapons. Be very sure that they understand it all."

Like one feeling his way among words, Labiche began to translate from English into French, with Charbonneau's help, for the squaw-man understood English almost as well as Labiche and pretended to understand it much better. Suddenly there was a wild cry that made everybody start. It was Sacajawea. Leaping up, she ran over to the Indian chief and first threw her blanket over him and then flung herself upon him, shrieking so hysterically in a babble of joy and devotion that Lewis felt it an impertinence to look at her. Cameahwait struck the blanket aside and stared hard at the girl. Then his face relaxed and he drew her to him and embraced her. To the astonished captains and their men Charbonneau was saying that these two were brother and sister.

"I know damned well I'm losing my mind," Lewis muttered to Clark. "For if this is true, the Almighty must have been guiding us when we told her she could come."

Clark said, "We should have no difficulty getting horses now."

"Let's hope he doesn't look at her too hard. He might figure she isn't his sister."

"She told us she was a princess, you remember."

Still wildly weeping the girl returned to her seat, her whole body shaking. Lewis looked curiously at the brother and saw that he was deeply moved. He had not known that Indians could be so emotional.

When Labiche and Charbonneau were in agreement on what the captains wanted them to say, the latter began to talk in halting Minnetaree to his wife and she seemed to be listening; but a moment later she was sobbing so wildly that nobody could hear a word. The council had to be postponed until she could recover her poise. This she was not able to do at once. On the contrary, after her brother had again talked to her she fell into grief so terrible that Lewis had no doubt that she was out of her senses. He asked Labiche what the trouble was. Labiche said that during her long absence all her family had died except two brothers and a small son of her eldest sister. At the moment the other brother was away hunting.

Clark came over to Lewis and the two captains stood together, looking at the girl where she knelt sobbing, her blanket over her head.

"I never knew," Lewis said, "that Indians can be so emotional."

Clark said she had been under a strain all the way up the river. He had supposed it was because she was getting close to her people. Or maybe it was because of her man, for he had been beating her again.

"He has?" asked Lewis, looking over at Clark. His emotions and thoughts completely masked, he added, "What was his reason?"

"I don't expect he has to have much of a reason."

"What do you think of these Shoshone Indians?"

"They don't look like they had ever had enough to eat."

Lewis told about killing the deer and how the Indians had wolfed everything down including most of the feet. Then his attention was drawn to a scrawny elderly bowlegged man who was walking round and round Sacajawea, looking at her. He was looking at her, Lewis thought, as he might have looked at a pony or a dog, or at anything whose value he was trying to determine. Bending over, he seized the blanket and hurled it off her and seemed then to be peering at her hair.

"I wonder if that's her other brother," Lewis said.

The Indian now clutched her arm and, dragging her to her feet, knocked her forearm away from her face so that he could see her features. He then turned and spoke shrilly to Cameahwait. He seemed to be enraged. But as suddenly as the rage had come it passed and in a quiet sinister way he moved round and round the girl, looking her up and down and at last, because he was half-blind, feeling her over.

Observing that she suffered his examination, Clark said, "He has some rights in her or thinks he has."

"Maybe he bought her when she was a child."

"I expect that's it."

The scrawny Indian was now demanding to be heard and the captains could tell by the faces of other Indians and by the way the girl cringed before him that he had a right to be heard. From what they read in faces, especially in Charbonneau's, and from what Labiche now whispered to them, they were able to make out the story. When a small child she had been betrothed to this man, who though not a chief was a Considerable Man, and under Shoshone tribal laws he now owned her. He seemed to be proclaiming to all ears that would listen that he was a betrayed and outraged husband and Charbonneau was an impostor and a poacher. He also seemed to be enjoying himself immensely, now that he had a large audience in the way he looked at her and gestured at her and then harangued the spectators he reminded Lewis of an auctioneer. The man might have yanked her toward him and taken her then and there if her friend had not come forward with her child. Sacajawea took the child

her arms and the friend went away. The scrawny Indian had been
omentarily silenced, while he peered at the child and felt over it.
hen he shouted more wildly than ever, pausing now and then to
eer at the child's face or the mother's, his own face steadily filling
ith disgust and disdain. Labiche said he did not want her now. Had
ie borne a child by another? Then she was of no use to him.

"It's pretty hard on her," Lewis said to Clark. "He has such con-
mpt, yet it's none of her fault."

"She doesn't want to stay with her people," Clark said. "She wants
go on with us."

"I'm not surprised," Lewis said drily. After a few moments he said,
These squaws look to me like they have ganaraehah and Louis
enerae."

Clark looked over at his friend, his face showing astonishment.
How could they have? They've never known white men."

"You made that sound pretty terrible," Lewis said. "Well, I've been
ondering about that. If they have it, then they've known white men
· it's native to them. I'd never heard it's native to them."

"Neither have I."

"We should be sure. Nearly all our men are pretty weak and a lit-
e venerae would put them on their backs."

When the last of the boatmen came up and had been hugged by
l the Indian men the captains had them build a council shelter of
.ils and willow boughs, and under this they met with Cameahwait
id two minor chiefs. Lewis now told them through translators that
e would need horses to go to the Salt-Water-Everywhere but would
ay for the horses; that the Indians would profit immensely later,
hen white men came to trade with them, for then the Shoshones
ould have guns with which to drive their enemies back and estab-
h themselves in buffalo land. Cameahwait's hunger-ravaged face
iowed bitter disappointment. He said that his warriors expected
ins now, a rifle for each: how many moons would it be before these
ime? If the white men went all the way to the ocean and then all
e way back home; and if he and his people had to wait until still
iother party came up the long river, how long would that be? He
ight be dead before then, they might all be dead. If they kept
eir horses, well, at least they would have horses. They could go
inting. They could ride down the rivers after fish, they could go
r afield after berries. They could live as they had always lived.
ut if they gave some of their best horses to the white men, for no

more than a promise that it would take a hundred moons to fulfill . . .

To Clark, Lewis said, "We're dealing with a pretty smart Indian."

He had learned among the Sioux and Mandans that the red men did not like long-winded councils. The Indian's patience, like a child's, was short. He decided therefore to terminate this council and soften the chiefs with a few gifts. To Cameahwait he presented a medal with an image of Jefferson on one side, a tomahawk on the other; and a worn uniform consisting of a coat, shirt and a pair of scarlet leggings; and a carrot of tobacco, together with awls and beads. To the minor chiefs he gave small medals with an image of Washington, and a knife and a little tobacco. To other Indians round-about he gave awls, beads, mirrors and knives. Then he presented to Cameahwait some corn. The Indians were delighted with their gifts and walked around uttering their shrill cry of joy.

Seeing the gun-envy in their eyes, Clark said, "Let's shoot off the airgun. It will be good to impress them with our power."

Lewis sent for the airgun and with the braves gathered round he fired it a number of times at a target and after each shot the Indians ran pellmell to see if the target had been hit. To their amazement it was hit every time. After the firing ceased the Indians gathered round the gun but seemed afraid to touch it. Cameahwait told the squawman that this gun was the greatest medicine they had ever seen, except the black white man.

This evening the captains pitched their skin-tent and withdrew inside. They were both aware that a grave decision had to be made, but before coming to it they talked of a more pleasant subject: they had both been enormously impressed by the three forks area and they agreed that it was an essential spot in the geography of the western world. Its wide beautiful valley, watered by three rivers and many creeks, had the Crows on the east, the Blackfeet on the north, the Snakes on the west, and they did not know what on the south. The three forks junction seemed to be a geographic hub and they hoped to give Mr. Jefferson a very full account of it.

Coming then to their problem, Lewis said, "As I understand the chief, one route is about as formidable as the other: either we go down a river where no man has ever dared go, or over the mountains which, according to him, are practically impassable. He admits that the pierced-nose Indians come over the mountains horseback but says there is no game, and so much fallen timber it's almost impossible to get through."

"Has he mapped it all out for you?"

"Yes, he has drawn several maps but I wonder how well he knows the country. How far has he been. He draws lines for rivers and makes piles of earth for mountains and by the time he's done a bighorn couldn't get through."

"We'll get through some way," Clark said, his face looking wan and sunken in his red beard. "I think maybe this is what we should do: I'll take a few men and find out if there is any canoe timber and if the river is navigable. You could be making the cache here and getting him in a mood to trade horses, if we have to go by land."

"All right, let's do it that way. You take the squaw and her man with you to the main camp and have them send Indians and horses over here, so we can get the baggage over. Every mile counts. Will, this country is just a hell of a lot bigger than Mr. Jefferson thinks it is."

"Or than I thought," Clark said.

"It's a thousand miles, the chief says, to the ocean. And between us and the Columbia, he says, there are big valleys."

"This river here, how long is it?"

"He doesn't know. He says no man has ever been down it. Somewhere it runs into a bigger river and that river flows for hundreds of miles through mountains and then God only knows how far before it reaches the Columbia. The mountains are so rocky, he says, that a goat can't get through."

"Yes, but if this river is navigable we could go on water all the way."

"The chief says not. Says we can't go down this river, and even if we could we couldn't go down the one this flows into."

"He knows of no river further north that goes to the Columbia?"

"None." Lewis filled and lit his pipe, saying, "The only tobacco they've ever had is bark. When the chief smoked our good old twist he nearly choked to death."

"He like it?"

"It made tears run from his eyes. A funny thing. These Indians have never known tobacco, I guess, yet they smoke. So is the habit just to be puffing at something?"

They listened. Their men outside were singing and a few of them seemed to be dancing. They could hear Bob Frazier's baritone tripping along his foolish rimes: "Now there are men who think it's great if legs are shaped to hold their mate! If legs from hips down to the toes are shaped just like a wagon's bows . . . !" Potts took it up in shrill falsetto. Shannon came in with the bugle; and then there was loud laughter.

"That's about right," Lewis said. "Some of the women do have legs like wagon bows."

"You think they have the disease?"

"They look like they have the symptoms."

"How do the men here treat their women?"

"About like all Indians. The brave rides the horse, the squaw walks and carries the baggage."

"I mean their chastity."

"Oh, that. Not held in very high esteem. For a trinket a husband will lend his wife for a night but the women here are not so importunate for our caresses as the Sioux and Mandans. Still, they're crazy as bedbugs over your black man."

"It beats the life out of me," Clark said. "You figured it out?"

Lewis put a hand to his mouth to hide a smile. "I expect it's because women are pretty fond of colors."

For a moment Clark looked at his friend. "I expect it's more than that. Do we take the corral bars down here?"

Above the violin they again heard Frazier's voice: "O form divine, wilt thou be mine?"

Lewis said: "If young men have been away from women for months—— Still, I agree with you: all the boatmen have been weakened by this long pull up the river. If they should get sick in this mutual exchange of good offices we'd have a problem on our hands."

Again Clark looked at him. He thought Lewis had the damnedest way of saying things.

"Those who are most squaw-crazy you might take with you."

"I was thinking of that. Well, I'll put out early in the morning, for I figure we have no time to lose. It's freezing already and we're still this side of the Rockies. What would we winter on if we got caught here?"

"Wild berries don't stick to a man's ribs. Fish and berries, that's about all these poor devils ever have but I've noticed that the happiest people are those who have to dig hardest to eat. They haven't any time to get philosophic."

For the third time Clark looked at him. He said, "I thought the women gather some kind of seed."

"They do. They mix it with berries to make a kind of cake."

"We'd have to go back to buffalo land," Clark said, and turned to roll his bedding out.

The next morning he was up at daylight and gathering his men and baggage, and soon he was off, with Sacajawea leading the party. Lewis had got up early too and had traded for three horses on which Clark and his men carried their heavier luggage. The three beasts cost him an old coat, a pair of elkskin leggings, a half-dozen hand-kerchiefs of gay colors, three knives and some awls, beads and mirrors. The men who had traded the horses were soon gambling in a strange game unknown to white men, in which they kept up a sing-song chant and made queer motions with their hands. The white men watching them supposed that in their own way they were invoking magic, as white men did when they spit on the dice. After an hour of gambling one of the three men owned everything and the two losers, it seemed to the white men, did not mind at all.

After helping Clark off, Lewis turned to his duties. He told the men to open all the baggage and air it, for in case the river was not navigable, which he fully expected, they would have to pack everything in parcels of suitable size and shape for loading on beasts. They were to keep a sharp eye on the Indians, though the red men here, he said, did not seem to be thieves. They had borrowed a kettle and tin cups but had returned them. Just the same, their eyes stood out with envy and astonishment when the men began to unpack. Indians stood all around them, both men and women, mouths open, eyes staring, the only movement in them being that of their eyes as they looked from wonder to wonder. Lewis had other men soak hides and cut them into rope-thongs, to use in lashing packs to the horses. Another group under the command of Goodrich he sent to the river to fish.

This was Sunday, August the 18th, Merne Lewis's birthday. He had the fact in mind all day long. All day long he was thinking that he had lived a pretty selfish life and hadn't been good for much at all. Lord darn, what a broken-off horn breeze! He was thirty-one years old and what had he accomplished? What had he done for anyone but himself? He had lived about half his life-span on this old sublunary world and had done little indeed, if anything at all, to promote the happiness of mankind, or to gather information for generations still to come. What a selfish creature he had been!

All day long he persisted in morose self-criticism and this evening he put his thoughts on paper, concluding: "I viewed with regret the

many hours I have spent in indolence, and now soarly feel the want
of that information which those hours would have given me had they
been judiciously expended. but since they are past and cannot be recalled, I dash from me the gloomy thought, and resolved in future,
to redouble my exertions and at least indeavour to promote those
two primary objects of human existence, by giving them the aid of
that portion of talents which nature and fortune have bestoed on me;
or in future, to live for *mankind*, as I have heretofore lived *for
myself*."

He read over what he had written and though he approved the
sentiments he thought he had expressed them badly. Filling his pipe,
he went outside and sat by the fire. The Indian men were dancing
and making a terrible racket. A part of his own men and all the
squaws seemed to be nowhere in sight. Little he cared about that.
His thoughts were deep tonight, almost as deep, he liked to think,
as Mr. Jefferson's own. After this he would try to be more like Mr.
Jefferson, the noblest and greatest of all the men he had met or
hoped ever to meet. He sighed and knocked his pipe out and went
to bed.

He lay for a little while trying to realize fully his situation in the
world at this moment—to project himself to a platform ten or twenty
miles above the earth and from this vantage point to look down at
himself, here in what he had named Shoshone Cove; and then to
look around in every direction. What would he see? Eastward he
would see the plains and prairies, the hills and rivers, which in a way
were now familiar to him; but in all other directions he would look
upon vast areas which no white man had ever seen. In fancy he saw
the great mountainous expanses to the south, the west, the north-
for a thousand miles—yes, for two thousand or more to the north and
the south: what a world it was and what marvels remained to be discovered in it!—what rivers and lakes, what minerals, what immense
forests, and what untold wealth in wildlife! It was what the United
States needed—all this, all of it—to become the greatest of the nations, to fill the dream that Tom Jefferson had for it. . . .

He was still looking down and marveling when he fell asleep

24

While his men were busy making leather ropes, packsaddles, and garments for themselves, or were off hunting or fishing, Meriwether Lewis was busy gathering information to delight Mr. Jefferson's soul. His Journal entries during these few days were long and detailed. Knowing that Jefferson wanted all the facts he could get on every Indian tribe in the west, Lewis now set down a great many observations of the Shoshones—that in this particular village they seemed to have about a hundred warriors but three times that number of women and children; that they had many more children than a man would expect to find in a tribe that seldom got enough to eat; that among them were only a few old people but that these were treated with tenderness and respect. He recorded for Mr. Jefferson the fact that the husband completely owned his wives and daughters and could do with them as he pleased; that a plurality of wives was the rule but that, unlike the Minnetarees and Mandans, the Snakes did not marry sisters, but purchased their wives from different fathers. The price was usually paid in horses or mules.

Now and then he would pause to mutter, "If only I could see Mr. Jefferson's face when he reads that!" meaning, "They seldom correct their children particularly the boys who soon become masters of their own acts. they give as a reason that it cows and breaks the sperit of the boy to whip him, and that he never recovers his independence of mind after he is grown." On the other hand, Mr. Jefferson would not be surprised to learn that these Indians treated their women, except the very old, with no respect at all, and forced upon them every kind of drudgery. This was true of the red man everywhere and

Jefferson knew it. Here the squaws cooked the food, dressed the skins, made the clothes, dragged in the wood, built the lodges and became pack-beasts on the journey to buffalo land. Here the red man thought himself degraded if compelled to walk more than a few yards.

Down the river Lewis chose a spot for a cache and had his men bury a part of the goods. A cache had to be made with the utmost care if it was not to be found by the red men: a dry spot was chosen and the sod was cut into small squares and gently removed. A hole was then dug, the earth from it being piled on skins. After the moisture-proofed parcels were buried the hole was filled with tramped earth, the sod was replaced exactly as it was before, and the excess of earth was thrown into the river. Experts in making a cache then built a fire on the sod that had been removed, or fed horses on it. Lewis's men built a fire. The men had cached goods at the Great Falls and at the three forks and had said, as they said now, "We'll never find it in God's world. Look, you can't even tell where it is."

George Shannon had said, "The captains will tell with their instruments."

Joe Fields had retorted, "You're quite an expert in finding things for a man who gets lost all the time."

In a cool level voice George had replied, "Did someone imagine I was lost?"

The second day after Clark left, Lewis spent smoking with Cameahwait and the minor chiefs and asking a multitude of questions. He had the chief draw with a cinder on a white robe the rivers and mountains and passes, as well as he knew them—and suspected more and more that he didn't know much about them. Through the translators the red man said that this small river on which they were camped flowed into a larger river down which no living thing could go except fish. As for the country on either side, only the bighorns lived there. He said there was an old man present who knew the country south and west and who told a horrible tale about it: yonder —he indicated the southwest—were high waterfalls, boiling infernos, yawning chasms and gorges, broad areas of black desolation, ice caves deep in the earth, and whole rivers that plunged into crevices and disappeared. It was a land of horrors. If Lewis and his men were to go that way they would have to climb high mountains of nothing but solid rock, where they would find nothing to eat, not even berries. They would come to a nation of savage red men who wore moccasins with holes in them (in his Journal, Lewis dubbed them the broken mockersons): these people lived like the bear, feeding on roots and berries. If the white men were to try to go this way with horses they would soon find their hooves raw and bleeding and they would have to abandon them. They would then come to a waterless desert, where the only moisture was a little rain in stone basins in the spring of the year. The old man begged Lewis to postpone his journey to the next summer.

The rivers he told about, Lewis was thinking, must be southern branches of the Columbia; the route he indicated must lead to the Vermilion Sea or the Gulph of California. Turning to Cameahwait, he asked through the translators over what route the pierced-nose Indians went to buffalo land. The chief said they came down an almost impassable trail through heavy forest and fallen timber, where there was nothing to eat but a few berries. Lewis was thinking, If Indians can do it, taking women and children with them, we can do it! In his mind the route was settled, provided Clark did not find a waterway: they would go north through the forests and over the high mountains to the pierced-nose Indians. He wished Clark would send a messenger to tell him what he had found.

The morning of Wednesday, August 21st, he left his tent and looked round him and his anxiety grew. It was almost a white world. Ice had frozen a quarter of an inch thick in the kettles; wet deer skins that had been spread out were as stiff as boards. Even the ink for his pen had frozen. The coves and vales were so deep with frost that they seemed to be white with snow. He sent three men out to hunt and told the other men to get packsaddles and baggage ready to march. If it could freeze so hard in August, within a month the high mountain barrier might be impassable.

Another day passed and another, and still no word from Clark. Lewis saw that the red men were getting restless; they wanted to be off to buffalo land but the chief had promised to wait until the captains and their party had gone. To keep the Indians in a cheerful mood Lewis gave them generously of beans and corn, though his own men were on short rations. He gave the chief some dried squashes which had been brought all the way from the Mandan villages. Cameahwait had them boiled and then fed a big helping into his bony haggard face. He said it was the finest food he had ever eaten except a piece of sugar that his sister had given him. That little rascal! Had she been stealing sugar?

Another day passed and still there was no word from Clark. Lewis had his men take the canoes to the middle of the river and fill them with stones and sink them. Cameahwait said his men would not bother them if they were left on the bank but Lewis did not believe that. He figured that if they were filled with stones at the bottom of the river the red men would be too lazy to bring them up. He sent a man down the river to see if there was any sign of Clark, and when the man returned to report none, the captain forced his anxious and restless mind to dwell on matters that would interest his President. He observed and made note of all the ornaments these Indians had; in what manner they fished; how they made bows of elk or bighorn and spoons of bone; the ingenuity and patience spent on their leather shields, and on a dressed leather club, which he called the Poggamoggon.

Another day and another—two more nights of heavy frost—and still no Clark.

Lewis now decided to trade for more horses, convinced that they would have to go overland. He asked Cameahwait if his men would trade and was dashed by the response: his men, the chief said, would first have to see what the white man had to offer. At Fort Mandan the smiths had made some crude battle-axes. Lewis brought them out. The red men looked at them, hefted them, swung with them and were delighted. For an ax and two or three trinkets Lewis got a horse or a mule. He traded for nine horses and a mule, hired two, and told his men to pack and get ready to go. After the twelve beasts were laden he hired a score of squaws to shoulder the remainder of the baggage and set off down the trail Clark had taken, feeling, he told himself, inexpressible joy at again being on the way.

He had been on the march only an hour when an Indian rode up to tell him that back at his campsite one of his men was sick. Lewis halted his party and walked back two miles, to find Pete Wiser flat on his back with what Lewis diagnosed as colic. Ordway was with him. Lewis had brought a few medicines with him and now gave Wiser a huge dose of laudanum mixed with essence of peppermint. He was not at all surprised after half an hour to see the man stagger to his feet and hear him say, "I feel fine now, I'm ready to go."

Ordway said, "Captain Lewis, you're a better doctor than most doctors."

Lewis was pleased but he said nothing. He suspected that Wiser had been with the squaws, and he wondered what Clark's men were thinking, who had been taken away from them. On returning to his main party he found that the Indians had made camp for the night. He was vexed and angry but he made the best of it by gathering from Cameahwait more data on big-horned animals that lived high in the mountains.

The next morning he sent his best hunters out and about noon they returned with three deer, most of which Lewis gave to the Indians. It was during this hour that the squawman came shuffling up with an astounding piece of information which he gave as though it did not matter at all. Early this morning, he said, Cameahwait had sent some of his warriors over the mountains to the village, with orders to the Indians there to come at once, so that they could all leave for buffalo land. Doubting his ears, Lewis asked the squawman to repeat the words.

"And you've known this ever since early morning?" asked Lewis, turning red with anger and vexation. "Answer me!"

"Yes, Cap-n."

"And you waited all these hours to tell me? Do you realize, you damned dumb stupid fellow, what the consequences of this may be? And who told you this, anyway?"

"Me vife."

"Oh, your vife. Didn't she tell you to tell me?"

"Yes, Cap-n."

"But you didn't! Can you get it in your head that if they all go buffalo hunting we'll be stranded here? Can't you understand that the whole success of our enterprise depends on—but of course you can't or you wouldn't have waited seven hours to tell me! If they take all their horses on the hunt what will we do? Sit on our baggage?"

"I dunno, Cap-n."

"And I dunno why the Lord ever made men like you. Come."

Lewis hastened over to the Indian camp to call the three chiefs together but to put them in an agreeable mood he first smoked a pipe with them. After the smoking he asked through translators if they were men of their word. They said they were.

"All right, remind them that they promised to help us get our baggage over the mountains, or to Captain Clark, if he's building canoes. Ask if they made such a promise."

Looking crestfallen and shamed, Cameahwait admitted that they had.

"Then ask why he has told his people to come to the buffalo hunt. Explain to him—and be sure he understands this—that we'll not trade with them, we'll not bring weapons to them, we'll not be their friends if they break their promises to us. Ask him if what I told him on former occasions was true. Ask if I have ever lied to him or broken a promise. Ask if I've not generously shared our meat with them and all that we have. Ask if we haven't gone hungry so that they might eat. Ask——" Too filled with emotion to continue he broke off.

The minor chiefs were now speaking. According to the translators, they were saying, "Oh, it was the big chief! It was not us! We said no no, we have promised to help our white brothers; but the big chief, he said, we go hunt now. . . ."

Lewis was looking at the big chief, who was silent. "Ask him if what the other chiefs say is true."

The big chief, the translators said, admitted that he had done wrong—and the poor scrawny half-starved long-jawed fellow seemed at the point of tears. He had done the wrong only because his people were hungry, they were half-dead for want of something to eat besides berry cakes. He was sorry. He would break his promises no more.

"Tell him to countermand the order at once. Tell him to send his fastest rider."

Cameahwait summoned a young man. Lewis gave him a colorful handkerchief to speed him on his way and he rode into the west. Turning to his men, Lewis said they would now resume their march. He felt ill. He felt utterly miserable, not so much because he had had so little to eat as because he had again looked into the face of failure; it was just one damned thing after another: if it was not bruised and bleeding men in ice-cold water, or men weak from eating little but unnourishing berries, or impassable rivers and mountains then it was a stupid lubber like Charbonneau, who should have been left with the Mandan squaws.

The next day about noon Lewis looked round him and perceived that one of his squaws had disappeared. Had she run off with a hundred pounds of equipment? Calling his translators, he went to the head chief and demanded to know where the woman was. After a few moments Labiche turned to Lewis and said, "She back there have baby."

"Have baby! You mean she's having a child?"

"She have baby, come soon."

Again feeling that he must be losing his mind Lewis stared back down the trail and presently saw her coming, the hundred pounds of baggage on her back and a fresh babe in her arms. What in the world would Mr. Jefferson think of that! He went close to her to be sure that it was a child. It was a babe all right, swathed in a piece of soft buckskin, its little red face puckered up, its tiny black eyes squinting, its skull covered with black hair. The mother looked wan and tuckered out but when she saw the white chief looking at her babe she smiled. She had been gone, Lewis thought, not more than an hour, surely not more than two: in that time she had given birth and recovered all the lost ground, with a hundred-pound burden upon her shoulders! It was almost more than a man could believe.

As the party was approaching the Indian village John Colter rode in from the northwest. When Lewis saw him coming he broke into a run, stumbling and almost falling in his eagerness. At last here was news from Clark!

Colter handed Lewis a note which he read and reread. Then he looked up at the youth and said, "Is there any food down there?"

"No game, sir. We lived on chokecherries and red haws."

"No fish?"

"There's fish in the swift water but they're hard to catch."

"Is Captain Clark coming?"

"He's on his way, sir."

"Well, he offers two plans here: we buy more horses and go overland, or we divide the party and one group will try to go down the river, the other will go by horse over the mountains. Do you know which plan Captain Clark prefers?"

"Captain Clark and all the men with him prefer to go over the mountains. The river down there is so swift in places you just can't stand up in it. It's full of big rocks and riffles and falls. The mountains on both sides—well, nor man nor horse can walk on most of it. You can't tow boats—the river walls on both sides are straight up and there's no bank to walk on."

"Timber for canoes?"

"No, sir, none that's any good. Sergeant Gass, he tried all of it."

"Then we go over the mountains," Lewis said. "But they tell me there's no game there either. How far behind is Captain Clark?"

"About two days."

"Didn't you see any game on your ride over?"

"One crow, Captain. That's all."

"What have you been living on?"

"Berries."

"Ah, those delicious berries! I can smell them, taste them, feel them and at night I dream I'm drowning in berry pudding."

John Colter smiled. He had a nice frank eighteen-year-old smile. Lewis responded to it, thinking, Yes, if I were to have a son he would suit me. He would have suited Clark too: both captains had become fond of this quiet well-mannered youth who had in him more of the spirit of adventure than a hundred ordinary men.

With his translators Lewis now went to the chief and said he wanted to trade for more horses. He wanted twenty more, at least. The moment he understood what Lewis asked for the chief began to droop and look terribly woebegone. He said he hoped his people would be able to spare a few but he was not sure that they could, for they did not have many——

Impatiently Lewis cried, "Tell him not to insult me with such nonsense! I've seen his bands of horses, I know they have over seven hundred, yet no more than a hundred men. The squaws always walk. Ask him if each warrior can ride seven."

All this was communicated to the chief. Then the translator was saying, "The Earth House people—the warriors far away——"

"Yes, yes, the Big Bellies."

They stole many horses from the Shoshones, the chief said. His people had to have many horses for their enemies to steal.

"Oh, come now!" Lewis cried. "Tell him a battle-ax is of more use to him than a horse up a canyon waiting to be stolen. Tell him we'll give him axes for horses."

"Says he will talk to other chiefs. . . ."

Children! Lewis thought. Nothing but children! You had to treat an Indian as a child to get along with him. Though his men were weak from hunger he had them range far and wide around the village to gather wood for a big fire; and this evening he told his men to play the fiddle and dance. Before supper Lewis gave to the Indians a part of his corn and beans and then had his men eat in plain sight of them, so that they could see for themselves that the white men had no more than they. They could see for themselves that the white men were also gaunt with hunger. Lewis himself went supperless to bed, telling himself that early in the morning he must get the horses or he would never get them.

At daylight he was studying the list of Indian presents:

12	pipe tomahawks	2	doz: Earings
6½	lbs strips sheet iron	8	Brass Kettles a 4/ Per lb.
1	ps. red flannel 47½ yds	12	lbs Brass Strips
11	ps. hancherchiefs assd.	500	Broaches
1	doz. Ivory Combs	72	Rings
½	Catty Inda. S. Silk	2	Corn Mills
21	lbs. Tread assd.	15	doz: Scissors
1	ps. Scarlet Cloth 22 yds.	12	lbs Brass Wire
5½	doz fan: Floss	14	lbs Knitting Pins
6	Gro: Binding	4600	Needles assd.
2	Cards Beads	2800	Fish Hooks assd.
4	doz: Butcher Knives	1	Gro: Iron Combs
12	doz: Pocket Looking Glasses	3	Gro: Curtain Rings
15	doz. Pewter do. do.	2	Gro: Thimbles assd.
8	doz. Burning do.	11	doz: Knives
2	doz. Nonesopretty	10	lbs Brads
2	doz. Red strip'd tapes	8	lbs Red lead
72	ps. Strip'd silk ribbon	2	lbs Vermillion
3	lbs. Beads	130	Rolls of Tobacco (pig-tail)
6	Papers Small Bells		
1	box with 100 larger do.	48	Calico Ruffled Shirts
73	Bunches Beads assd	15	Blankets (from P. store)
3½	doz: Tinsel Bands assd	1	Trunk to pack sundry Ind: prests.
1	doz: Needle Cases		
2¾	doz Lockets	8	Groce seat or Mocka-sin Awls
8½	lbs Red Beads		

The captains had realized back in Fort Mandan that they had too many of some items and too few of others: eight gross of awls were a lot of awls and forty-six hundred needles were a lot of needles; but twelve tomahawks or four dozen butcher knives or a dozen ivory combs or two pounds of vermilion were only a fraction of what they should have brought. They had a lot of beads but they didn't have enough blue beads. Scarlet cloth and striped ribbon were not as popular as they had thought they would be. One brass kettle was worth more than ten gross of thimbles; one roll of tobacco more than a cartload of brooches. He imagined that they would be out of tobacco long before they got home: all but seven of the men used the stuff and some, like Paddy Gass, were never without a quid except when eating.

Well, by offering axes, knives, beads, mirrors, fish hooks, needles and old military garments he hoped to get enough horses to carry the baggage to the next navigable river. In his note Clark had suggested that he trade for the kind of horse that would do for both packing and eating, in case they were driven to eat their beasts; and so all day long Lewis haggled with the braves, his eyes in every instance scanning the animal's depth of shoulder, thigh and loin. The red men were not so eager for the white man's goods as when he first met them. He knew the reason: Sacajawea had filled their ears and minds with tales about the wealth of her captors, the Earth House people, who lived in warm lodges that shut out the cold; had huge gardens of plant food which they gathered and stored for the winter; and all the buffalo, elk, antelope and deer they could eat. She had told about their weapons, their clothing, their bedding, their ornaments. She had told of the many luxuries the white men had, who moved up and down the river to trade. And so her people, whose sole possession was horses, besides their crude weapons and leather garments, were determined to drive sharp bargains and take all that they could get. They wanted weapons above all but Lewis offered them only a few axes and knives and some pieces of iron and brass for arrowheads.

Thursday, August the 29th, there was an infernal din in the Shoshone village: a bold young brave who had gone away to seek a scalp had lost his own, and almost his life; and when his relatives saw him they set up a shrill wailing that could have been heard for two or three miles. It was the women, and the children imitating the women. Lewis walked over to learn what had caused all the racket and saw the young man with his bone-bald head and his face filled with shame. He was a picture for woe, all right: his enemies had taken more of the scalp than usual—had in fact skinned this man down to his ears and his nape. His skull was still raw and the sun had cooked it, the insects had been feeding on it. The women were making such horrible sounds that Lewis walked from one to another to look closely at their faces, wondering if this grief was dissembled or real. He knew it was put on when one of the wailing squaws caught his eye and suddenly fell silent. When she turned away he would have sworn that she was giggling.

A little later Clark and his men came in, ragged and gaunt and pale but quite cheerful, though for days they had lived on wild berries and a few fish, yet had climbed mountains every day. Lewis hurried over to his friend and searched the long lantern-jawed face. It looked leaner, harder and more determined than ever. What a lucky dog he was when he chose Will Clark as his partner!

The two captains went to their skin-tent. On the way over Clark said, "Captain Lewis, are we ready to go?"

Lewis smiled inside. Damn it, these Clark brothers really had the military spirit! His face grave, he said, "Almost ready, Captain Clark."

"We have enough horses?"

"Twenty-nine. We could use more but it would take a rifle to get another." After they had entered the tent he said, "The river is impassable?"

"Absolutely. Have you found any guides?"

Clark's manner was so grave, so stern almost, that Lewis was amused; but quickly, in fairness to his friend, he told himself that Clark had been away on a difficult and dangerous journey, climbing every day like a bighorn and living on berries!

"There's an old Indian here from some other tribe," Lewis said. "Uncle Toby, our men call him. He has agreed to go, and maybe his sons."

"He knows the land route?"

"I can't tell just how much he knows. He pretends to know a great deal. I think he knows the route to the pierced noses."

"That should be good enough," Clark said. "You agree that we should go north rather than south?"

"Beyond all question. Toby says the southern route is an inferno of waterfalls, chasms, vanishing rivers, waterless deserts and hostile Indians. The northern route, he says, is no picnic and there will be nothing to eat but berries."

"Berries," said Clark, and made a face. "When I get home I'll never eat another berry in all my life. For days we had nothing but chokecherries and red haws. They made us all sick. We puked and groaned and thought we'd die."

"Colter told me. Well, we still have some pork and corn meal. I'll have a cook fix you a bite."

When Lewis returned to the tent Clark said, "Haven't your hunters here had any luck?"

"Not much. A deer now and then. These starved Indians have chased all the game back into the mountains."

"I expect that's it."

"What's it like down the river?"

"Bighorn country. Real rugged."

"And north is timber country. When we find timber for boats we have no river. When we have the river there's no timber. I sometimes wonder about the Almighty's sense of humor."

When the cook brought a bowl of salt pork and meal gruel Lewis sat back and watched Clark eat, his mouth watering, for he was as hungry as a Shoshone Indian.

Clark said, "This tastes a lot better than haws. Aren't you eating with me?"

"I ate just a little while ago," Lewis said. He thought that would end it. He had forgotten Clark's capacity to astonish him at the most unexpected moments.

Perhaps a full minute passed in silence. During that minute Clark glanced once, quickly and sharply, at his friend's face. Then, quietly, without looking at Lewis, he said, "Merne, you're a damned liar."

Lewis was startled and then delighted. He wanted to go over and hug his friend but, masking his emotions, he said gravely, "I think I hear Sergeant Ordway calling." He rose and left the tent.

25

At daylight the next morning the white men left their beds. While the cooks were busy making a thin gruel for breakfast, other men brought the twenty-nine beasts in and on some of them cinched pack-saddles made of green deerhide thongs and canoe paddles. They interrupted their labor to drink a cup of gruel and then packed the beasts and turned them to face the northwest. The captains and their men now had to say goodbye to Cameahwait and his warriors, who again insisted on hugging every white man in turn. The farewell took an hour, and by the time it was concluded, the Corps was a scowling and rancid-smelling group of men. George Shannon, oblivious of all eyes, was sucking his cheeks back against his gums and grimacing with his lips as he stared down over his leather jacket. Every man among them detested what Lewis called the Shoshone national hug. Bob Frazier was saying, "Wonder how the New Hampshire girls would like that kind of squeeze." He looked round at the squaws and saw that some of the bolder ones were hugging York. Now and then the big black man would sweep one up off her feet and press his black skin to her copper-cheek, while Frazier stared incredulously at a dangling and kicking pair of bowed legs. Paddy Gass was wondering aloud in a muttering brogue how many Shoshone babies a year hence would have kinky hair.

Frazier was singing a farewell: "I hate to leave my Indian rose whose legs are shaped like wagon bows! If I come back, my valentine, O tell me, dear, wilt thou be mine? Across the mountains to the sea will bowlegged lassies follow me . . . ?"

Some of the men were laughing like mad at Frazier's nonsense, and the younger squaws, seeing them laugh, laughed too. When the Corps turned down the river half the Indian village trailed it, hoping for food or gifts or love. Among them was a small nephew whom Sacajawea had adopted, toddling at the side of the woman who had been captured with her years ago. By late afternoon of the second day all the trailing Indians turned back. The two captains, again emotionally stirred in spite of themselves, watched the slave-girl say farewell to her friend and her nephew. It was such a tearful frenzied parting that Lewis's inner voice spoke to him, saying, "This impassive surface of the red man is only skin-deep, yet how it deceives all but the most discerning! For see this girl, crying as if her heart had broken; and this small lad clinging to her, his face all wet with tears!"

He turned to Clark. "Who started the idea that the red man isn't emotional?"

"He certainly is emotional," Clark said. "Maybe that's why he wears a mask."

"Our little squaw," Lewis said, still watching the farewell, "seems to arouse great devotion in those who love her."

"I expect she's had a lot to tell her people."

"Too much," Lewis said. "She made my horse-trading almost impossible. It takes so little to arouse greed in the human breast."

"They have so little that they have a lot of room for wanting."

"She acts to me like she doesn't intend to come back to her people. You suppose she intends to go back with us?"

"I was wondering."

"This is no goodbye for just a few months. This is farewell."

Down the main river the party went thirty miles and then turned up a creek that emptied into it from the north. All the Indians had left them now except old Toby and one of his sons. Toby said the route lay up this creek but there was no sign of a path and after a mile or so the brush was so dense that the men had to cut their way through it. How far, they wondered, would they have to swing axes in deep thickets, on thin gruel and berries? They looked to the right, to the left, and saw hillsides of stone fencing them in: either they would chop their way through the creek growth or risk their horses trying to climb to higher ground. By the second evening after leaving the Indians, Clark was gloomily writing in his Journal that the pack-beasts were in perpetual danger of "Slipping to their certain distruction & up and Down Steep hills, where Several horses fell, Some turned over, and others Sliped down Steep hill Sides, one horse Crippeled & 2 gave out. with the greatest difficuelty risque &c. we made five miles & Encamped."

Both captains felt terribly discouraged. If they averaged only five miles a day winter would catch them in the mountains—and Lord O Lord, what mountains these were! The mountains in the United States were only hills by comparison. Each morning they sent hunters out but there was no sign of game here, nor any sign of fish in this creek. They were all on extremely short rations of salt pork, corn meal and berries—and it was chiefly berries. Some of the men were so sick of berries that they gagged them down and immediately vomited them up. Those with axes, chosen from the strongest, labored from dusk to dusk, their faces gaunt and pale, their bellies empty. They had thought it would be heaven to get out of the cold wild-running Jefferson River, where all day long they slipped and fell, half-frozen and half-drowned. But swinging an ax all day, with nothing to eat but two ounces of pork, two ounces of meal, and berries —this was worse, this would do a man in in no time. The captains each had a horse to ride but no man could ride a horse in such hellish thickets. They climbed up out of the creek; turned to the east and then back to the west, looking for an easier route. The impassive and timeless Toby refused to scale the steep and dangerous hillsides with them. This was the path, he said. This was the only way to the pierced noses.

If, standing above the creek and looking round him, Lewis or Clark heard a sudden loud curse he would say to himself, "Another horse has fallen." They started with twenty-nine and already had left three behind them. Clark had wondered if they should not eat them but then learned that some of the men were sentimental about horses. "They'll come to it," Lewis said. "These mountains will take the squeamishness out of any man."

Only Paddy Gass was really cheerful. A carpenter, he loved woods, he loved trees, and here he found a most extraordinary tree to love. It was a species of pine that grew tall, and as straight as a rifle barrel, sometimes without a limb in the first sixty feet. There were vast forests of this tree and what forests they were! Paddy would stand for five or ten minutes just looking up at trees, marveling at their perfection; or he would marvel at the way the big bushes were laden with dead-ripe serviceberries and chokecherries. A man could stand and fill his belly in a few minutes, feeding with both hands, though on a serviceberry now and then there was a tiny reddish bug that had a most horrible taste.

The next day, the 3rd of September, they broke their last thermometer when a horse fell and rolled. They climbed up a mountainside of loose stone; went over the crest and down into another creek; and then for hours fought their way through creek growth, covering in all that time only two miles. This was the worst country, Clark told himself, that he had ever seen horses traverse—and on military expeditions he had seen horses in all kinds of places. The mountains to the east of them were white. At dusk of this day it began to snow and snow fell steadily until it was two inches deep, and all the brush was bowed and white-laden. The men this night sat around a big fire in the storm. They had no wish for fiddle music, no wish to dance: they were bone-weary with fatigue and hungry clear through their marrow. The cooks had announced that even the corn meal would soon be gone. Each man for supper had a tin cup of thin gruel, a tiny piece of salt pork—and yes, O Lord, all the berries he could eat! Sacajawea, carrying her seven-month child and her own baggage, hustled busily from morning to night gathering berries—and the men were grateful, knowing that she would pick only the ripest and fattest ones; knowing that she would not pick those with the red bug on them or the wormhole. They were grateful but just the sight of berries made some of them gag. Oh, for a haunch of venison, a hind quarter of fat elk, a buffalo hump or a beaver tail! And why, oh why, were there no beaver in any of these streams?

John Colter, a trapper at heart, said he had thought of that. He figured that the Indians had eaten them all.

"There should be otter," Alex Willard growled. "All the salmon in the river down there and no otter? What does the Almighty think he's doing?"

A number of the men looked at Alex, some of them amused, some shocked.

Bratton was lying on his back looking up into a wilderness of snowflakes. He had been fat at Fort Mandan but he was not fat now: his elkskin sagged down over his gaunt belly, his cheeks were sunken. "Holy grandma," he said. "I'm sickern a dog tonight."

Reuben Fields said, "All I have to do, I just say, Look at that great big beautiful bush of sarvisberries and I bend over double like a jackknife."

"O God," someone groaned. "Now you've started me all over again."

"Them great big beautiful sarvisberries."

"Serviceberries," Shannon said.

"Listen to Mr. Knows Most. It's about time he got lost again."

"What I want to know," said Willard, the young man who as a child had run away from home, "is what do the pierced noses eat?"

"Dogs," Reuben said.

"Dogs?"

"Toby said, but I think he's a liar. He's so old his mind is gone."

"Berries and fish," Shannon said.

"No big game?"

"Dogs," Reuben said. "Big fat waddling dogs."

There was silence. Then Frazier said, "Where did Sergeant Ordway say his Betsy lives? These beautiful squaws make me think of Betsy. Oh tell me, sirs, do you suppose that Betsy's legs are wagon bows?"

There were snorts and snickers.

George Shannon spoke next. He had more education than all but two or three of the men. Lapping snowflakes into his boyish mouth, he said: "You mean the sacrifice at the shrine of Hymen?"

"Hymen, that's it. What city does she live in?"

"She's Ordway's gal," Bratton said. "Get your mind offen her."

"She blisses me up," Frazier said. "Everywhere I see dimples. A gal who writes to a man that way——"

"Has bowlegs," Reuben growled. "We know what's on your mind."

"I'll tell you. It's the smell of sarvisberries. If I belch, it's sarvisberries. If I sneeze——"

"It's sarvisberries."

"Dogs," Alex Willard said. "I don't know as I could eat a dog. When I was a little shaver I had a dog and he was like a mother to me. He got killed."

"You have me bawling," Frazier said. "What killed your mother?"

George Shannon said a man would eat anything before he would starve to death.

"Even his own children, you say?"

"Some people in the Bible did."

"What I want to know," Frazier said, "is not the Bible. It's squaws."

He broke into song: "A darling with dimples up and down from her waist is just like a dream-girl who's built to my taste! A squaw with deep saucers all over her—ump——"

Some of the men snorted.

"Her ump!" Hugh McNeal cried, and folded with laughter.

The next morning the captains perceived that the morale of their men was the lowest it had yet been. It was a cold night, so cold that they had all found their moccasins frozen. The wilderness around them was white. So little food was left, and there was so little hope of finding anything but berries that the men were told there would be no breakfast. Clark had said to Lewis that they might as well test their men right now, for if they were going to break it should be not too far from buffalo land. While the cooks told the men there would be no breakfast the captains sharply observed their faces. Not a man among them seemed to wince. Not a man seemed to care.

In the presence of most of the men Clark said to Drewyer, "Take the best hunters and go. It's perfect tracking and if there's a living thing around you'll find it."

The other men packed the horses and set off. Sacajawea, with her child on her back and a pail in her hand, entered the silent white woods and disappeared. Charbonneau, sullen and sniffling with a cold, was at the tail end. A little before noon Drewyer came in with a deer across his shoulder and the party halted for breakfast. The deer dressed out only about thirty pounds of flesh but that was almost a pound to each person. Old Toby and his son devoured the stomach, the lungs and all the small guts and then sucked at the bones and hide.

When the party marched again Frazier said to Shannon, who walked at his side, "I can't figure it. At the falls the captains refused to take the north river but took the south river and we went south to hell and gone. Now we're going back north. Why didn't we go straight across?"

"We had no horses," George said.

"We could have carried the stuff a few miles a day and still saved time."

"If you're an expert geographer why don't you lead the party?"

Frazier turned to look at him. "Smart, aren't you? So damned smart it makes sense to you to go four hundred miles south and then four hundred miles north, when all the time we want to go west."

George said patiently, "The captains are looking for a transconti-nental water route."

"Honest?" said Frazier, sneering. "I thought they were looking for the ocean."

Both captains were agonizing over the matter that Frazier and some of the other men were raising in their own minds. It was true that from the falls on the Missouri they had gone hundreds of miles south by southwest and were now going back north. Old Toby said they would have to go north five or six sleeps. In the minds of the captains the journey from the falls to the point where they would cross over the divide stood as a great V and they wondered how far it was across the top of the V. Was there any waterway there? The Big Bellies had said there was not. If they had gone up Maria's River would they have had to travel so far? Other questions tormented them as they pushed across this nightmare of wilderness and stone, watching their men grow weaker day by day and sensing in themselves a steady sapping of their strength. The risk of failure was now so great, the danger that they would all perish in these mountains so menacing, that all day long day after day Jefferson's words stood as a warning light in Lewis's mind—"To your own discretion therefore must be left the degree of danger you may risk. . . ."

He recalled the words when he caught the men looking at him; when he saw the pallor of fatigue and exhaustion in their starved faces; when he heard their attempts to jest and keep their hearts up; when he heard some of them muttering in their sleep. Was he risking too much? He was afraid that it might be so. He did not put the question to Clark and Clark did not put it to him. For both captains this was no time to ask questions to which there was no answer. It was a time to push on with the last of their strength and reach a safe haven.

They never dreamed that Three Eagles, head chief of another tribe, which they were to call the Tushepau, had his black eyes fixed on them. He was on his way with his people to buffalo land when one of his scouts brought astounding news: yonder in the deep timber was a strange party of warriors, moving forward in a long thin line of pack-animals, with one squaw and a child, and a tall man painted black. Was only one of them painted for war? the chief asked. Only one. And they had a squaw with them? What kind of war-party was this?

He himself went stealthily forth and his astonishment was great when he perceived that only one was painted for war, that a squaw trudged with them with a child on her back, and that not a man among them wore a blanket. Had they been robbed?

It was so mysterious that the chief ordered that all his party's horses should be driven within camp and all weapons made ready. Then he waited. These incredible men with their pale faces did not send scouts ahead, but came right on as if they owned the whole world! Where were they going? Where had they come from?

The white men had no idea that a band of Indians was just ahead of them until suddenly thirty-three Indian lodges were before them and friendly Indians were rushing toward them, shouting cries of welcome or joy and offering them buffalo robes, fine white robes, which the red men threw over the white men's shoulders. A little later men, red and white, were sitting round a fire smoking and staring at one another. Off and on the red chief harangued his people but the white chiefs didn't know what he was saying. The language these Indians spoke was unlike any that the white men had ever heard: it was a kind of gugling speech, Clark was to say in his Journal. For most of the men it was a speech with a strange impediment —a brogue, one said; a bur on the tongue, according to another.

Lewis said, "I expect maybe these are the Welsh Indians."

For generations there had been widespread belief that a tribe of Welsh Indians lived somewhere in the Western Hemisphere. Away back in 1170, the story said, a Welsh prince named Madoc had dared the wide ocean and had discovered the new world. Returning to his homeland, he had raised a large company and had again sailed west. The legend said that the descendants of this colony still had white skins, still spoke Welsh, though another legend said they had become indistinguishable from the red people. With a twinkle in his eye the tall gangling redheaded Tom Jefferson had said to Lewis, "Keep your eye open for the Welsh Indians." Did he really believe the story? Lewis had asked; and the President had replied, "I neither believe nor disbelieve where I have no evidence. There are strange things in the world. This may be one of them."

Lewis neither believed nor disbelieved but he told himself that *if* the story was true and if these were the Welsh Indians, who made such weird gurgling sounds in their throats, it was his duty to record as much of their language as he could. John Shields said he was Welsh: he listened to the gurgling speech and shook his head no, this was no language he had ever heard. Lewis summoned Shannon to assist him. Making the chief understand that he wanted to know by what sounds they called things, he pointed to a tree, a horse, a man and to many other objects around him; George Shannon spelled the sound as phonetically as he could, and Lewis wrote it down. All the men gathered round, curious, staring. Were these actually Welsh people?

"We think perhaps they are," Sergeant Ordway wrote in his Journal; and Private Whitehouse wrote: "We take these savages to be the Welsh Indians."

The captains gave medals to the chief and his principal men, and two flags, and tried to tell them who they were and why they were here; but all the translators together couldn't get over the language barrier. And so they talked in sign language. Then the captains traded for eleven horses, and seven of their own for stronger beasts. These Indians, Clark wrote, "possess ellegant horses," and he foresaw that now, with stronger mounts, their journey over the mountains would be less difficult. From his deep contempt for the British, Lewis was now willing to exempt the Welsh.

The next day was cold; water froze, and snow fell in the uplands. After the trading, after Lewis was done with recording words, the party climbed again, following the Indian trail. The red men had had only dried or fresh berries and a little dried salmon; they too were weak and starved, and eager to get to buffalo land. The day the white men left them they ate the last of their flour and the next day had nothing but berries, a few pounds of corn meal and some soup being held in reserve. "Chokecherries!" the men said, standing by tall bushes and stuffing the purple astringent fruit into their mouths and crushing the bitter pits between their teeth. Others, too sick to eat, watched them, in the way men will when starved and enfeebled and thinking of death. "The red man eats bark," someone said. "Why don't we?" Some of them ate bark. They said it tasted like old leather soaked in turpentine. Some searched the earth for roots but knew there were none or Sacajawea would find them. Some stared at the cheerful girl and her cheerful child. It beat hell out of the moon, one of them said, how she kept going. Did Clark slip her some food from the hoard?

"You ought to choke on that," John Colter said.

"Shut up," Hugh McNeal said. "All this useless jabber uses up your sap."

They ate only berries the next day, only the bitter acid choke-cherry, but they still moved forward, creeping like a line in slow

motion, covering less than a mile in an hour. The next day the hunters brought in some meat. It was not much but it was enough to give
each man a small piece, with three or four pounds left for breakfast the next morning. The next morning the hunters set off in a world
of white-and-dark and returned after two hours with three geese.
After Toby and his son had eaten their portions they sucked the juice
off the feather ends; they skinned the lower legs and feet and ate
the skin and sucked at the bones; and the white men sat and
watched them. They hardly knew what to think when they saw the
old Indian pull the tongues out of the mouths and eat them and
break the jaws apart and suck at the throat.

Toby now told them that east from here it was only four or five
sleeps to the Missouri. The men tried to figure up the number of
days since they had turned south from the falls: it was fifty-four, one
said; another argued that it was fifty-seven. The captains said it was
fifty-two. Fifty-two days, and straight across it was only five!

"I tell you we could have carried the stuff that far."

George Shannon said, "Who knew it was only that far? We're in
an unmapped land."

"Fifty-two days up that damn ice-cold river!"

"Forty-seven days, that's what we lost."

The party was now going down a river and a valley. Toby said
they should leave the river and turn west, and so where a creek
dumped into it the captains pitched camp and decided to let the
horses fill up and the men hunt. This spot they called Travellers Rest.
It was Monday, September the 9th.

The next morning Lewis sent out all the best hunters—Drewyer,
the Fields brothers, Colter, Collins, Shannon, Goodrich and a few
others. He told them to go as far as they felt they could but to be
in camp by evening. With Clark he spent most of the day taking
observations, pausing at bushes to eat cherries, and twice accepting
a few roots which the slave-girl brought to the captains. They speculated on the length, direction and headwaters of this river they had
been following, and the river not far away which Toby said it emptied into. Toward evening they were startled to see John Colter coming to camp with three Indians.

He told them this story. He had been hunting along a creek when
suddenly he saw these three red men, forty or fifty yards away, looking at him and putting arrows to their bows. Knowing that they intended to kill him, he quickly laid his gun down and with hands

above his head advanced toward them. With arrows aimed at him they waited till he came up. In sign language he convinced them that he was their friend, and that a whole party of their friends had come a long way to see them. This had warmed the Indians and made them talkative. They had made him understand that twenty-three of their finest horses had been stolen by the Shoshones. They were on their way to avenge the loss.

"So that," said Lewis, "is how the Snakes get all their horses!"

He decided that these three Indians were Tushepaus. When the hunters came in with three deer he asked the Indians to remain for supper. In sign language they said they were not hungry. Because any Indian in this area who said he was not hungry was a liar the captains kept a sharp eye on them, and were not at all surprised when two of the red men ran out of the camp and disappeared. The third one sat eating and looking nervously round him. Lewis moved over by him and called Drewyer and had Drewyer ask the Indian if he would serve as a guide. Lewis offered him a tomahawk and a knife. "Find out where his people are," he said. Drewyer and the Indian talked in signs; they made drawings on the earth, they pointed, they used their fingers, their arms, even their feet. Drewyer said that this man's people were beyond the mountains, on a large river, down which canoes could be ridden clear to the ocean. The canoe journey, the Indian said, would take only five sleeps. It would take four sleeps over the mountains.

Some of the men had been listening. One of them said, "You hear that? Only nine days to the ocean! What is this?—September tenth? Think of it! September nineteenth we'll be there!"

"Walking on water like St. Peter?" asked Frazier.

"Only nine days?" Silas Goodrich said. "In nine days we'll be there?"

"Yes, yes," Frazier said. "A ship will be waiting for us loaded with Virginia hams and Pennsylvania whisky. There'll be a whole ton of tobacco, five white women for each one of us, and letters from our mothers."

Several of the men came up and looked at Frazier. They looked over his face—at his golden-brown beard; his mouth; his eyes; his long tangled hair hanging down his shoulders; and again at his eyes. They were eyes, George Shannon decided, full of mockery and lunacy. He asked himself, "Are we all going crazy?"

He said to Frazier, "You think you should lie down awhile?"

"He's got it figured out," Joe Whitehouse said. "A ton of tobacco and five white women for each one of us is just right."

"I forgot to tell you mountain pirates," Frazier said, "that President Jefferson will be on the ship to welcome us."

"The British ambassador with him, I suppose," George Shannon said.

"Blondes or brunettes?"

"Two blondes, two brunettes and one redhead for each man."

"Mither uv God!" Paddy Gass said. "All that and Virginia ham."

Frazier said, "And the complete works of Shakespeare."

The next morning the third Indian vanished and again the party had only Toby to guide it. Two horses had strayed off and got lost, and almost the entire day was spent looking for them. Hunters went out and returned empty-handed. Late in the afternoon the party moved up the creek, and after about seven miles camped on an old Indian site, with white mountains on the left.

They all went to bed without supper. They all rose at daylight and without breakfast set off again, up over hills and down into canyons with fallen timber everywhere. This path, Clark said to Lewis, was simply intolerable, and so he scouted to the left, to the right, but again there was a choice of only two ways—along the creek through almost impassable growth and fallen timber, or up the steep rocky mountainsides where horses were likely to slip and roll. The men in the lead encamped at dark, built a fire and waited for the stragglers to come in. The tail end did not arrive until ten o'clock, and both men and beasts were staggering. Looking round him, the exhausted but undaunted Clark observed to Lewis that both men and horses were much fatigued. This day the men had had little to eat, the beasts nothing at all. There was no grass. There was not a thing a horse could eat, save a few leaves hanging to bushes, these and twigs.

The next morning the weary but cheerful hunters again climbed the mountains, and returned with a small deer and a few grouse. The men ate breakfast and grinned at one another, though in the belly of every one the lean meat was like a physic. After a mile or two the party came to hot water steaming out from a stone ledge. Indians had shaped a basin into which the water ran, and in that some of the men sat naked, to ease their aching feet and bones. It was good to feel hot water again.

York shoved his black legs in up to the knees and made sounds of delight. He said a man nevah knowed what was bestest till it was all took away. Hot water was bestest now.

"Bath-un and woman-un," someone said.

The old cud, Paddy said, that was best. A man jist warn't a man without his old chaw of terbakky.

"The mother of Shannon!" Frazier cried. "Look!" He pulled a foot up from the heel of which a great roll of calloused hide half an inch thick was peeling off.

Reuben said, "It's all the dead weight you carry around that tuckers you out."

"Especially in his head," said Alex Willard.

The next morning it was raining and the rain turned to hail. On the high mountains all around them snow was falling. By noon they knew they had again crossed the continental divide, for they saw a small stream flowing west. This creek, the captains said, was surely a tributary of what they called the Kooskooskee River. The party staggered along for eleven miles this day and then halted when Lewis saw that some of the men were falling in their tracks. He looked north, west and south to the vast curving masses of mountain ranges and spurs, the watersheds, the craggy peaks, the enormous hogbacks, swinging in tremendous curves and falling down, lost, into the dim deep canyons. There were peaks, he judged, that rose ten thousand feet or more, and deep saddles lying four or five thousand feet below them. It was a fearful view for weak men. So far as he could tell, the immense slopes of the main backbones of the system had been cut deep, as though by ancient glaciers or by millions of years of wind and weather. The general ruggedness of it was little short of terrifying.

He went to Clark and Clark said, "I expect we better kill a colt."

"First, let's climb that hill and see what we can see."

But they saw only what they had seen—saw this stupendous mountain barrier lying upon the eastern and western watersheds. Most of it was on the western side. Nowhere around them could they see the smoke of campfires, or sign of life. How far would they have to go before they again found food? They had only three colts. They had lost a number of their horses and needed all that they now had, and more, to carry their baggage.

"Some of our men are pretty weak," Lewis said.

"Pretty weak," Clark said. "I don't think Bratton can even get up."

"Yes, I expect we'd better kill a colt."

They went down to the camp and walked among the men to see which of them seemed strongest. Bratton was stretched out like a dead man. So was Whitehouse. So were Potts and Labiche and Wiser and several others. The Fields brothers were moving around, Colter, Shannon, Frazier, Willard, Drewyer, Collins and the three sergeants.

To Ordway, Clark said, "Choose some men and dress out the fattest colt."

And so this evening they all dined on boiled horse flesh and stared round them at pine, spruce and tamarack and breathed the aroma of these woods, around them and from the fire. This tall country smelled good. They were about seven thousand feet up, the captains said; the air was sharp, the smoke of burning pine and spruce had a wonderful clean scent. Roundabout were the horses, all their ribs plain under their stark hides, their bony faces reaching up as bared teeth seized a few leaves or a twig. The Lewis dog had filled himself with stuff from the colt that not even Toby and his son wanted and now lay moaning, a shaggy listless half-dead thing: he didn't have the energy even to bark any more and he never ran or trotted but merely walked.

Still, nearly all the men felt cheerful tonight. There would be a part of the colt left for breakfast, but even better than that, they were again on the western watershed, most of the time they would be going downhill. If it was a hundred and fifty miles to food could they make it on the flesh of two more colts? Most of those who talked about it thought so.

The next morning they went into a deep vale and then had to climb a steep mountain. Some of the men thought they would never make it. They thought most of the horses would never make it. One horse after another lost his footing on slippery stones and fell and rolled; and one of them, on whose saddle was strapped Clark's small desk, tumbled over and over down the mountain for fifty yards. Watching him roll, Clark said, "There goes my desk." The horse fetched up against a tree. With three of the strongest men Clark went down to it and stood a few moments looking at the beast's eyes —eyes so wide open that a lot of the white was showing; eyes full of terror. Poor dumb thing! Clark thought, and bent over to look at his desk. It had been smashed to kindling. They got the horse to his feet and were astonished to observe that he did not seem to be hurt at all. He didn't even limp. "No bones broke?" Reuben said, feeling over him. Clark led him and the men prodded him or put their shoulders to his thighs to boost him up, and when they were back with the main party they unbound the pack and hurled the pieces of desk down the mountain.

Some of the other men, with Lewis at their head, had been down after other horses that had slipped and rolled. Only one horse limped of five that had fallen. This would have seemed a miracle to men strong and well-fed but to these gaunt men who trembled with hunger and fatigue nothing was miraculous any more. They hadn't the strength to think about such things. All they wanted was to get out of these damned mountains before they all lay down with the horses and died.

They fought their way to the top of this backbone and then searched wearily up and down its crest for water. There was none. They went down and climbed again. They would melt snow, Clark said, for even if they did not eat they had to drink. Colter came in with two grouse and some of the men looked at him under lowered brows, wondering if perhaps he had killed three birds and eaten one. Why were the hunters all so strong? And of what use were two small birds for thirty-five hungry people? The captains brought out a few tins of what they called portable soup: it was a thin tasteless broth that all the men detested but they drank half a cupful, ate their tiny portion of grouse and, rolling under blankets with a gentle snow falling to whiten them over, sank again into sleep.

Three hours before daylight the snow really set in and it came down steadily all day. Even by daylight it was four inches deep on the old snow. Clark was the first man up but a few moments after he left his bed all the men were pulling on their cold frozen moccasins. They had all slept in their leather clothing. They were all pulling on their moccasins but the squawman. Sacajawea always had to arouse her man, for he was lazy, among the Big Bellies he had got the habit of sleeping late. There was nothing to eat this morning, and so no reason to tarry: as soon as the beasts were packed Clark moved off at the head of the column and discovered right away that following the Indian trail was difficult because of the new snow. It was a heavy deep storm now, into which he could see less than a hundred feet, or not that far when he looked through forest. It was not a cold day; the big flakes clung to the men and melted, and by noon most of their clothing was soaked through. Clark decided to halt and build a fire to dry them out. Besides, he had seen a few bunches of pine grass above the snow and wanted the horses to graze it.

He moved around stiffly while some of the men got a fire going, telling himself that never in his life had he been colder and wetter. He could hear the shussh of water in his moccasins when he stepped; could feel the cold damp where the underside of leather hugged his skin. He was afraid his feet would freeze. Deciding that the best thing for him was to walk as rapidly as he could, he told Lewis that he was going on ahead; and with his rifle across his wet arm he looked for a moment at the men around him. It was significant both of what he was and of his power to judge men that he called to John Colter. At a brisk pace the two of them walked about six miles, when, seeing a spot that would make a good campsite, Clark said, "I expect we better not go any farther or they'll never catch up."

"Captain, shall I go back and help them?"

Clark looked at John a moment—looked as a father might look at a son in whom he saw what he had hoped for. "No, it's too far to go back. Let's get a nice fire going. They'll see the smoke," he said, looking up through the trees, "and it will give them comfort."

While gathering wood for fires Clark now and then glanced at the youngster laboring with him—for even now he was barely eighteen years old. But he was all man. He was one of the three or four best hunters in the party—fearless, resourceful, self-reliant. There was no swagger in John Colter, no brag. If a job was to be done he was always ready to tackle it. He was always cheerful. Yes, Captain William Clark would have been proud to have a son like him.

Lewis meanwhile was encouraging his men to keep going. Now and then one would sink into the snow by the way, with a look on his face that said, "I'm a goner, I am! This is the end of me!" But when Lewis approached and said, "Get up from there," the man staggered to his feet somehow, a foolish little grin of shame back in his beard. They were still no more than halfway to the smoke of Clark's fire when two men were down, and then five; and Lewis, himself almost too feeble to stand, tottered back up and down the line saying, "Get up from there. . . . Get up from there. . . ."

Suspecting that Lewis was having trouble, Clark told Colter to keep the fire up and he would go back up the trail.

"Captain, do you want me to go?"

"I'll go," Clark said.

He was barely out of sight when he heard a sound off in the woods and, looking over, saw four deer standing broadside. He began to tremble a little and knew then how weak he was. Quickly bringing his rifle up, he pressed the trigger but there was no explosion. He pressed it again and kept pressing it, and seven times his gun failed to fire. Beside himself with vexation, he examined the gun and found that the flint was loose but before he could adjust it the deer were gone. "I'll be damned!" he said. That was as profane as Will Clark had ever been, for he thought that profanity, like obscenity, showed weakness of character. He was terribly vexed with himself. He stood a long moment looking over at the clearing where four fat deer had stood and looked at him. What, he wondered grimly, if it had been a grizzly facing him! He turned back up the trail, telling himself that he had better take care of his gun, he had better get possession of himself. What was happening to him and the men, anyway?

After a mile or so he saw Lewis coming toward him. He thought his friend was staggering. He waited till Lewis came up when, looking sharply at his face, he said, "Captain Lewis, I think you are badly fatigued."

So tired that he thought he would die, Lewis nevertheless was amused. He drew his cheeks back in a bearded grin. "Captain Clark, you were never more right in your life. I trust that you have supper ready."

"And so I might, if I hadn't been so stupid. Four fat deer within forty paces and I snapped my gun seven times."

Lewis was about to say, "Didn't two or three times tell you something was wrong?" but held his tongue. Some of the men had come up and had heard Clark's statement.

Joe Fields said, "Where, Captain? Where did they go?"

"They went," Clark said. "They're gone now."

"I could track them in the snow."

"It'll soon be dark, but come, I'll show you where they were." After Joe had taken the deer trail and vanished the captains walked in single file with Clark leading. Lewis said he supposed some of the men were down back along the trail but he had told them so many times to get up that he had decided to leave them, thinking that if left alone they would find the strength to rise and walk again.

Clark said, "I expect we better kill another colt tonight."

"I expect so," Lewis said.

"How many are falling?"

"About half of them."

Were the captains wondering if the entire party might perish here high in the mountains? If they were they would not have said so. They were not the kind of men who talked about such things. They knew that plain recognition of possible defeat always gave hostages to the enemy.

Clark looked up at a tree and said, "We could make canoes of this timber."

"All we need," said Lewis, "is a river."

Instead of smiling at the witticism Clark said gravely, "I figure it can't be much farther."

"Not much," Lewis said. "We'll sup heartily on fat colt steaks to-night and all feel like new men in the morning. I'm sure all the men are cheerful, even if a little weak."

"There's the fire," Clark said.

"Good old fire," said Lewis. "How many people in the world know what a wonderful thing fire is?"

"Provided," Clark said, "it's the right size in the right place."

26

Except Joe Fields, the last of the men came staggering in, after another colt had been butchered and most of the men were sitting round a big fire, with boiled flesh and hot broth in their tin dishes. Bob Frazier was looking speculatively at the scarecrows standing roundabout. "Look at them crowbait," he said. "I could eat a whole horse at one meal." All the men now looked at the horses, standing with one thigh fallen, heads down, razor backs wet from the snow, ribs coming up as stark as slats with each breath.

Now and then some of the men glanced at their captains to see how they were feeling. They found it impossible to tell. They seemed nearly always to be cheerful and to look on misfortune with such indifference or contempt that the men would have been ashamed to utter a complaint. The few of them who looked deeper, like Shannon, Pryor and Sacajawea, knew that Captain Lewis was not all right. They knew that he was sick. They suspected that he was living on pure grit. He was forcing the boiled flesh down but they saw him with a hand to his mouth trying to hide his nausea. Yes, he was living on nerve, but so were most of them. Instead of making Shannon feel better the meat made him ill. As was his way, he sat quietly looking round him from face to face and at last fixing his gaze on the slave-girl. She seemed about the same as always, even though she starved herself for her child. Clark had the cooks give the child half an adult's portion, but even so, the mother gave it a part of her own. The men had given up trying to figure out from what source came this small woman's strength. As for the child, it was a wonderful little boy, George thought: though still unable to walk Pomp would clap his hands and shriek with glee when the men danced. But the men weren't dancing any more. Even at the man-killing Great Falls portage they had danced but they were too weak now. Thoughtfully for a few moments George looked inside himself at his muscles and bones: yes, he was too weak now. Lord, thought of dancing filled him with nausea!

He was still looking at the Indian girl when suddenly she met his gaze and flashed a smile. He liked her smile but he wished she wouldn't smile at the men when her man was watching. The jealous fool hadn't struck her since Clark chastised him but George felt that he was hoarding his resentment and would beat the daylights out of her once he had her alone. Charbonneau had not seen the smile she gave George. The squawman had his face down in his tin cup, his long tongue licking up the morsels.

It was nearly midnight when Joe Fields came in, walking erect and firm. What a man he was! George Shannon thought, watching him come. He and Drewyer and two or three others seemed never to tire. Oh yes, Drewyer had tired, but Joe never. He had followed them for miles, Joe said, but had never caught a glimpse of them, nor of any living thing. There were not even birds in these woods.

The next morning the party set forth without breakfast and after a few miles found themselves out of the main range of the mountains; but the terrain was still rugged and strewn over with fallen timber. The horses were so weak that they would no longer step over a log without being shoved from behind; and if one of them fell it practically had to be lifted before it would make an effort to stand. It was the sullen behavior of the horses that angered some of the men: did the damned fools want to lie down here and die? Then they heard their philosophic captain say:

"I expect the will to live is in exact proportion to the intelligence."

The men gathered round a fallen beast looked over at their captain and considered his words. One of them said, "If that's true, this horse hasn't any brains at all."

"Less than a dog," Lewis said.

The men looked over at the wet shivering dog, sitting on his skinny rump. Reuben said, "Then a really dumb guy don't care if he lives or not."

"About like a horse," Joe Whitehouse said.

This was a party of geniuses, Lewis said. They would all live for ever. Whether he had chosen his words, as Shannon suspected tha he sometimes did, to cheer his men none of them knew but they felt better. Shannon pushed ahead to Clark and told him what Lewis had said. Did the captain think that was true?

"I'd never thought about it but I expect it might be."

"It gives you something to think about," George said.

Clark glanced at him and said sternly, "It gives you reason to stay on your feet."

This day the hunters found no game except three birds that they called pheasants. The only thing the party had to butcher was a rack of bones called a horse but they needed all their horses for the baggage. Even as it was, with less than a hundred pounds on each beast, the horses staggered and fell all day long. The worst part of it, the men had now decided, was getting the horses up; for again and again after one was lifted it shuddered and closed its eyes and sank. The men went supperless to bed tonight, all of them restless with pain. If they could have been warm it would have helped but they had to kick the snow away and spread their blankets on the wet cold earth, and all night they shivered, because they had no resistance to cold, being so starved and enfeebled.

Clark was thinking, while lying in his cold blankets, I must take a few men and push on ahead or we'll all die here. He would take the best hunters; two or three of the strongest horses to carry their baggage; and they would all fan out so that they would walk over an area several miles wide. With luck they might find a deer.

But they found no deer, nor any sign. All day long, with not a thing to eat, they waded in the snow, each man alone, save that three of them led the gaunt beasts. Colter would stop and stand leaning against a tree and he would have bet his life that he heard living things moving but he knew that he heard nothing. He knew that he was suffering hallucinations because of his extreme weakness. He knew there was no deer over there where he now heard one but he walked over nevertheless and looked round at the smooth unbroken snow. He supposed he was losing his mind. Yonder, over the hill, was Clark; in the opposite direction was Joe Fields; and beyond him —but who was there? It made him dizzy to try to think. He felt nausea when, picking up his gun, he raised a foot and thrust it forward and walked again.

This night the seven men gathered supperless round a fire and not a word was said. One might have said, "I guess the snow has chased all the deer down to the valleys." And another might have replied,

"The red men are eating them now." A third might have said, "It's going to be colder tonight." But men did not speak when they were too tired even to think. All the grouse seemed to have gone. The wolves had gone. There was nothing around them but snow and cold; vast forests; stupendous black-and-white mountains in the east, the south, the north; and the unknown in the west. They had climbed a hill thinking, We'll see a valley now! But there was no valley, only another hill. All day it had been one hill after another.

They rolled into their cold blankets on the cold earth and waited for morning. Clark's last thoughts before he fell into restless slumber were of Lewis back on the trail, back there eight or ten or twelve miles, with nothing to eat, with a few of his men so weak they could barely sit up, with two or three of them delirious. Well, he would have to go farther tomorrow. . . .

Just before daylight they set off again, in the deep cold dusk of morning, feeling desperate but striving with all their will to look cheerful. Each knew privately that they could not go much farther without food. How far away, O Lord, was the nearest village? Clark was thinking, Back there on the trail Captain Lewis listened all day yesterday for gun shots and heard none. He is listening again. He is looking at some of his men, sitting, too weak to rise, and he is listening. . . . If they got nothing today would this be the end of all of them? Clark was not a man to dwell on a prospect of defeat, or to admit that defeat was possible; but he was a realist, he was an old campaigner, he knew that some of the men with Lewis could not live much longer. He knew that Lewis would soon face the problem of abandoning a few of them (for he had no horses strong enough to carry them) and pushing on without them, or of remaining with them. He knew that he would never leave them. He knew that his friend was in a desperate plight by this time and this knowledge made him look so grim that John Colter was startled when he glanced at his captain's face. The seven of them went steadily on, stumbling, sometimes almost falling, their ears and eyes straining in a land where there was only the deep-winter silence of trees and snow.

Or was there a sound?

"Listen," Clark said, for they were all walking together this morning. He looked at the men. "Did you hear anything?"

The men looked at him and then at the horses. "I've been hearing things for days," Reuben said.

"I'm sure I heard something," Clark said.

Most of the men doubted it. They were thinking, Our captain's mind is going now. But Clark's mind was tough and it was not yet going. The thing he had heard was a horse.

It came into plain sight and stood in a clearing looking at them. "An Indian horse," Clark said. He handed his espontoon to Drewyer. "Can you break its neck?"

"I kin try," Drewyer said, kneeling in the snow. Clasping the top end of the staff with his left hand, he laid his rifle across the hand and took careful aim. He fired, and the horse fell. John Colter hastened forward with a knife to open the jugular vein.

While the men dressed the beast out and built a fire to cook breakfast Clark explored roundabout in the woods. The presence of the horse meant that Indians were not far away. On coming to the fire he said, "Was it pretty skinny?"

"Kind of," John said. "But fat compared to ours."

"What we don't eat this morning, hang in a tree for the party. Drewyer, fire your gun again and after half an hour again. I want Captain Lewis to be sure to hear it."

The seven men sat by the fire and ate boiled lean horse flesh, without salt or pepper. It was stringy and tough and tasteless and it doubled instead of easing the pains in their bellies. After eating, Clark wrote a note to Lewis and tied it to the tree where the meat hung; it said that he and his men would go to lower country, to find food. It was a brief stiff unemotional note—the kind Lewis thought of as a military note.

The men built up the fire, hoping that it might serve as a beacon light to those behind, and went on. The snow here was a foot deep. They saw no sign of Indians, no sign of a living thing. When night came, two of the men gathered wood for a fire and the other four men gathered twigs or anything they could find that the horses would eat. They were all so tired, both beasts and men, that they could barely move. The men kicked the fire away and laid their blankets on the warmed earth and tried to sleep; and the next day, still trudging along, they unexpectedly came in sight of a small band of Indians. Clark went on ahead and in sign language convinced these red men that he and his men were friendly. He then told the one he took to be a chief that his party was hungry and weak and wished to eat. The chief spoke to his women, who rushed away but soon returned, and set before Clark and his men the two principal foods of the pierced-nose Indians—dried salmon and the camas root.

Clark and his men sat in a half-circle, and facing them were about forty men, women and children, their black eyes staring. Had they ever seen white men before? It was possible. Perhaps they had gone far enough down the Columbia to meet white traders. Clark took a piece of salmon and politely sniffed it. It smelled rancid. He bit into it and knew then that it had not been smoked. It had merely been sliced thin and laid in the sun to dry. He then bit into a root and thought it had a fair flavor. It tasted a little like potato. While chewing he was thinking, If the red people can live on such food, so can we. Did they have an abundance of it? He looked at his men sitting round him and thought they all seemed to be eating heartily.

John Colter said, "It tastes like pumpkin, sort of."

"Sort of."

Clark again turned his gaze on the Indians. On meeting them he had looked critically at their noses but had seen none that looked pierced. He had then looked at their clothing but only for a moment: the men here seemed more immodest than any other red men he had known: they quite exposed themselves, and seemed to do so with a kind of wanton impudence. The squaws, on the other hand, appeared to be more modest and hidden than any squaws on the Missouri; they wore a loose garment of leather that fell almost to their ankles, clasped in at their waists with a girdle. These were handsomer Indians than most, Clark thought, and quite dressy in their way. The men wore buffalo or elk or deer leather, adorned with beads, most of them white, with sea shells and what looked like mother of pearl attached to snippets of otter or mink skin, hanging from their hair or necks. The paints on their faces were green, blue and white.

"Thank God," said Joe Fields, "these Indians don't want to hug us to death."

"I see a girl over there," his brother said, "who can hug me any day she wants to."

"My brother," Joe said, indicating Reuben. "So weak that he staggers, yet he thinks about women."

"She does look sort of nice," John Colter said.

"Sort of," said a fourth.

When the girl became aware of the men looking at her she simpered and, turning, wiggled and giggled, hiding her face.

"I guess women act the same the world over," Joe said.

"They seem like a rather timid people," said Clark. He ha

observed, on approaching them, that they had made movements toward flight; and even now, standing back and watching, they seemed ready to run at a moment's warning.

After Clark had eaten more than he believed he should he rose painfully and with difficulty to his feet, and felt sharp pains all through his lower body. Looking round him at his men, he said, "If I can buy a packload of food I'll send it to Captain Lewis." He looked from face to face, as though trying to decide which of his men was strongest. "Private Reuben Fields, you will take the load back."

"Yes, sir," said Reuben, but he was thinking, By God, yes, it would have to be me! I show a little interest in a girl and back up the mountains I go!

For colored beads Clark traded for about a hundred pounds of salmon and roots and had the food packed securely on the strongest of the beasts. For a knife he persuaded a young buck to go with Reuben, thinking that if a heavy snow were to fall, Reuben would not be able to find his way. Then he watched the two men off, the Indian going ahead, Reuben following him and leading the horse.

Reuben felt sullen. He had been chosen as a member of Clark's party to go down the river with him—and to the day of his death he would never forget the taste of red haws. Now he was chosen from six to climb back up these white mountains. He supposed he would find Captain Lewis and all his men down. Lewis had been a sick man when they left him and half the men with him had been sick. Maybe they had never got as far as the horse meat. Maybe they would be scattered back along the trail for miles, down, dead or dying. . . .

They were not down but they were almost a forlorn hope of a party. Even the big Negro was so weak that he tottered. They awoke one morning buried under half a foot of snow, and though Lewis had left his bed at daylight, most of the men had only looked out; had put out an unbelieving hand to feel the snow and measure its depth, and had thought, Oh, to hell with it! Why should I get up and shiver around in that!

It would not have been such an effort to get up if they had had warm sturdy boots instead of thin frozen moccasins, and socks instead of a few rotten rags with which they tried to wrap their feet. Their moccasins had worn so thin that every evening some of the men sat by the fire with needle and thread, patching holes. They still had a little soup but it was no good for a man. September 18th they had watched Clark and his six picked men vanish and then the main party had followed the middle path, knowing that it was Clark's. The weather had turned colder, and all night the men had shivered from cold and hunger. All night in their own private hearts they had asked themselves questions but not a man among them, save Charbonneau, had yet faltered; not a one of them had ever thought of giving up. How could they, when present with them was a girl like Jawey! All day long she carried her child, and the bedding and dishes for her and her man; smiling if anyone looked at her; searching among the trees for something to eat. If men saw her while she and her child chewed on the inner bark of the spruce she would then offer them some but none of them would eat bark. They had all tried it and spat it out.

And all day long, every day, Meriwether Lewis, though almost the weakest of them, smiled and quipped and cheered them on. "Away out there," he would say, looking into the west. "That looks like the thin line of a river." He would say, "Down there—there are the prairies. The game is down there. Indians are there and they have food." The men would bug their eyes and stare but they could see no sign of fires, no sign of life in the whole wintry world around them. Their captain's face was so fleshless and gaunt that he did not look like the man they had known; but his smile was the same, the smile they had seen all the way out. They all knew in their hearts that no man could sit down and die with a leader like that. "We'll make it!" each man said privately to himself. "By God, we'll make it!"

Or would they? A few of them were now delirious and talked in their sleep. Whether their captain did none of them knew but most of them knew that no man in the party was living more wholly on grit. They knew that he, the captain and leader, was striving with superhuman will to keep from staggering and falling; but he fell now and then. Not a man let on that he saw his leader fall or thought he had fallen. Not a man ever spoke about it. They all pretended that their captain had merely sat down. For in all of them now was a kind of dread that they had never known: what if their leader were to fall and die, what would they do then? The sergeants had some power of leadership, more especially Pryor, the quiet one, but he was no Lewis, he was no Clark. None knew that better than George Shannon. None more closely watched the leader's face for sign that the will was failing. . . .

On the day Drewyer shot the stray horse Lewis and his men, with the sweat of exhaustion pouring from every one of them, came to the crest of a hill and, looking out, saw a vista that warmed them more than a glass of brandy might have done. They were looking at a broad distant prairie marked by the unmistakable line of a river. There would have to be a river in a wide area like that, lying, as it did, at the base of mountains. And surely Indians were there. Toby said there was a river. He said there were Indians. They took their horses to trees roundabout to let the feeble beasts nibble at bark and after sitting a little while to rest they all drank about a fourth of a cup of soup. A hunter went off into the woods and they heard a shot but they knew it would be only a pheasant and they would give that to the girl and her child. Hearing another sound, they discovered that a horse had slipped and rolled a hundred feet down a mountain, with a load of ammunition on its back. Before any of them could reach it the beast had staggered to its bleeding feet and was standing, trembling.

Lewis's mind was not clear today and he knew it. Trying to figure out how much food the party had, he could think of nothing but a little bear grease and twenty pounds of candles. He was not sure that candles could be eaten. Did they have some peas?—or was it beans? Did they have any squash? He looked off to his right and, seeing a tree that he called bolsom fir, he forced his mind to think about it; and while sitting here he identified eight species of conifer around him. It always made him feel saner when he botanized. He was feeling better with himself when the thought occurred to him that there could not possibly be twenty pounds of candles. They had no candles. Was it twenty pounds of bear grease or was his mind wandering?

He forced himself to stand up. How far ahead was Clark? Had he found food?

Standing up, he felt dizzy and he wanted to sit again. Instead, he looked round him. He had read in Clark's Journal, "These immense mountains and our lack of food have so dampened the spirit of our party that I must go ahead and find game and kill it and send it back. . . ." Good brave levelheaded Will! If there was any game in the country he would find it—but what could there be except a coyote or two, a blue bird of the vulture kind, a gray squirrel, a pheasant or two. . . .

He was aware that a few of the men were covertly watching him.

Then he heard a sound and, looking over at a group, doubted his senses, for some of the men seemed to be babbling in a frenzied weeping way, while pointing to the far prairie. Well, at least the prairie was no mirage. Toby said the Columbia flowed across it but Lewis could see no line of a great river and he doubted that the Columbia was there. He suspected that it was farther north.

The party now moved ahead, its spirits lifted. Toby said they would reach the plains tomorrow. This evening Lewis gave his men a half-cup of soup each and strolled among them to see how they were. Most of them were suffering from dysentery; some had open sores from which pus was running; all of them had a deathly pallor that looked all the more ghastly in faces that had been bronzed. Bratton was moaning like a man dying. He had vomited his soup. But the next morning he took his place in the line and staggered off, as dauntless as ever. All of the men, Lewis decided, even Charbonneau, were showing marvelous grit.

This morning, feeling dizzy and depersonalized, Lewis forced himself to give his attention to a bird—he supposed it was a bird—to note all its markings so that he could describe it for Mr. Jefferson. A little larger than a robin, it was bluish-brown on its back and wings, black on its tail and striped white down its neck. The top of the head, the neck, breast and belly were a yellowish-red. He also forced himself, as he moved along, to put his description of the pheasant into phrases, so that he could enter the matter in his Journal this evening.

About noon they came to the carcass of the horse hanging from the tree and some of the men thought it was an illusion. They staggered round the tree to view it from all angles. George Shannon went up and smelled of it. He said, "It's real, all right." Then he saw the note that Clark had left for Lewis and, gently pulling it out of the crotch of a forked stick, he took it to his captain.

Lewis read the note and said to his men, "Captain Clark has gone down to the level country southwest of us." The men looked into the southwest but only for a moment. They were far more interested in the horse flesh. Lewis told the men to build fires and cook as much of the flesh as they thought the party could eat but his own dinner was spoiled when he learned that one of the packhorses was missing. It was the horse that had all his winter clothing on it. After sending two of the best woodsmen back to find it he tried to take his mind off his worries by studying the plants around him, the huckleberry, alder and honeysuckle, but botanizing today could not make him forget his internal miseries. The tough half-boiled horse meat had made his own dysentery and that of most of the men far worse than it had been and some of them had such violent abdominal seizures that they cried out with pain. Everywhere in the timber roundabout Lewis could hear groaning. When suppertime came a few of the men refused to eat any more of the crowbait.

Bratton shuddered with sickness and shook his pale thin face. All he had done, he said, was to chew it for the dog.

"Shame on you," Lewis said. "Fine fat grain-fed beef and you turn up your nose at it."

"Captain, it makes me sick just to think of it."

"I hear a wolf. Would you rather have wolf?"

"Beaver tail and buffalo hump," said Bratton, and went on groaning.

The next morning Lewis killed a coyote and one of the men a crow and they all gingerly tasted boiled crow and coyote. Some of the men thought the coyote was better than the horse. Toby and his son refused to touch it but sucked the bones of the crow dry and chewed at its tough flavorless stringy legs. Before evening of this day came Lewis was forced to realize that he was so weak, from dysentery and hunger, that it took the full effort of his will to rise again after he had sat. Knowing that he was leeched out, he wondered which of the medicines might do him some good. What had his mother given for dysentery? While thinking about it he dozed and then sank forward into deep sleep. A half-hour later he was up and staggering away into the woods, as most of his men were, clutching their convulsed bellies and seeking a private spot. All night it was this way. All night men moved back and forth between thickets and their cold beds.

The next day a little before noon they met Reuben with his packhorse load of roots and dried salmon, and the men were so overjoyed that they embraced him. "Ah-hi-e!" George Shannon cried, and most of them took up the Shoshone call. "Ah-hi-e!" The slave-girl stood apart, holding her babe and smiling at them. Then the stronger men stripped the food off the horse. Lewis was examining a root.

"Did Captain Clark cook these?"

"We ate them raw but they give some of us a bellyache."

"I think we should cook them," Lewis said. He would have had no doubt about it if he had known that Clark was suffering horribly and saying to his men, "I hope to God Captain Lewis and his men show more sense and cook these things." After the roots were boiled the men thought they were not bad at all but they overate of both roots and salmon and then thought they would die of cramps. Lewis lay stretched out over his bedroll, with his head and feet lower than his belly, trying to ease his pain. Even while he grimaced and shuddered his eager and curious mind speculated on the cause: was it the roots, or the salmon?—or the weeks of hunger and starvation? —or the enervated condition of the bowels? "Private Fields!" he croaked, and when Reuben came up he said, "Did it give all of them bellyache?"

"Captain, I don't know. It did Captain Clark and me. I've had cramps all the way back."

"Is Captain Clark feeling all right?"

"Except for cramps."

Lewis staggered to his feet and began to walk. He tried to walk at a brisk stride but the cramps were so violent in their seizures that they bent him to his knees. He heard men around him vomiting. He was looking round to see who was ill when his eye was caught by the compassionate face of the girl. He went over to her.

"Aren't you sick?"

"No seeck," she said, shaking her coal-black hair.

"And Pomp, he no seeck?" He looked over at Toby and his son: they were not sick either. What in thunderation was it that filled the white man with horrible pains and left the red man untroubled? Was it too much civilization? He went over to Bratton, stretched out on his belly. "Where do you hurt worst?" he asked.

Bratton rolled over. Lewis was startled when he saw the agony in the youth's face. He could see that William Bratton was in terrible pain and, forgetting for the moment his own ills, he hastened to the medical supplies and mixed together a huge dose of laudanum and jalap. He took it to Bratton and said, "Down this," and Bratton gulped it down. Lewis then went among the other men, privately chiding himself, saying, "Only recently I said I would be less selfish and give myself more to mankind, yet here I was, concerned only with my own miseries!" Refusing to think of his own pains, he spent the remainder of the day doctoring his men. None of the medicine seemed to do them any good. It was, he supposed, the kind of thing they would have to endure until it wore itself out.

Silas Goodrich wiped slobber from his pale bearded lips and said, "It's the salmon, Captain. I reckon it has cured me of fishing for life

"How you know it's the salmon?"

"I belch it up. I can feel salmon all through me."

A few of the other men thought it was the salmon and not the roots but Lewis decided that if it was not the roots it was general debility from weeks of privation. By late afternoon he had his party marching again and he then discovered how weak most of them were. They were staggering and falling. They would rise to their feet with an effort that drained their faces still whiter. But it was not long before those in the lead came to an Indian village, and Lewis smiled wanly when he saw all the women and children mount horses and flee. What a formidable appearance we must present! he reflected. Not a one of us could strike a blow to save his life, yet see how they run!

A few of the Indian men came forward. They seemed friendly. Lewis's astonishment would have been boundless if he had known what was in the minds of these red warriors. After Clark and his men had left them the chiefs had gone into council and had decided to massacre the white party. Their will had been softened by the pleading of an old squaw. Many years before she had been captured by an enemy tribe and taken to Canada, and there had escaped with the aid of white men and covered the long distance back to her people, though almost dying of hunger and weariness. At the moment when Lewis and his men were chewing the tough sinews of coyote she was begging the chiefs of her nation to be kind to these strangers and do them no harm.

Lewis did not know this, but even if he had known it, he was almost too sick and weak to care.

27

The next morning he was unable to rise from his bed. His mind was so clouded by sickness that he did not know that not all of his men had come in—that some were back along the trail, fallen and unable to rise. Clark meanwhile had told himself that Lewis was taking a long time to get out of the mountains and on a strange horse he had turned back to find him. The horse took fright and threw him, and threw him twice again, and Clark was not sure that he had not suffered a broken hip; but he mounted after the third fall and rode on. He found Lewis stretched out on his blankets, his gaze on the sky. Clark sat by the bed and looked at him.

"My friend, you sick? But of course you are or you wouldn't be here."

"Weak," Lewis said. "There's a bird up there in that tree——"

"Never mind the bird," Clark said, looking at the sunken eyes and cheeks. "You can't get up?"

In a voice so weak it was barely audible Lewis said, "I don't seem able to."

"Have all your men come in?"

"Will, I just don't know."

My God! Will Clark thought. He brought them out of the mountains, all right, but it has almost cost him his life. He decided that it would be wise to talk about other things. The principal chief, he said of those he had seen, was named Twisted Hair, which seemed a peculiar name for an Indian. On a white elkskin Twisted Hair had drawn for him a map of the downriver country. It was about five sleeps by boat to the big falls of the Columbia; white men, the chie said, might be found there. The Indians here seemed to live on nothing much but dried salmon and the root which some of the men were now calling the wild potato. Either the fish or the potato had made practically all the men sick. Clark himself had thought he would die of bellyaches.

In his low feeble voice Lewis said, "I think it's the exhaustion, not the food."

"It might be."

"Five sleeps. How far is that?"

"The Almighty knows but I wouldn't guess, for we've been wrong so many times." They had thought, Clark went on, to find a short portage between the waters of the Missouri and the Columbia, but there were two valleys and hundreds of miles between them. They had thought the Columbia was just a river but knew now that it drained a vast interior, and that between the two rivers there was not one mountain system but two. They had thought the Missouri headed far north of its actual source.

"The mountain of salt," Lewis said, "where can that be?"

"Mr. Jefferson is going to be disappointed."

"Only in that. This tall country will delight him."

The gaunt half-starved dog had been uttering low growls at Clark. Lewis now moved his head to look at the beast. Clark, he said, was the only person the dog had let approach him.

"He doesn't like me today."

"His mind is affected, like his master's."

Amused, Clark looked at his friend. "Well, how about a big dost of medicine?"

"I'm full of it," Lewis said.

There was a brief silence. Then Clark said, "You know what impresses these red people most? The hair on our faces. Next to that is the way we make fire. That's real big medicine. Next to that is York's color."

Lewis smiled faintly. "Are they friendly?"

"Fair. They're a good tribe, one of the best I've seen." Clark stood up, hiding from Lewis the pain in his hip. "I have to go find a campsite and timber for canoes. Anything I can do for you?"

Lewis shook his head no. He would be all right, he said. It took a little time.

This evening Twisted Hair invited the two white chiefs to his lodge and Lewis knew that he would have to rise and go. He told himself that it would do him good to get up on his feet. With what he took to be the last of his strength he rose to hands and knees and then thought he would faint, so awful was the nausea that filled him. He remained in this position several minutes, trying with a sheer effort of will to shake off his sickness; and then he managed to get to his feet and to stand as though propped, looking round him. He was glad that nobody had seen him. Walking slowly, like one trying out a pair of new legs, he went over to the lodge, a shambles of pine brush and bark. He went inside and sat by Clark and at once Twisted Hair had a squaw serve them dried salmon. Lewis forced a little of it down and then sat paralyzed with horror, for he was afraid he would vomit right here in the chief's hut. As soon as he could excuse himself he went back to his bed.

Hundreds of Indians remained around the white camp all night. All night the dog growled his warnings. Having discovered that these red men were sneak thieves, Clark had told his men to keep an eye on them all the time. Most of the men were too sick to keep an eye on anything.

It was Frazier who said what most of them were feeling. Stretched out on his blanket, his handsome face now haggard, moist with sweat and of the pallor of wet yellow clay, he said, "Well, here we are, between three and four thousand miles from home . . . on the west side of the Rockies . . . probably given up by relatives and friends and now forgotten . . . sicker than dogs and flat on our backs . . . but not licked yet. Think, fellers. We get some canoes made and we just float down a big river to the sea; and there President Jefferson will have a ship loaded with Virginia hams and tobacco and two blondes, two brunettes and a redhead for every one of us."

"Holy grandma!" Bratton croaked, and turned his head to look over at Frazier.

Whitehouse said, "How do Drewyer and Joe Fields and John Colter keep going?"

"They're hunters," Alex Willard said. "They've had more to eat."

Trying to look over at a group of squaws watching the white men, Frazier asked, in a squeaky falsetto, "O form dee-vine . . . wilt thou be mine . . . ? What legs are these . . . with bowed-out knees . . . ? The shapes that fit . . . good God, that's it . . . !"

He kept it up till some of the sick men around him were choking with laughter.

Frazier's nonsense, the comical stuttering of Potts, the never-failing smile of the slave-girl, the round baby-faced cheerfulness of little Pompy—these for the sick men were better than medicines. These kept them jesting and mocking at themselves all day. What a gang of weaklings they were! Why didn't they all get up and build the canoes?

The next morning Clark found his friend no better, and then counted the men who were too feeble to stand. There was a dozen of them. They complained of loose bowels and cramps and of a heaviness drawing down from their hearts. Clark gave them huge doses of pills and then hustled off downriver to locate a campsite. His hip gave him a great deal of pain but, having decided that it was not broken, he tried to be indifferent to it. Before dark he returned to camp and it was then that Lewis told him of the loss of three horses, with valuable packs, back in the mountains. Clark decided to send a man into the cold white world to find them. But which man?

He sat by Lewis and said, "Which man is most likely to find them?"

Lewis did not reply at once. He was thinking of the men. They were all good men. He thought that as a group they were the hardiest, most dependable, most valiant in the whole wide world. But some were better for one thing, some for another. Goodrich could catch more fish than any ten of them; Drewyer was by far the best hunter; Cruzatte was the best riverman; Shields was the best smithy. Joe Fields was perhaps the boldest, George Shannon the most resourceful, John Colter the most adventurous. . . .

"Colter," he said.

Clark went to Colter. "Private Colter, Captain Lewis's men lost three horses and their packs back in the mountains. Think you could find them?"

Colter looked his captain straight in the eye and said, "I could try, sir."

"Then choose your horse and anything else you need and be off."

Clark's task now was to move the party down to the campsite. Twisted Hair brought a gentle horse for Lewis to ride and they put him on it. At once he doubled over and almost fell off. Then, clutching the mane to steady himself, he managed a wry grin and said, "Who was the man who fought the windmills? That's me." The big Negro for a while had been too weak to walk but was now a little stronger—but not strong enough to show off his muscle and strength. Clark had him lead the horse so that Lewis could give both hands to the mane.

The party had not gone far when one man after another sank by the trail and stretched out, faces bathed with sweat. A few of them were put on horses; the others were left to rest and recover and come along in their own time. When, two hours after dark, some of them had not come in, Clark sent a few of the strongest men back with horses to fetch them. The next day, with the pain in his hip so sharp that it made him suck in his breath, he went down the river to look for canoe timber, and all day he hoped that when he returned to camp he would find Lewis feeling better. Half-sick himself, he had more than he could manage alone. But Lewis was not better. He seemed worse, and so did a number of the men. In his short entry for this day—he was too dog-tired and full of pain to write much— Clark wrote, "3 parts of Party sick . . . Capt. Lewis verry sick." Later he rewrote it, saying in this part, "when I arrived at Camp found Capt. Lewis verry sick, Several men also verry Sick, I gave them Some Salts & Tarter emetic, we deturmined to go to where the best timber was and there form a Camp."

And so they moved again the next morning, downriver, to the junction of the middle and north forks of what they called the Kooskooskee, being unaware that these Indians did not give rivers names. In his own mind Shannon spelled the word as Cooskootske —and told the captains that as well as he could make it out, coos meant water; koots meant little; and ke meant the. And so the captains assumed that the word meant The Little Water. They made camp by a grove of large yellow pine trees.

Though their axes were small and poorly balanced and hafted Clark said they would have to do. Canoes must be made. After choosing a few men to fell trees and hack out the canoes he assigned to each an ax, and then gave his sick friend and all the other sick men a big dose of pills, salts, jalap and emetic. A number of Indians had followed the white party, hoping to trade food for trinkets; and this evening after he had doctored the men Clark forced himself to take ribbons, beads and fish hooks and go to the Indian camp to barter for wild potatoes and dried salmon. He was himself too sick to eat. He was so sick that on his return he kept out of sight of Lewis not wanting him to see his face. He suffered so all night from cramp and from his hip that he barely slept at all, but at daylight he was up and directing the men who were felling trees. In the late afternoon he felt a thrill of joy go through him like a spurt of fire when he saw John Colter riding in, leading a horse across which was flung half a deer. Clark went over to him and gravely the youngster told him that he had found Indian tracks and had no doubt that the re men had made off with the other two beasts. He could not understand why they had not taken this one also.

While listening Clark looked at the venison. It was a godsend. He summoned a cook and told him to prepare it at once for the men who were sick. "Boil it gently and make a nice rich broth." When the broth was ready he took a tin cupful to each of the sick men, together with choice morsels of flesh. There was no salt for it but they were getting used to being without salt. Lewis swallowed a little broth and made a face. He was not sure that he could keep it down but said he was feeling a lot better. That was a lie and Clark knew it. In his Journal this day he wrote, "Capt. Lewis very sick nearly all the men sick. . . ." Nearly all. He too was sick but he refused to admit it and he drove himself on day after day—because canoes had to be built, the party had to get down the river before winter set in. The men with the axes were so weak that labor made them burst with sweat; for every ten minutes that they worked they had to sit for an hour.

The next day all the men but five complained of their bowels and stomach. Even Drewyer had taken to his bed. Lewis was still unable to get up or to keep anything on his stomach. It took all the will Clark had to force himself from the bed and to stand up. Anyone looking at his face could tell that he was sick—and grimmer too, for he was determined to put this party to the ocean, and then back home. He would allow no other thought in his mind. He was determined that all these men should get well but he knew that they would have to have meat or they would all die. This day he encouraged the men hacking at the logs; took broth and medicines to the sick; and told those few still on their feet to stay on their feet.

The next morning he stood above Drewyer and said, "Can't you get up?" Drewyer said he guessed he could if he tried hard enough but he had vomited everything up, even his organs, it seemed to him, and he was as weak as a seven-month baby. He struggled and rolled over and got to his feet, trembling. "Fine," Clark said. "Now you and Colter go hunting. We simply must have meat."

"Yes, sir," he said, and picked up his gun. With nothing in his stomach he climbed to the back of a horse and with Colter headed for deer timber.

Before dark the two men returned with three deer. Men lying on their blankets forced themselves to sit up and look at the wonder of what two sick men had done—for even Colter was living on grit. "Holy grandma!" Bratton said. "It makes me plum ashamed of myself." It made George Shannon so ashamed that he staggered to his feet and then stood, shaking all over, his shoulders sagging, his face drained white. "God in heaven," he said, "what has happened to all of us, anyway?" He was looking round him at more than twenty men lying on their beds in broad daylight.

This evening in his Journal, Clark again wrote, "Capt. Lewis very sick. . . ." He himself was so sick that Sacajawea hovered near him, her anxious eyes on his face. He gave her the task of boiling deer flesh and making broth for the sick men. When he saw the eyes of the men light up as she served them he thought impatiently, What a stupid fool I am! Why, of course that was it: when men were sick and thousands of miles from home, flat on their backs in an unknown land among an alien people, what on earth could cheer them like the gentle ways of a woman? He should have known it!

Either the venison and broth or the gentleness of the slave-girl was big medicine, for almost at once the men began to improve; and by October 1st Clark was able to take up pen and ink and write, "Capt Lewis getting much better. . . ." Captain Lewis's sunken face had an amiable grin on it; in his sunken eyes there was again the whimsy and mischief. He was a gaunt shadow of a man when he stood up; he looked like nothing much but skin and bones and he said he felt like skin and bones. He was so weak that he tottered but his will was mighty, he was determined to be a well man soon. He looked over at Will Clark, thinking, What a man he is, for he brought us all through! Lewis thought they would all come through, after moving through the camp to look at the men. John Potts, Pete Wiser and William Bratton looked closest to death but they were cheerful.

"Holy grandma," Will said, looking up at Lewis. "Captain, you don't know how plum ashamed I am."

"Sickness is divine punishment," Lewis said. "Private Bratton, you'll simply have to change your ways."

"You mean about the squaws, Captain?"

To hide from Bratton his grin Lewis moved away. He paused by Bob Frazier. Frazier had one of the heaviest and handsomest beards; it was now spread over half his chest. With a dead-pan face Frazier looked up at his captain and softly intoned, "O form dee-vine! Will she be mine?"

"She says she will," Lewis said. "Now you'd better get up from there."

Most of the men did get up because they saw their sick captain up, and of those who got up not a one returned to his bed in daylight. They were too weak to do anything but they could sit by the river and jest with one another or watch the men burn out the canoes. For these, laboring with axes, Clark had a horse butchered. Shields had decided that it was easier to burn the canoes out than to hack them out; and so all day long he and his men fussed with their fires on green wood, looking up now and then to see the sunken eyes of Lewis watching them, or turning to retort to one of Frazier's quips. When not watching the men Lewis cast a botanist's gaze on the plant growth roundabout or studied the river's waters and wondered about the ways of the salmon. He thought the salmon industry should become a huge one and that it should belong entirely to the United States.

By October 5th some of the men felt strong enough to brand the party's horses and cut off their forelocks. Five young braves, to each of whom Clark had given a knife, had promised to take care of them. This evening the two captains sat by a small fire of their own. When food was brought to them Lewis said his appetite was returning but he looked long and hard at the food on his tin plate. It was dried salmon and camas roots.

"Wonder how dog tastes," he said, looking at Clark. "These people have lots of dogs."

Clark did not meet his eyes. He could form no picture of himself eating dog flesh.

After sniffing at the salmon Lewis took a bite. These Indians were cleaner in their habits than the Mandans or Snakes but a man could never tell what a squaw would do. He chewed a root and swallowed it and then saw that Clark seemed to be eating with gusto.

"You like these wild potatoes?"

"Not especially but they help to keep a man going."

A cook now brought about two quarts of boiled roots, without salt or seasoning. Finding them tender and easy to chew and swallow, and knowing that they were clean, the captains ate them all. In only a few minutes they were suffering distress and in half an hour they were swollen with bloat. Lewis stood up with hands pressing against his belly and bent over, breathing hard. "I feel," he said to Clark, "like I'm going to bust wide open."

Stretched out on his back, Clark also was breathing hard. Never in all his life, he said, had he been so puffed up with wind. Feeling sharp pains in his chest, he supposed that the gases in his belly were pressing upward against his heart and he was a little worried. He tried rolling over a few times but that did no good. Lewis was heaving and trying to belch. All night the captains dosed themselves with medicines and groaned and suffered, for they could find nothing to relieve the flatulence. Now and then Sacajawea came over to their tent to look in.

Stretched out on his belly with a folded blanket under it, Lewis said, "I'm thinking of Virginia hams . . . and Albemarle honey . . . and Mr. Jefferson's vintage wines."

Clark thought his friend was breathing like a bloated steer. He said, "What you should be thinking of is something to make you bust wind."

"Did I ever tell you Jefferson developed a Frenchman's taste in wines over in Paris? He has a good cellar and that's what I need right now."

"I expect," Clark said, "it wouldn't be a bad thing to stick ourselves."

The next day both captains were sick but Clark forced himself to keep going. He had some of the men make a cache of the pack-saddles, a few canisters of powder and a bag of balls. By evening all the canoes were ready for the water and a more ungainly hideous set of boats had never, Lewis supposed, been seen in this world—for they were only chunks of trees with most of their insides burnt out. The next morning the canoes were loaded and the party set out downriver, in four large boats and a small one, the pale and haggard Lewis in the prow of one, the pale and haggard Clark in the prow of another. They covered twenty miles. The next day they came to a series of rapids and one of the large canoes, with Sergeant Gass steering, struck a stone and, turning broadside, split wide open. In only a few moments it sank. Most of the men unable to swim had been in this canoe. They always were, Lewis reflected! And there the silly fellows were, clinging to river boulders and bawling for help. Clark had a canoe unloaded and sent it over for them, and then sent another canoe, manned by expert swimmers like Colter and Frazier and Ordway, to retrieve the baggage from the sunken canoe and bring it to shore. John Colter was so valiant in this enterprise that Clark named a nearby creek for him.

They were all busy drying out the baggage and rearranging it when George Shannon cried, "Holy Moses!" and on looking up the captains saw old Toby and his son running at full speed up the river. "They haven't been paid," Clark said. He sent Drewyer to fetch them back but after a while Drewyer returned to say that it would do no good, for if Toby was paid, the pierced noses would rob him before he reached the mountains. He asked the white chiefs to be his friends and let him go while he still had a chance at his life.

A great number of Indians had come from villages along the river to spy on the white men and to steal from them. This evening the captains entertained them with violin music, singing and dancing. York, after submitting a few minutes to inspection and rubbing with wet fingers, jigged and clogged for them, the red people howling with laughter, for they thought him very wonderful. A few of the stronger men square-danced, while Potts, stuttering worse than usual, called the figures: "Swsssswing old Adam! Swing old Eeeeeeve! Swing them fuf-fuf-fellers before you leave. . . ."

Suddenly with a horrible shriek the fun-makers were silenced, as an almost naked squaw, frothing and drooling from her toothless mouth and tearing at her long filthy hair, rushed forward from darkness to take the stage. In a voice pitched at the very top of frenzy she seemed to be singing—or shrieking curses—or invoking her gods: the white men had never seen such an Indian and couldn't tell what she was trying to do. After a few moments she interrupted her wild dancing and shrieking to dash forward to a white man and offer him a gift—a tiny piece of shell or obsidian. If the white man refused it or seemed reluctant to take it then her frenzy was too horrible to look at. For then she took a knife from somewhere and slashed at herself—across her upper left arm, across her skinny breast-bags, or down across her lean belly and her thighs; and as the blood poured out of her with a hand she flung it over her like red rain, and over the people nearest her, her open mouth shrieking horribly all the while.

The captains and all the white men were too amazed to speak. Clark was asking himself, "Is she mad or is this an act?" Lewis was observing that though she was in fact a repulsive old crone, in her wild dance there was something astonishingly beautiful. She now rushed at one of the men and offered a trinket; then slunk back three steps and stiffened as though she had been struck; held the dramatic taut posture a long moment; and with a shriek that smote ears like blows again gashed herself on her bony chest and down her left arm. Each gash, each flinging of her blood, each wild swift gesture of a hand across an open wound was a rhythmic part of her dance. Were her people, Lewis wondered, pitying her or laughing at her? It was impossible to tell. Was this a ritualistic dance, a tribal dance?—or was it only a strange compelling exhibition of this creature's madness? Lewis supposed that she had danced before, for she was scarred all over.

As suddenly as it had begun it ceased. She was gone. Some of the men went to look for her and Lewis heard one say that she had rushed to the riverbank and fallen there, and was either senseless or dead.

The next day they witnessed another curious thing. These Indians had bath-holes in the earth, six or seven feet deep and three or four feet square, roofed over with timber and earth, with a hole in the roof through which a man could crawl. To cure themselves of certain ills they heated stones in a big fire and threw them into the hole; and after a man had crawled in they poured water upon the hot stones. In the pit he took a steam bath that, in the words of George Shannon, really filtered him out. Sometimes they threw hot stones into a small pond and bathed there but it was the steaming in the pit that drove sweat in torrents from their body and left them looking pale and purified. Lewis watched some of them steam themselves and wondered if this treatment would not be good for him and his men. None of the men would try it. They said they'd rather eat dog meat. Labiche, the Frenchman, said that dog was a fine dish, a delicacy even, if properly cooked. Lewis was game to try anything but he hesitated, knowing that these Indians were not dog-eaters. He took the matter to Clark.

The men, he said, were sick and tired of dried salmon and roots. Most of them were ready to eat dog.

Clark was thoughtful a few moments. Then he said, "Why don't you let them try it?"

"These Indians don't eat dogs. If they see us eating them what will their attitude be?"

"Contempt, I expect."

"You think they'd become hostile?"

"Why not start in a small way, with two or three?"

So Lewis traded for two small fat dogs and told the cooks to do their best by them. He himself ate a portion and thought it tasted about like beaver. He liked beaver. So did most of the men. He asked them how they liked dog, and though they were eating it as if the expected to bite into spiders they said it was all right. A few of the Indians were standing round watching them, contempt plain in their faces. Among the dogs which he traded for next was a pup that belonged to a squaw. Her man traded it for a few beads and at once she began to wail and tear at her leather skirt and her hair, as though all her children had been stripped from her. Lewis had never seen a woman weep with such wild abandon. He was about to give the pup to her when he thought, No, if I give it to her, the whole damned tribe will be weeping around us!

Captain Clark quietly wrote in his Journal, "our diet extremely bad . . . all the Party have greatly the advantage of me, in as much as they all relish the flesh of the dogs. . . ."

Clark refused to touch it. While eating dog flesh Lewis would look over at his friend, his eyes twinkling humorously, but he never twitted him about it. He knew that such prejudices lay deep against the human heart. But he did speculate, in his restless way, on Clark's motives, especially after catching a look of disgust and horror on the face of the slave-girl. She wouldn't touch dog either, or feed it to her child. Had Clark's repugnance, Lewis wondered, been determined in part by the woman's? It was impossible to know but this he did know, that Clark had become fond of her and her son, and she of him. Hardly a day passed that she didn't try to do something special for Chief Red Hair. On perceiving that Clark would not eat dog meat she took a few of the beads that she had brought on her person and traded for choicer pieces of salmon and in her shy way offered them to him.

At the junction of two big rivers, one coming up from the south out of stupendous mountains, the other down from the Divide in the east, whose waters they had ridden from the canoe camp, they paused to make observations. The river from the south was greenish-blue, the other as clear as crystal. It was down these two rivers, flowing as one, that they would ride to the Columbia. The men liked to dream of a journey on calm waters, while they lay back snoozing in the canoes. After the man-killing struggle up from the Great Falls they had convinced themselves that the Columbia would be a broad lazy stream like the Mississippi. But the pierced noses told them, by drawing maps in the dust or on elkskins, that they would encounter wild water innumerable times, all the way to the ocean.

"But at least," George Shannon said, "we won't have to buck it. It will be going our way."

28

They now discovered that different bands of the Flathead nation lived along the river, in small villages six or eight miles apart. Their first day out from the junction they stopped at a village and bought seven dogs; fifteen miles farther on they bought five dogs; and a few miles farther this same day they bought three dogs. The men had been so long used to meat, Sergeant Gass said in his Journal, that they didn't like fish, not even boiled salmon, and thought dog flesh a great treat. While eating supper the men would look now and then at the leashed dogs, yet to be eaten, or at Lewis's dog; and some of them decided that a man could get used to anything. Most of the men here were dog-lovers, yet here they sat, George Shannon reflected, stuffing their stomachs with nothing but dog meat. How strange it was, he thought, looking over at Lewis: the one captain was a dog-man, inseparable from his own beast, yet was smacking as loud as any; while the other captain, who had never shown any particular interest in dogs, sat apart eating tasteless camas roots and rancid fish. The slave-girl was sitting not far from George. He saw Clark glance at her a time or two but could not tell what the captain was thinking. George was thinking that she had been worth more than her weight in gold. Every time the party approached a village the Indians showed fright and hostility until they saw the girl. Then they came forward, smiling and friendly, for she was a token of peace. George doubted that any man in the party would be alive this day if she had not been with them.

The second afternoon out from the junction they suffered a disaster. Another dugout swung broadside to a stone, in swift rapid and both men and baggage spilled out. The canoe sank almost at once, and articles floated away—bedding, clothing, hides, shot pouches; while even more precious articles, such as tomahawks, a bag of powder and all their dried fish, went to the bottom. The men clung to the big stone until rescued and then all the other canoes hastened downstream to recover such articles as were still floating. Clark, watching from the shore, was thinking that by the time they reached the ocean, if not before, they would have nothing but the leather rags they stood in. If President Jefferson did not send a ship to take them home—if they had to retrace the long journey overland, what would they use for barter? How could they buy horses, or even feed themselves, if they had nothing to trade? He could see them parting with a gun, and another gun, a third, a fourth, until, having no guns left, they would stand defenseless. He felt terribly depressed this evening while chewing rancid salmon and camas roots but he forced himself to make a long recording in his Journal and there confessed nothing of his state of mind.

The next morning he sent hunters out but before noon they returned to say that there was no sign of game anywhere. Along the river there was no timber, not even sagebrush. The captains had resolved never to take from the red people but the previous night they had stolen two poles from a fish scaffold, and this evening they stole two rough planks. They had to have a fire to cook the dog flesh.

"I hope the Lord is looking the other way," Lewis said to Clark, while watching the men cut the planks into firewood. "I've observed though that it's a human habit to think that He looks the other way for us but not for those who oppose us."

"I expect," Clark said, "it's the Indians who aren't looking the other way."

There were no Indians in sight and no fish drying on this scaffold but the captains had no doubt that red men were watching them. They suspected that all the way down the Columbia they would never be free of them. The next day they had just made their evening fire when they were startled by wild sounds and loud singing; and on looking up they saw two hundred men marching toward them, while beating on leather drums and singing to the music. They came up and formed a half-circle round the white men and kept singing until they were given tobacco; and again Clark's thoughts turned gloomy. Almost all the men smoked or chewed or did both: what would their morale be like after all the tobacco was gone? Of course if there were trading ships at the mouth of the Columbia they could replenish their stores, for Lewis had a letter of credit. But if there were no ships? Lewis meanwhile was presenting a medal to the principal chief, and a shirt and a handkerchief; and smaller medals and handkerchiefs to two other chiefs. The Indians then went away to smoke but most of them soon returned, to beg or steal. One of them offered Clark a parcel of old dried horse meat that was chiefly fat. Clark accepted it, though he knew that a red man expected to receive ten or a hundred times as much as he gave.

The next morning Clark chose two men and went exploring. He expected to make a big map, put together from many small ones, of the entire region covered and he wanted it to be as complete as he could make it. So he went off up a branch river, pausing again and again to look at the huge quantities of fish drying on scaffolds, or at the piles of salmon along the banks which the squaws were getting ready to dry. At every village it was the same. There were also thousands of dead salmon along the shores or afloat in the river or on its bottom. He wondered what had killed all these fish. Squaws came to him, leading dogs which they wished to trade, for up and down the river had gone the word that the white men ate dogs. In one of the villages he was invited to enter, and the moment he was inside, a squaw brought a mat for him to sit on. Her man then brought a piece of driftwood and, using a wedge made of elkhorn, he split it into kindling and made up a fire. In the fire he put stones, and when these were hot they were dropped into a basket of water containing a large salmon. After a few minutes the fish was taken out and laid on a neat platter made of rushes. While Clark ate, the Indian boiled a fish for each of Clark's men waiting outside. After eating, Clark offered to smoke with his host, forgetting for the moment that these Indians smoked only in ceremony.

On his way back to camp he fell to thinking of the women in these villages. They were an ugly lot. They were fatter than most Indian women he had seen, with low broad faces, and heads so flattened that the line was straight from the nose to the crown. They wore, at least at this time of year, only a piece of leather tied round them at their hips, to which before and behind was attached a second piece drawn between their legs. In his Journal the shocked captain wrote that the squaws barely "hide those parts which are so sacredly hid & scured by our women." He did not think himself overly fastidious in these things but looking at these Columbia River Indians made him feel ill: they were just too fat and filthy and naked. But he did reflect, with pleasure, that here the men took on themselves a part of the drudgery, and that youth showed respect to age. In one of the lodges he saw an old woman who was, the Indians told him with signs, completely blind, yet she occupied the choicest position in the hut and when she spoke she was listened to. He did not like to reflect on the appalling prevalence of blindness, and eyes hideous with partial blindness, sores and pus. Was blindness caused by the brightness of the sun on river waters, or by the diet? The captains, and their men too, had also observed the lamentable condition of these people's teeth. In nearly all of them the teeth were bad. Many had no teeth at all. In some they were worn even with the gums. Had they abraded and ground their teeth down by eating roots without washing the sand off them?

There was one advantage to his party in all this: the women were so shapeless and hideous, their heads were so fantastically misshapen, their mouths were so ugly and their breath so dreadful that not even the most woman-hungry man in the Corps could feel amorous toward them.

William Bratton, looking at one of them, had cried, "Holy grandma!" and had gone on staring. Bob Frazier was expressing his wonder in jingles, to the delight of the men: "Oh, her lips unclose on the breath of the rose! The shape of her skull, oh, it's beautifull . . . !"

When a score of the squaws gathered round, to twitter and fall against one another, showing to the fullest their unsightly teeth and, in profile, the horrible deformation of their skulls, George Shannon looked at them and sucked his apple-cheeks in. Then from somewhere he took a fishbone and thoughtfully picked at his teeth. Silas Goodrich bugged his eyes at them, his mouth open. Alex Willard scowled. Even York seemed to have no interest in these women: when three or four came up to him and, twittering and acting frightfully silly, rubbed at his skin and examined his kinky hair, and when after a few minutes a half-dozen of the short bandy-legged braves came up and also began to rub, the big Negro exploded with a terrible howl of rage and, snatching a knife from his jacket, he waved it and cut the air with it, his eyes rolling in such a hideous way that his master became alarmed. Clark shouted at him and York at once subsided and returned the knife to his belt. He still looked surly and dangerous. The Indians backed away from him, their eyes saying plainly that they didn't know whether he was man or beast.

Frazier was intoning, "Please, my love, please give me part of your fleas! Take me to your home, doll, where ten billion fleas crawl . . . !"

"Hop," said George Shannon, still picking his teeth.

It took a lean flea to hop, Frazier said. Those on these beautiful maidens were so fat they could only crawl.

October 16th was a day they would never forget. After running another series of rapids and getting a canoe stuck and wetting everything in it, after taking their midday meal and floating down calm water for an hour, the men in the rear heard the men in the lead canoe yelling their heads off. Those behind knew that it was the Columbia. "The Columbia at last!" an awed voice said, as it might have said, "So this is heaven!" The Columbia! The men were standing up and craning their necks. The Columbia! They had come four thousand miles to find this river and there it was, with the Kooskooskee and the Kimooenim pouring into it. And there was a host of Indians coming to greet them, singing, dancing and beating on drums. The captains decided to camp here. The fire-makers, the wood-gatherers, the cooks first had to get a better look at this great river, about which they had heard all their lives, about which they had been thinking and dreaming for more than a year.

With an ironic smirk Frazier gestured at the river, at this point about half a mile wide, and said to the men around him, "The Columbia."

"You never thought it was here, did you?" Shannon said.

"Georgie boy, do you believe in the Euphrates?—the Ganges?—the Po?"

"All right, what proof have we that this is the Columbia?"

Brannon said, "Our captains have taken hundreds of celestial readings. They know."

"Did you hear that?" Frazier asked.

"If it isn't the Columbia," Alex Willard said, "what is it?"

"The Mississippi," Frazier said.

"The Ohio," said George.

"It might be the Ganges."

"Or the Thames."

"I expect," Frazier said, "we'd better call it the Columbia or our captains will go on forever."

The next morning the captains were busy, Lewis writing down, with Shannon's help, a few dozen words in the language of the Indians here, whom he called the Sokulks; while Clark with two men was off *up* the Columbia to see what it was like. Throughout this day and for several days to come a man would suddenly cry out, "Columbia!" The other men would look at him, some gravely, some with grins in their dirty beards. For a few of them, led by Frazier, it became a kind of sport, this sudden shouting of the word when the other men least expected it; and the nonsense went so far that in the dead of night the lone incredible word would ring out like a bugle. That they had actually reached the Columbia was a little more than some of them could believe. The captains seemed to take it for granted but those who looked deepest into the captains knew that they were both so self-disciplined that their emotions and thoughts rarely came to the surface. That was it, Shannon thought, lying in his blankets and looking up at the stars: not military discipline, as he had imagined, but just plain self-discipline. It was a wonder in both of them, but especially in Lewis, for whom discipline came hard. Neither captain had betrayed by a gesture or a word that he was happy, after almost a year and a half and nearly four thousand miles, to see this river which he had risked his life to see. . . .

At this camp forty dogs were purchased with a few thimbles, needles, beads and bells. Like the upriver dogs, they were small. The men wondered if they would taste fishy. What else did they have to eat? They were of many colors—black, white, brown and spotted —with a long head, small ears erect like those of the wolf, and short smooth hair except on the tail. Because Lewis's dog was three times as large as any of them they showed him wonderful respect, hardly daring even to sniff him. Still refusing dog meat, Clark shot a river bird now and then, preferring the stringy and almost fleshless crane to dog.

For two days now the journey was uneventful. On the 19th, while sitting on a high stone by the river, waiting for the canoes, Clark saw a crane flying overhead and shot it. Below him, across the river, he had noticed an Indian village, and he now saw some Indians running downstream, as though in fright. Afraid that they might arouse the nation and come against him, Clark entered a canoe when it came up and told the men to put him across. On the other side he approached the lodges but saw no sign of Indians anywhere. The entrances had been closed with reed mats. He had brought the three men in the canoe with him and now told them to wait.

With his pipe in his hand he drew the mat aside and stepped into the nearest lodge, and was astonished to see it jammed full of men, women and children. His astonishment grew when he saw that the women were sobbing with terror and wringing their hands, the men sitting with bowed heads, as though awaiting the executioner. Clark offered his pipe to the men to smoke but they seemed paralyzed. He then took from a pocket a few needles, awls and pieces of ribbon and pressed them on the squaws. One or two of them smiled and tried to hush their grief. What on earth was wrong with these people!

Leaving this lodge, he entered another and found the Indians there in a frenzy of fear. Again he offered a few gifts and tried to smoke with the men. He entered a third lodge, a fourth, a fifth. He told the three men waiting for him, the Fields brothers and Drewyer, that the Indians here were scared to death. Drewyer went forward and tried to convince the Indians that the white men were friendly. Clark went off a few yards and, sitting on a stone, beckoned to the red men to come over and smoke with him. They refused to budge. The squaws were sticking their heads out with tears running down their cheeks, and children were clinging to them, crying. Trying to solve the riddle, Clark now recalled that he had twice in the lodges kindled his pipe with his sun glass. But surely that was not it.

Lewis now came over with two upriver chiefs, who were riding with the party. In sign language Drewyer now told the chiefs what had happened, and they went over to talk to the Indians. They came back and told this story. These Indians had seen the big bird fall from the sky but because a bank of cloud obscured it they thought that Clark himself had come down. There had been the thunder of his gun—and what was that, they asked, for they had never seen a gun. Then in the lodges he had put his pipe to his mouth and with medicine so big that it dwarfed their minds to think of it he had brought fire down from the sky.

"Have never seen a gun?" Clark said. "How can that be?"

Lewis said, "I think you can take over this tribe now as head chief. Look, they're bringing you gifts."

This was true. The poor terrified creatures were bringing wood, which for them was more precious than food. They were begging him to accept dried fish and dried berries. The red men, beside themselves with joy because the dreadful one from the skies was not going to destroy them, also begged Clark to take their wives and daughters. Clark was embarrassed by their gift-giving. He was wondering how he could convince them that the white men were friendly when, looking over at the canoes, he saw Sacajawea. He beckoned to her and sent her among the squaws to tell them why the white men were here. As if by magic the fear and suspicion left Indian faces and all the red people came over to watch the white men make camp.

This evening Lewis had Cruzatte play his fiddle, and York dance. The Indians were delighted. Like children who after sorrow had found kindness, they were embarrassingly effusive in their expressions of joy: they brought wood to the cooks, dried fish and berries to the captains, and several trinkets to the slave-girl. Knowing that all the Indians were covered with fleas, the men tried to keep away from them but they kept crowding in and all but the cooks kept moving back—and back—with the Indians following them, black eyes staring with childlike envy at the pots, the utensils, the guns and knives, all of which they had never seen before and could only regard as magic beyond their understanding. George Shannon found it painful to look at their faces, yet was so fascinated by what he saw in them that he had to look; for never in white faces, not even in the faces of small ignorant children, had he seen covetousness so absolutely naked—so naked and unashamed and elemental that he could not resent it, could only wish to say, "Take the things, damn it, take them, and get that look out of your eyes!" But George, an abnormally sensitive young man, saw things that most of the men missed. For such as Werner and Windsor, Hall and Howard and McNeal they were a gang of ugly stinking thieving rascals, with cheekbones so high they looked swollen, with misshapen bodies that smelled of fish.

The party was approaching a timm. This was the Indian word for the great cataracts on the Columbia, pronounced with a resonant humming sound that suggested the distant pouring of waters. There would be a lot of timms, the red men said. Five days after sighting the Columbia they came to the first timm, whose sound they had heard for two days and one night. Beaching the canoes, they all went down to have a look at it.

This one would not be difficult, Cruzatte, their riverman, said, but the men unable to swim the captains sent down the bank. Sacajawea and her man were among those who walked. Soon the girl slipped away from him and searched the area for roots, berries and nuts for

Chief Red Hair. Every day she tried to find food that he liked, for he still refused to eat dog, though once he had tasted it after hearing one of the men say that it was better than elk loin or buffalo hump, better even than beef. Instead of dog, Clark ate anything he could find, and shared what he found with the girl and her child—a crane one day, which was little more than the bones of its long legs and neck; a coot another day, a tough insipid waterfowl that tasted of bogs; and on a third day a mallard duck.

Hidden away inside her leather jacket Sacajawea had a two-ounce piece of bread that she had carried so long that it was hard and soured. She had hidden it for her child, afraid the time would come when there would be nothing to eat, not even tree bark. Lately she had been wondering if she should offer it to Clark. She decided against it as long as he seemed active and vigorous. Her son seemed to thrive on anything she gave him and would eat anything. He was not yet nine months old but he was trying to walk and trying to talk, his round black eyes looking everywhere. Once in a while Clark would go up to the boy when he stood in his saddle on his mother's back and pinch his little chin or tweak his small lump of a nose. No matter what Clark did the child would gravely regard him as though speculating on his nature and motives. "How's my boy Pomp?" Clark would say.

Below the first timm was wilder water, where enormous stones, looking as if they had fallen from the sheer walls that confined the river, lay scattered in the current, forcing the boatmen to use all their strength and skill to get the dugouts through. The whole day October 21st was spent in toil down a series of rapids. That evening John Collins, grinning all over, offered the captains a drink of what he called beer. He said he had made it with pashicoquarmash, the captains' name for bread made of camas-root flour. At the head of the Kooskooskee River they had baked a few large loaves of bread and brought it with them but it had molded and soured. Collins had put the bread in a kettle and fermented it. Though Lewis was non-committal, Clark said the beer was excellent. Collins said, "Captain, I figgered we need something to cheer us up. Our faces get longer by the mile."

None of the men had their former zest. Not a one of them had fully recovered from the ordeal of crossing the mountains, when they had nearly starved to death. They all said that they felt well but most of them lied about it. They were as bold as ever, as faithful in their duties, as uncomplaining, but a part of the dashing adventurousness had gone out of them. They had overworked too long and starved too long. They had endured, Lewis told himself, as much as men had ever endured, and lived, but something had gone out of them. He saw this when, smoking by the fire in the evenings, he watched them: they just didn't move with their old zip. They didn't have their flesh back, their color, the health-glow in their eyes. They were not as unfleshed as they had been when they came out of the mountains but they were all underweight, their cheeks were sunken, their step slower. If only Mr. Jefferson had a boat waiting for them at the mouth of the Columbia!

The next day they came to a real timm, where the whole stupendous body of the river was driven through a narrow channel, the water foaming white over great stones and then plunging into falls whose roaring could be heard for miles. They would have to portage here. The distance was less than a mile but was strewn with sharp stones. The men carried the baggage while the captains, still exploring, found a small side channel down which the canoes could be taken. Red men came eagerly to help carry the burdens and it took white men some time to discover that while an Indian was carrying a parcel he was all the while slipping various articles inside his clothing, or to squaws and children, who then made off in great haste.

"I'll be damned!" said Sergeant Ordway, after examining a parcel which an Indian had carried. "By the time I'm an old man I'll have no faith left in the human race."

"By the time he's an old man," said Frazier, leering round at the bearded faces. "The sergeant says by the time he's an old man."

"If he wasn't my superior," George Shannon said, "I'd say he was a little slow learning."

"My God!" said Ordway in a stricken voice. "They stole a tomahawk!"

"The sergeant says they stole a tomahawk," said Frazier, again leering.

"They'll show it to everybody," Shannon said. "We'll feel like thieves when we take it away from them."

"Him," said Frazier, indicating George, "he takes Captain Lewis real serious when he talks about us and the Indians being brothers. We just all steal from one another, like any big family."

John Colter came up. He said the Indians here had a curious way of storing dried fish and the captains thought the men would like to see it. Most of the men did not have Meriwether Lewis's insatiable interest in everything under the sun, from the way a root grew underground or a coot's feet were shaped to Indian language, dress, lodges, customs—or the drying of salmon. They might as well go, Frazier said: it would be a chance again to feast their eyes on the squaws, to observe how delicately they were formed, and with what sweet scents they made themselves irresistible.

"A brow divinely formed. Did Shakespeare say that? He must have seen the Flatheads. See yon child, his head under the spruce plank, flattened out like the bill of a platypus. My little red brother! See yon damsel, how beautifully her legs are swollen from calf to crotch, because she binds leather straps round her ankles. Lift her arm gaily in the dance and sniff the sweet odors. Pull back the leather girdle and count the fleas. My flatheaded red sister! Bend above her in the moonlight and touch your lips to the fish grease in her hair. Take up her hand, and notice how much old salmon fat is under her fingernails. My red sister, my red brother . . . !"

Some of the men were howling with laughter but George Shannon's blue eyes were fixed on Frazier with a kind of innocent wonder. He hurried on ahead, for he had spotted the captains with a group of Indians. The squaws were making salmon stacks.

After drying the fish and pounding it into fish meal they put it in baskets made of grass and rushes. These, about two feet long and a foot wide, were lined with salmon skins. After the baskets were solidly packed with the meal they were stacked one on another, each wrapped in a grass mat. Twelve baskets, each holding almost a hundred pounds of meal, formed a stack.

Lewis said, speaking to his men around him, "As far as I can learn, this fish meal keeps for years. They sell it to white traders at the mouth of the river."

He spoke with such enthusiasm that the men stared at him, wondering why he was so interested in the matter. One of them said politely, "And what do the traders do with it, Captain?"

That's what he intended to find out, Lewis said. This species of fish seemed to be in the rivers by the hundreds of millions. There might be a world market for it. If the United States got control of the salmon, instead of the damned British—— But at that point he broke off, feeling that he had said too much.

Did the traders, George Shannon wondered, sell the meal to unsuspecting people who had never seen a squaw's way with salmon?

This evening he sat with a plate of boiled dog but he had no appetite: he was thinking of the filthy hands of the squaws; the way fleas fell off them and into the salmon baskets as they bent over, sweating and toiling; and of the sweat that dripped to the basket and was kneaded into the meal. If only the buyers could see all the things that went into a stack of salmon!

His mouth stuffed full and his speech thick, Dick Windsor said, "Whuh matter, George? Not hungry tonight?"

"Not very," George said.

Windsor was staring at George's plate. Reaching out with his own, he said, "If you got more there than you want——"

With his knife George shoved the dog meat off to Dick's plate.

Bill Bratton said, "He's thinking of big fat juicy elk steaks."

"Or mebbe the pie his ma used to make. You got a ma, George?"

Setting his plate aside, George moved over to the shadows and stretched out on his back. He was a little homesick tonight. When his father got lost two years ago and froze to death he left a widow and nine children, of whom George was the oldest. He was glad he had come on this great adventure, he would not have missed it for the world, but he just couldn't get used to the things some of the men did. Well, they were all getting dirtier, mile by mile; they all had fleas now because these Columbia River Indians were lousy with them. They all smelled of rancid fish. He thought they all smelled like men who had been sick.

He wished he had a chance to get lost again. He could then dress and cook his own meat; find clean water and soak for an hour in the luxury of a bath; clean his toes and trim his toenails, dig out his ears and scratch the dandruff out with cactus thorns, without having men stare at him and think him effeminate. Lord in heaven, he might even get rid of the fleas!

29

It wasn't hell enough, the men said, to struggle all day long in the most terrible water they had ever seen. They now had fleas. They had had them ever since they came to the fish-eating Indians, and the farther down the Columbia they went the thicker the pests became. October 23rd they came to a stretch of river that one man in his Journal called terrifying and another horrible; and they had hardly begun to take the larger dugouts through when they realized that fleas were practically eating them alive. At the head of these rapids the Indians had recently camped, leaving strewn about an immense quantity of old dry grass and salmon skins. In the skins and grass the fleas had taken up their abode by the millions.

The first cry came as usual from Bob Frazier. "Holy St. Peter!" he said, standing knee-deep in water and staring down over his leather garments. "Look how they're swarming over me."

Other men were brushing at their clothes or across their long matted hair and down over their beards.

Frazier waded to the bank and began to strip off. "If any women come around," he said, "they'll just have to look."

Silas Goodrich said, "What do you have they'd want to look at?"

"I'll be damned if I'll let bugs eat me alive, just to be modest."

All the boatmen stripped to their moccasins. Up the Missouri they had gone day after day stripped to their waists, and the upper part of them was now almost as brown as an Indian. Their lower torso and upper legs were white. Some of them, like Frazier, Labiche and Cruzatte, had long beards. Wrinkling his nose, George Shannon was looking at the naked long-bearded ones. He thought they looked preposterous, with long hair falling down their shoulders, beards hanging down from their chins, half of them white and half of them brown, with their feet in moccasins. There they stood, searching in their beards and in the hair of their bodies for fleas.

"What in hell is a flea, anyway?" said Frazier.

"Captain Lewis would know."

"A flea," Shannon said, "is a hard wingless bloodsucker with a hop twice that of a kangaroo and ten times that of a frog."

For a moment the men looked at George. "Where they suck they leave a red spot," Silas said.

George said, "We're all flea-bitten sons of disaster."

Again the men looked at him.

"You can't drown them," Frazier said. "Yesterday I sunk my shirt and piled rocks on it and left it an hour. Every flea was still on it and as spry as ever. Cooled off and hungrier, that's all."

"What wonders me," said Goodrich, searching his beard, "is how the Indians stand it."

"You notice they keep moving, from camp to camp, with millions of fleas hopping right along after them."

"If you look at the Indians close," Goodrich said, "you see flea-bites all over them."

"My God, have you been in their huts? You can see ten million fleas sitting in rows looking right at you and if you step inside they all jump."

"These," said Joe Whitehouse, holding one by a jumping-leg and looking at it, "are four times as big as those back home."

"They get more to eat," Frazier said. "They chew on these fat squaws all day long."

"We better get going," George said.

Frazier said, "On a journey like this it's nice not to be able to swim. Where are the men who can't swim? All gone hunting."

"It's better to be a good shot," Silas said. "John Collins, when we started he couldn't hit the broad side of a barn but now, look, he's almost as good as Drewyer."

"Oh no, Clark is next to Drewyer."

"Anyway, is John in the river?"

The men had waded back in, leaving their garments on the bank, and Frazier now thrust his head under and made underwater howls and gurglings. He brought his head up and shook water from his long wavy hair. "It does no good," he said. "It just cools them off so they can bite harder."

The Indians always came to watch the white men struggle with their boats down the rapids. Today word spread that the men had stripped off their clothing, and as thick as waterfowl along the banks stood women and children, gawking. Attached to each canoe was a long rope of elkskin: the men would ease the boat down the rapids ahead of them, feeding the rope out, until the boat came to safer water. Four of them, in water to their waists, had braced themselves behind huge stones and were letting one of the two largest dugouts down over boiling white water when the rope broke and all four men fell backwards and went under. They came up, clawing and cursing, and stood together, the water bursting white against their backs, and watched the ugly ill-balanced canoe riding down over the waves, headed straight for the next cataract. A dozen Indian men were running down the bank. Some of the squaws were shrilling at the men out in the river but they had no idea of what the women were saying. Frazier waved to them and wafted kisses, and shouted across the roaring waters, "Pick all the bugs off of you tonight and I'll be over! Oh, my adorable flea-bitten cuddly little red-squaw kitten!"

"You'd think," Silas Goodrich said, "you could stick your head in this swift water and it would wash them away. Hold me." The men braced themselves and seized his arms, and Silas thrust his shaggy wet head under white water where it came foaming down from great stones. He kept thrusting and turning his head, letting the water drive full in his face, into his ears, across his forehead and over his skull. Then he clasped a strand of hair close to the roots and brought it through his clenched palm. He looked at his palm and saw two fleas. "Holy Mother!" he said.

This evening the men sat naked by campfires searching their clothes. The captains had been talking to an old Indian who had come up the river. This man, a minor chief, had in sign language told Drewyer that the Indians down below intended to massacre the white party. Drewyer took the news to Clark, and Clark to Lewis. Now the captains were talking about it and looking round them. There was something queer all right, Lewis said, because at sunset two hundred and fifty Indians had surrounded their camp, but the moment dusk came they had all slunk away. These river Indians had never done that before. On the contrary, the pests had always tried to stay all night.

"Yes," Clark said, looking everywhere, "they've all left us. That means they think we are going to be attacked."

"It couldn't mean anything else."

"I'll give orders to have all weapons inspected and our ammunition brought up to a hundred rounds." Clark went to the fire and summoned all the men to a single group. When they were attentive and waiting he told them what the old Indian chief had told Drewyer. They were to see that all their weapons were in first-class order and that there was plenty of ammunition. He looked round him and said, "Haven't Drewyer and Collins come in?"

Ordway said, "No, Captain."

"Proceed at once to get everything in order."

While the men were melting lead and pouring bullets they talked about this new menace but they were not alarmed. They had developed a vigorous contempt for the red man as a fighter. Even though they supposed that there were hundreds or thousands of warriors downriver, all with weapons furnished by white traders, they jested about it.

"Did you notice how they all slipped away tonight? They're up to something."

One of the men pouring bullets looked round him and said, "Have the two chiefs gone?"

The men all looked round them then. There was no sign of the chiefs.

"Well, I guess our red brothers are going to come after our scalps. And pretty damned fancy scalps they are too," Ordway said, looking at the long-haired men.

"Holy mother of Moses," said Joe Whitehouse. "They might even take our beards too."

"Peel us right down to our collarbones, maybe."

The scowling Alex Willard looked round and said, "How many is each one of us good for?"

One of the men who had been an Indian fighter spoke up. "Ten," he said.

"Ten? Only ten?"

"It depends on the man," George Shannon said. "Drewyer, he would be equal to five of me."

"More than that," Bratton said. "More than that of me, anyway."

"Well now, if we could all shoot like Drewyer and Captain Clark—

hell, if we was all as good as Collins and Colter and the Fields brothers . . ."

"Yeh," said Joe. "You should a-seen me miss the crane yesterday."

"They're all good for ten each," said Frazier. "Some of them are good for five. Me, I'll wrassle the squaws."

"One squaw down," said George, "and a hundred and sixty dead Indians."

"But what if they all have good rifles? What if a thousand of them come with good rifles?"

"Shoot fifty and they'll all run away."

"How you think Captain Clark looked? Worried?"

"You never can tell about him. He always looks the same."

And so the men talked among themselves while pouring hot lead. The two elderly Chopunnish chiefs, now hiding out in darkness, had wanted to go home. They seemed, Lewis reflected, to live in deadly fear of the red men down the river, who were armed, they told the captains, with rifles, knives and tomahawks. The captains had persuaded them to linger a day or two longer, promising that they would do their best to make peace between them and their ancient enemies. The chiefs had said they would stay one more sleep, possibly two, but they were so afraid that they had slunk back into the darkness to hide. It was the behavior of these two experienced old warriors that convinced the captains that their party might have to face hostile Indians before it reached the ocean.

Lewis pretended to feel that all was well. He looked into the skin tent which he shared with Clark and saw his friend bent over his endless map-making. What a persevering man he was! Nothing neither cold nor wet nor hunger, sickness nor danger, could keep Will Clark from his duties. His desk had been smashed when the horse rolled with it down a mountain and now for a table he used a piece of smooth plank that he had found in a pile of driftwood. He was sitting on the earth with his plank on a pile of bedding, a make shift candle at his elbow. Nearly every night Clark wrote in his Journal. Lewis seldom bothered to write anything down on this stretch of the journey: there was not much to excite him along here and besides, he could copy from Clark later. Copying from his friend always amused him, because again and again he was convinced that Clark's spelling was wrong, yet could never be sure that his own was right.

He went over to the fire where men were pouring bullets. The looked up as their captain approached, their eyes searching his face. They could never read anything in Clark's face but in Lewis's face, or anyway in his eyes, they usually could see the lights of his thoughts. Was he anxious? O Lord, he always looked anxious, in a queer intense way. Was he mirthful? He always was. He always looked as though he were about to roll a quip off his tongue.

"Captain Lewis," said the grave Sergeant Pryor, "have you heard anything more?"

"Only the nightingales. Well, Sergeant, nothing really. We've persuaded the two old chiefs to stay for one or two more sleeps but I expect they'll sneak away before morning."

"They're afraid, are they, Captain?"

"All Indians are afraid. It's always the man who's afraid who is so earnest to prove his courage."

"You know, Captain," George Shannon said, "I've been thinking. It——"

"He really expects us to believe that," Frazier said.

"—seems we never have any trouble with the red men unless they've had dealings with white men. The Snakes and the pierced noses, they gave us no trouble at all."

"Well now, that's right," Bill Bratton said.

"I had thought of that, Private Shannon. I expect you're dead-right."

Lewis thought of George's remark while returning to the tent. Yes, he guessed Shannon was right: the Corps all the way from home had had the most trouble with those Indians who knew the white man best. The Shoshones had never seen a white man and, except for their eagerness to get to buffalo land, they had been as gentle as women—if anyone but simpletons could believe women gentle after seeing squaws. The pierced noses had been gentle too, at least until the captains began to purchase dogs. But the downriver Indians, they would be another matter: for many years they had been trading with white men at the Columbia's mouth, and no doubt they all had venereal diseases by this time and had learned that white traders were all damned rascals. Was there after all something in the myth of the noble savage, before the white man corrupted him?

Did Captain Clark think so?

Clark looked up from his labor and considered the question. "Innocent," he said. "Not noble."

"Oh. Innocent?"

"That's not just the word I want," said Clark, who had, though he lacked formal education, an extensive vocabulary. "Guileless, maybe that's it."

"Guileless in the way of children before they learn the ways of adults?"

"Yes, that's it."

"But they're crafty and treacherous."

"So are children."

"Maybe they have to be crafty because by nature they're so trustful. Would you say that?"

Clark considered the question. He was not an impulsive man. He said he would think about it and tell his friend later what he thought.

"Another funny thing," Lewis said. "No animal seems to be afraid of man until after he hears a lot of gunfire. We could almost walk up to buffalo, elk, deer, antelope, beaver, otter. But the time will come when at sight of us they'll run."

"I expect so," Clark said.

"I hope," Lewis said drily, "that time also comes for the British."

Lewis unrolled his bedding and, stretching out, lay in thought. He was full of worries and anxieties tonight. His President had said, "When you reach the mouth of the Columbia, send two of your most trusted men back by sea if you can, with a copy of all your notes and maps." Good Lord, had Mr. Jefferson not foreseen what a huge task it would be to copy all the maps and notes, of which they already had enough to make three large books! Lewis was a man who obeyed orders, but how could he obey that order? He was a man whose mind turned whimsical when looking straight at the plain implication in the President's words, that two were to come by boat, the others were all expendable. Still, Jefferson had said, "You may all return by sea if the way overland looks too dangerous." He didn't like those words either: they implied that there actually *were* things that could make him and Will Clark turn aside. Meriwether Lewis honestly could think of none. Not on this continent anyway.

If there was no ship waiting for them—and the captains had about decided that there would be none, lest its presence give alarm and offense to the Spanish down the coast—the party would have to return overland, and the return would be more difficult than the outward journey. The red man might be guileless but the guileless man when disillusioned was the most terrible of all men. The Indians were children. All those between the Sioux and the ocean would be disillusioned by the time they saw the captains again, for they expected traders to come at once, to bring them weapons, food, bushels of blue beads, cocked hats and red coats, medals and commissions. Every chief they had talked to was now dreaming of being a chief as big as the one in Washington. People who had little, Lewis had learned, placed no limits on covetousness, once their imaginations were kindled.

Every tribe along the way home would know just how many men were in the white party. They would know that they could safely attack it without danger of being surprised by a larger party, coming from behind, and without fear of vengeance. But worst of all would be the want of beads, knives and trinkets to trade for food, horses, boats. If there were traders at the Columbia with the merchandise the party would need, why, then, he had a letter of credit; but though a chronic optimist by force of will he was a hypochondriac in his depths. He drove himself to expect the best but privately expected the worst.

Feeling fleas biting, he moved over to candlelight and, stripping off his shirt, began to look along the seams, still thinking. He was recalling the President's words, "It is impossible for us to foresee in what manner you will be received by those people." In the library at Monticello, Jefferson had said, "It's impossible even to guess how many different nations you may find, of whose existence no white man today has any suspicion; or whether they will be warlike or peaceable; or with what amazement or fear they may look upon you. It is therefore impossible to say whether at some point you should decide to turn back, or whether you should persevere to the end. All such things must be left to your judgment. . . ."

Lewis had not told his President that not once during those after-midnight talks had the thought occurred to him that he might turn back. He was not the sort who ever turned back, nor his friend who sat here painstakingly drawing a map: not all the Indians in the whole world could make them turn back, nor any other danger known to him. It was not at all a matter of risking their lives: they would explore this immense unknown land and set the flag of the United States in so many places on it, and leave so many tree-blazings and records on it, that the insufferable British would never have the gall to lay claim to it. Even so, the claim to it of the United States might not stick if the party was wiped out: when the red man destroyed the white man, wishing to put himself beyond suspicion and vengeance, he left no evidence scattered around, least of all buttons and bones. If only they could send all the maps and notes safely to Washington—for if they returned overland, as they had come, the Blackfeet would be waiting for them. Loss of all their lives would be such a small price to pay for such enormous gain, but there might be no gain if the notes and maps were lost. Tree-blazings could be quickly effaced and flags perished in a little while, but such maps as Will Clark was making His Majesty's government could never laugh away. . . .

It was past midnight and Clark was still drafting. Lewis stood above him a few moments looking at the map.

Clark said, "The big job will be putting all the little ones together."

"I expect so," Lewis said. He went to the tent door and looked out. The fire had died down and was a tubful of glowing embers. Downstream he saw a night watchman slowly pacing, and upstream another. Clark had put some of the most dependable men on guard tonight but the captains knew that the Indians would never attack them here. Returning to his bed, Lewis laid the top blanket back and crawled in and then lay on his back with the blanket drawn to his chin, his beard above the blanket. His friend Clark said he snored turribel. At his side lay his dog, scratching. The sound of the waterfalls was still a tremendous roaring but down below, the two chiefs said, was water so dreadful that it could be heard beyond the southern mountains. Well, after they passed the narrows and the big chutes they would move on a river that became steadily wider as it approached the sea. Five more sleeps, the older chief said, and they would be looking upon Salt-Water-Everywhere. They would find the river choked with sea otter, and all around them would be herds of deer and elk. Yes, and Indians with the white disease, Lewis thought, sinking into sleep.

30

The great river here passed through a mountain range, with such a churning and roaring of its waters as no member of the party had ever seen. Clark in his efforts to describe the awesome spectacle searched his vocabulary for big strong words: "in those narrows the water was agitated in a most shocking manner boils swells & whorlpools. . . . I put all the men who could not swim on shore." But he well knew that even an expert swimmer would stand no chance at all in the stupendous plunging waters of this gorge, which the captains called the short narrows. The confining stone walls choked the river to a width of only fifty yards, and there the water "swels and boils with a most tremendeous manner." All the more valuable things, such as papers and maps, guns and ammunition Clark sent overland by the men who could not swim. The big green dugout canoes were much too heavy for portaging: the men could only try to ease them down the cascading water with long leather ropes. Other ropes, attached to stones on the bank, were flung out into the current for the men to seize, if they fell or were hurled down. Indians lined the precipices above to watch the intrepid white men, astonished that they would undertake to pass boats over such waters, even more astonished when the men did it without loss of life.

The next series of falls, the Chopunnish chiefs said, would be worse. Clark found its first plunge to be a sheer twenty feet, straight down; and just below it "a tremendious black rock Presented itself high and Steep appearing to choke up the river . . . The whole of the Current of this great river must at all Stages pass thro' this narrow chanel of 45 yards wide." The boatmen were amazed to learn, after viewing this dreadful plunge, that they were still in the short narrows. The long narrows were still to come, and only the Great Architect, Frazier said, knew how many chutes. The men would not have believed that they could take boats down such water. Captain Clark, a determined man, had said, "Of course you can," and this evening he wrote in his Journal, "I deturmined to pass through this place notwithstanding the horrid appearance of this agitated gut swelling, boiling & whorling in every direction . . ."

Naked but for their moccasins and almost as tough as hawthorn, the men delighted in matching their strength and skill against a foe in whose thunderous downrushing maelstroms death could be swift, if they lost a foothold and fell. With a gallantry that both captains took note of and privately admired, the men would pause in their dangerous labors to look up at the squaws, half-overhanging on the ledges above, and blow kisses. With spray and foam blinding him and driving like stinging sleet over his naked body, with such a roaring in his ears that he could not have heard his own voice, even if he had shouted, Bob Frazier would pause, press a wet palm to his lips and gesture upward, crying, "O form dee-vine will you be mine?"

The next morning the two captains walked down the river to see the spot which the old chief said was the worst of all. Silent, the two men looked at it and then up at the sheer stone walls. In their minds was the same thought, that this part of what they called the gut could be passed only with the gravest risk. What if they were to lose some of their men here? Portaging was out of the question. Unless they were to abandon their dugouts and go overland they had to pass these waters. The river here, Clark was to write a little later, plunged "through a hard rough black rock, from 50 to 100 yards wide, swelling and boiling in a most tremendious maner. . . ." The men with the dugouts took one quick view of the scene and then went forth, with hundreds of Indians crouching above and looking down on them. One canoe half-turned broadside, dipped and almost filled with water; but, righting itself the next moment, it went straight and true, even though half-sunk, to a calmer haven. The last of the five also dipped and half-filled but bore away safely. It was, the captains told themselves, a marvelous exhibition of skill and courage.

It was along here, the old chief said, that certain Flathead tribes levied tribute on all who passed. They would demand guns, at least and possibly the girl. The two chiefs were now so filled with terror that with tears in their eyes they begged to be released; and so the captains smoked a farewell pipe with them and sent them on their way. Like old Toby, they lost no time.

Clark shrewdly figured that the Indians would not dare attack after witnessing the incredible heroism and gallantry of the men with the boats. Red warriors came to the camp every night but instead of looking round them, as was their habit, for articles they might filch they stared with unconcealed admiration at the boatmen. The boatmen, sitting naked by the evening fire and searching their garments for fleas, paid little attention to them. These Indians were even more flatheaded and ugly than those upriver. The squaws were so repulsive in both their appearance and odors that not a man among them, not even Gibson, Whitehouse or York, could feel any yearning toward them.

Through the long narrows and through the chutes—through all the most dangerous stretch of this mighty river that gathered so many big rivers to its bosom—with hundreds of Indians gazing down from the ledges above, the boatmen labored, with a skill and daring that astonished even their captains. And not once was there a hostile gesture from the red men. They would have applauded, if applause had been one of their ways to show admiration. For the most part they simply stared, their black eyes shifting from face to face; from face to powerful bronzed shoulders—for these Indians were even more stunted than those above. Both captains had been observing that the farther down the Columbia they went the more unattractive in physical appearance the red people became. These men did not look like dangerous warriors.

They were bowlegged flatheaded runts, Paddy Gass said, and that was the opinion of the men.

October 29th one of the Flathead chiefs made a special effort to be friendly. He took Clark to a lodge and proudly showed off a few things he had got from white men—a sword, a jacket, a hat and a piece of scarlet and blue cloth. He had picked up a few English words and with the humorless pride of a small child he used them over and over, often without sense. If Clark pointed to an object the chief would say, "Good," with the o's sounded as in food; or he would say, "Damn," or, "Son of a pitch." With an imperious gesture he ordered his wife to fetch his medicine bag and with pride simply bursting from all his pores he drew out fourteen human fingers. He pointed into the southeast and Clark assumed that these had been cut from the hands of Shoshone Indians. He had not known that Indians ever took fingers as trophies. All these fingers the chief had painted red. He would look at them and stir them to show them off, and then up at Clark's face, to see if he was really impressed. Clark wondered if the fingers represented fourteen dead men, or three or four: as nearly as he could tell, there were no middle fingers or little fingers among them. Like one handling the most precious things in the world, the chief took up one finger after another, all the while talking in a loud singsong voice. Clark supposed he was boasting of his prowess over his enemies. Then with extreme care he returned the fingers to the medicine bag and handed the bag to his squaw, who all the while had stood back looking morose and sullen, her black eyes never leaving Clark's face. Clark wondered, as he had wondered so many times, when thinking of squaws, how any motherly gentleness could be left in a female who lived with such savage males.

A little farther down the river he was exploring one day, with Joe Fields at his side, when he came to an Indian cemetery. The graves here were vaults, about eight feet square and six feet in depth, made of pine or cedar planks. In these vaults the dead bodies were wrapped in skins and bound round with ropes of grass and bark, and laid out on mats. In one vault they saw four bodies side by side; in another were old bones to a depth of four feet. Attached to the vaults were brass kettles, frying pans, baskets, wooden bowls, sea shells, scraps of cloth, small pieces of bone—all of which had belonged to those buried here. On the planks which formed the vault sides were paintings or carvings of the human form. Roundabout in the earth were old vaults decayed and almost covered over with moss, leading Clark to suppose that this had been a burial place for ages. Did these Flathead Indians worship wooden idols? The captains had discussed the matter without deciding whether the objects in the huts were idols or ornaments.

Clark said to Joe, "I never see such a spot without thinking of Shakespeare. Who else has so well understood the briefness of life?"

Joe looked curiously at his captain. Shakespeare was only a word to him. He said, "They'll give almost anything for a brass kettle. Funny they leave them here."

"Is it fear of the dead, or reverence? I don't know."

Both men were feeling unusually solemn, as most people will in the presence of the dead. They moved softly, slowly, almost with exaggerated respect, as they went from object to object; and when they walked away from the place, like persons at a funeral they did not speak. The scene had kindled Clark's imagination: what had these people been, what sorrows had they endured, what hopes had died with them?

-The Corps had not yet passed all the more dangerous parts of the river. They now came to what they called the Great Chute or Falls, where Clark found the water "passing with great velocity forming [he meant foaming] & boiling in a most horriable manner." But this kind of danger the men were used to now and they faced it with a courage so reckless that again the Indians were popeyed. Most of the Indians were expert swimmers too but never in all their generations of life on this river had any of them run the narrows or the Great Chute with a canoe. The squaws came with their men to the campfires and even the most dull-witted of the white men could not fail to be aware of their fascinated admiration. They were ready to give themselves without pay but no man in the party could stand the sight of them; they had tumors and open sores; some of them were blind in one eye or half-blind in both and from their eyes ran an ill-smelling moisture; and they had teeth so hideous that when they smiled the white men shuddered. As Clark was to observe in his Journal, the women were small and homely, with swollen legs and thighs, and with remarkably bulging knees. He conjectured that their malformed legs came from their habit of sitting on their hams —for in such manner they would sit for hours, picking fleas off. They were "nearly necked wareing only a piece of leather tied about their breast which falls down nearly as low as the waste, a small roabe about 3 feet square, and a piece of leather tied about their breach . . . They are dirty in the extream." If the men could have stomached their sores and their filth, their teeth, their hideous legs, their odor, there still remained their monstrous flat skulls rising to a cone.

Bug-eyed, the men had watched the Indians press the heads of their infants. They hollowed out from a piece of cedar a form in the shape of a bread trough, and this they carved or left plain, depending on their tastes. This *canim* or canoe or cradle was lined inside with the very softest cedar bark, after it had been pounded into a kind of cedar meal as gentle as wool. In this cradle the babe was placed as soon as born and covered over with a skin dressed as soft as silk, with its head raised on a pillow at one end. A cushion of feathers or wool was placed on its forehead. A long piece of thin plank, with one end made secure at the head of the canoe or cradle, was laid across the cushion on the forehead and the other end was gently forced down at the opposite end of the cradle and made fast. This plank was also tied by strings to the sides of the cradle. It looked to the men as if the plank weighed upon the babe's skull with enough pressure to crush it. The infant was so firmly bound in the cradle that it was unable to move hand or foot, and in this position it remained a year or a year and a half, being taken out only now and then to be washed or for a little exercise of its limbs.

This yearlong pressure on the babe's forehead forced the bone of its skull to expand at the sides, giving to its face an expression of flat stupid broadness. It was a wonder, the men said, that it did not affect the mind—or was there no mind to affect? Among these Indians were a few whose heads had not been flattened, and these were laughed at by the others and held in contempt. Their slaves were never allowed to flatten the heads of their children, because with these Columbia River Flatheads the more monstrous the skull the more aristocratic the person.

"It wonders the hell out of me," Joe Whitehouse said. "Is everything just habit?"

"Habit and prejudice," George Shannon said. "Did you ever stop to think how hideous they think your head is?"

"But it's the natural shape."

"It's natural to let your hair grow long, and your finger- and toe-nails. It's natural to go naked and never bathe and eat with your fingers."

"But where'd they get the idea?"

"Where'd you get the idea that a white skin is better than a black one?"

The men discussed the matter when sitting round the evening campfires. Most of them had been shocked and horrified, a few had been enraged, when they first saw babies bound in the cradles with the plank across their foreheads. To imagine that children had to suffer such torture for more than a year! Were all ideas of beauty nothing but prejudice and custom? For people with no noses would those with noses be thought monstrous? Getting a new perspective on themselves, the men stared hard at one another and asked, What is it that makes one handsome, another ugly? They looked at themselves in clear water. They talked.

"If you really get down and look at it," Bob Frazier said, "just what is beautiful about the human nose? It's a swelling on your face with two holes in it full of hair. If you could turn it inside out and smell it!"

The men were all looking at him. He was such a fluent show-off, this Bob, and they never knew when he was mocking them. But they did seem to see that the nose was not exactly a thing of beauty after all. Nor the human ear, they decided, after Bob concluded his lecture on that homely appendage.

"Well, what about the eyes? Wouldn't it be better to have them on the sides of the head, like the elk or the rooster? Each eye seeing what it could and minding its own business."

"Much better," George said.

"What about color? White man, red man or black man, what in hell does it matter?"

"It makes a difference to the squaws," said Frazier, looking over at York.

"Just the same," said Dick Windsor, "if I was married to one of these beauties I'd push her head back in shape."

"You couldn't."

"I'd put a lot of pressure on the sides and shove the bone back up."

"You'd kill her, you damn fool."

"The funny thing," said George, "is how some people think they're beautiful if just one thing is the way they want it. These squaws think they're beautiful because their heads are flat. They don't seem to care what their legs look like."

"Or their gooms."

"Or their smell."

"You're insulting the divine form," Frazier said. "You gentlemen forget what raptures await us."

The captains were not worrying about the white disease, at this stage of their journey. They had seen in the faces of their men the disgust and horror when the men looked at the squaws. They knew that the odors and fleas and malformations were too much for them.

"I hope," Lewis said to Clark, "that all the way down the river and at its mouth the damsels are still superlative in their beauty."

Clark looked startled. Glancing at his friend, he saw the sly mirth and responded with a grin.

Lewis said, "Have you noticed the way Shannon looks at these heavenly beauties? It's as good as a physic."

For Meriwether Lewis the beauties of nature were more appealing than those of the female face and form. Even before the Corps entered the Columbia he had been impressed by parts of the gorge through which the merged rivers ran, and down the Columbia his wonder had grown almost daily, in spite of terrible fatigue that was with him day and night. Day after day he marveled at the immense formations on the north side: there the mountain masses lay gently downward to the river like gigantic sleeping forms, covered over with blankets of deep tawny velvet. Great lions and tigers, a mile in length, lay asleep there, George Shannon said. As sensitive as his captain to natural spectacle, when he saw Lewis gazing up at the forms, George would look also and marvel at the superlative smoothness and the richness of the covering. The symmetry reminded him of a woman's thigh.

Steadily the nature of the Columbia's gorge changed. A gigantic monolith set at the river's edge and rising eight hundred feet, the captains called Beacon Rock. Just below it, on the north side, the mountain range fell back and away in stupendous rolling masses, mile upon mile, splashed with every conceivable shade of brown, russet, yellow and gold, all interspersed with green forests upon the saddles and flanks. When clouds covered the sun, all the mountain's colors were enriched and deepened; when the sun came out, the whole vast pillowed mountainside was brilliant in its own year-round colors and in all the tints of autumn. On down the river, on the south, Lewis looked with breathless admiration at the spectacular rock formations, the like of which he had never seen. All blanketed over with richly hued mosses, and rising hundreds of feet from the river floor, some of them stood like gigantic columns; some seemed to have been set upon one another, end to end; and still others were like great fat obelisks, standing side by side. All of them were deeply mossed over in exquisite colors, and sealed in their deep seams. Lewis could have sat for hours on the north bank to look across at the dramatic beauty of the canyon's south wall.

But there was work to be done. After passing the main falls and rapids the party entered quieter waters and made good time. November 3rd they met two canoes of red men from downstream and heard good news. In sign language and a few words of English the spokesman said that three ships were waiting at the mouth. Three ships from the President? Such a surge of relief and hope came up from Lewis's tired depths that he felt giddy. Had Mr. Jefferson sent boats to pick them up and take them home? Why had he ever doubted that the President would? Three ships! The most beautifu words in the language, he told himself, and hastened away to find Clark.

But the levelheaded Clark said, "Three trading vessels, I expect."

"Traders? Still, don't you think——"

"Three?" Clark asked, looking at him. "Why would he send three?"

A number of times in his life Lewis had been so completely the victim of unreasoning and unreasonable hope that he had wondered if he was sane. Chagrined, he now turned away, stubbornly telling himself that *one* of them *could* be from the President. But he knew better. Just the same, trading vessels would be a godsend to men whose clothing was in tatters and whose barter-merchandise was nearly all gone. For without food and horses they could never return overland—scrawny men, half-dead from months of starvation, who had given the best of all they had in the long journey to the sea. He *would* be insane if he imagined they could struggle up this mighty river, dragging heavy dugout canoes behind them! No men on earth could do that—no, probably not even men strong and well-fed. Clark would say they could, he would say they would, if the time came for it; but Lewis suspected that his indomitable friend did not know that human strength and courage had their limits.

He returned to the Indians to get the story again. Were these among the ships that came periodically to trade?

"Son of a pitch," said the red man, grinning.

It was Lewis's turn to be startled. To Drewyer he said, "Is my red brother swearing at me?"

He was just showing off his English, Drewyer said. The red man had no idea what the words meant.

The red man now beamed on Lewis and said, "Bass stirred."

That's what Lewis thought he said. Unable to restrain his mirth, he grinned at the Indian.

"Gull," the Indian said. That's what Lewis thought he said.

"Means girl," Drewyer said.

"Gull bass stirred."

"Gull bass stirred. I wouldn't be surprised," Lewis said. "Well, find out all you can about these ships."

If it wasn't one thing, the men said, it was another. If it wasn't Indians pestering the daylight out of them it was millions on millions of ducks, swans, cranes, storks, herons, gulls, cormorants and geese. The islands along here were simply covered with them. It was wonderful to have goose and duck and swan to eat but these millions of

creatures made a nightmare of darkness. Their loud shrill ear-splitting councils would seem to quiet down and the men would be dozing again, when a crash of honking would fetch them upright, as
though a million geese had spoken at once. Lewis was a nervous
light sleeper and so did not expect to get any rest; but Clark, a deep
sleeper, got no rest either. He confessed in his Journal that "it will
be impossible for me to sleap." The men actually growled with rage
when eating. Wrenching a leg off the body of a goose, one of them
would say, "This son of a pitch will keep me awake no more."

This night the tide rose eighteen inches close by their camp, and
the next morning they all looked at its mark and marveled. The ocean
at last! Could they hear it? Some of the men with ears to the ground
said they could. Anyway, here was some of its water and soon they
would stand on its shore. They came this day to a large village of
what the captains called the Skilloot nation and found that these people had stores of an edible root about the size of a small potato,
which they slowly roasted in embers. It was the wappato, Clark said
in his Journal—the same root that the Chinese cultivated—and called
sagit ti folia. Clark bought four bushels of it and the men ate it with
ravenous hunger. For supper they had roast goose and swan, with
wappatoes, and they all ate with the pride of kings.

More and more Indians were now coming upriver to meet them,
and when the men saw them in the white man's trousers, shirt, hat
and jacket, carrying muskets, pistols and tin containers for their
powder, they knew that they had crossed and come out of the great
unknown and were in white man's country again. These Indians,
even uglier and more repulsive than any others the party had seen, all
knew a few English words, chiefly the profane and obscene, gathered
from sailors and traders; and with preposterous pride they showed
off their learning. They were, the captains thought, extremely arrogant and obnoxious, but they smoked with them and tried to learn
from them. What a difference association with white people made
in red people!

Looking a captain right in the eye, one of the braves would split
his broad red face in a grin and say, with enormous gusto, "Yuh son
of a pitch." It was impossible to tell what the man thought he was
saying.

"Gulls?"

"No gulls," said Lewis, shaking his head.

"Gulls?" the man said again, speaking with what seemed to be anger. No gulls? He wasn't silly enough to believe that. The white men always wanted gulls. This enterprising rascal had been counting the number of men in the party. He held up the thumbs and fingers of both hands. "Gulls?"

Clark summoned Drewyer. "Make him understand once and for all that we want no women."

But neither Drewyer nor any man under heaven could have made the red man believe that. He had seen too many white men. He knew that they always wanted women. He had brought a whole big canoeload with him and he was dying to swap their good offices for guns, knives and ammunition. Not once down the Columbia, Lewis was thinking, had they been able to camp free of Indians, with their fleas and their quick light fingers. Soon after the captains said no to the gulls they were smoking with a half-dozen braves when, looking round, Clark realized that his pipe tomahawk had been stolen—the very tomahawk the Indians had been smoking! With anger rising in him he said to Lewis, "They've stolen my pipe tommyhawk and I expect to get it back." Both captains immediately began to search the red men, and then their canoes; and it was while they were searching for a tomahawk that they would never find that the scoundrels —for in his Journal this evening that was Clark's word for them—made off with Labiche's overcoat.

"You sure they took it?" Clark asked Labiche.

The Frenchman shrugged. Who else could have taken it?

"All right, let's find it."

It was found not far from where they had all been smoking, stuffed under the roots of an upturned tree. They again searched in vain for the tomahawk. Supposing that they had hidden it in the river, Clark was sick of the sight of them—of their sly thievish faces, their broad flat heads, their swollen legs, their decayed teeth, their stench. He liked Indians who were proud and well-formed. These did not seem to him even to be human. As for their gulls, not even the most woman-hungry men could stomach their shape or their odor. Not even York.

The day the tomahawk was stolen the party set off down the river and traveled till long after dark, trying, as Clark put it, to get shut of these red people, at least for one night; but a few minutes after they had pitched camp, somewhere out in darkness a voice cried, "Holy grandma, here they come again!" It was two canoeloads of the scoundrels pretending that they had food for sale but actually hoping to steal another tomahawk.

The party spent a miserable night here. Most of the time rain fell, and already in this wet climate their clothing and their bedding were damp. Besides rain there was the infernal pandemonium of tens of thousands of ducks and geese, cranes and herons. Lying awake and wondering about the hideous squawking and honking of this vast assemblage of fowl, the men would ask one another, "What excites them so?" Clark conjectured that it was the sounds that were not their own: if a flock of herons let off their raucous unearthly squawk, then after a moment the geese gave forth; and the geese seemed to arouse the ducks to frantic quacking; and the ducks and geese together stirred up the cranes or the bitterns, or marsh-birds with voices even more dreadful than the bittern's. The racket, in Clark's opinion, was simply horrid, and he was not a nervous man.

It rained the whole second half of the night and a heavy rain fell all the next forenoon. They were all wet, they were all depressed except the slave-girl and her boy; and this day, pushing hard for the ocean, they covered thirty-two miles and camped free of Indians. There was game in this wooded land—fat elk and deer, fat grouse; and the men felt a little more cheerful, with better food, even though wet day and night. The next day they met a boatload of Indians, one of whom spoke some English: he said that the principal trader at the mouth of the great river was named Haley—so George Shannon spelled it for them, after listening a number of times to the red man's guttural mouthing of it. The Indian, his crafty eyes watching white faces, said he had in his canoe a woman Mr. Haley was fond of. "Wonneral womans," he said, pointing to her. The wonderful woman at once stood up in the canoe and came ashore.

Clark said hastily, "No women. Understand me, no women."

"Womans no?" asked the astonished red man. "Haley womans no?"

"No women, no women!" Clark snapped, his temper short. It had been raining all day. They were all wet and they were in a bad mood, and a fool Indian came offering stinking repulsive women!

This evening, with timber abundant, the captains had large fires built, to dry out clothing and bedding, and in their light to search for fleas. Fleas, they had discovered, seemed to be twice as hungry and persistent in wet weather. While most of the men searched their ragged garments and their damp bedding already smelling of mold Clark sat in a great light and made a long entry in his Journal. His quiet perseverance amazed the men—for they knew that fleas were biting him; that because he was wet he was itching; and that he was dog-tired. Yet there he sat for two hours, writing—and he did not forget the women: "Serves as well for a girdle as to hold in place the Strans of bark which forms the tissue, and which Strans, confined in the middle, hang with their ends pendulous from the waist, the whole being of Suffcent thickness when the female Stands erect to conceal those parts useally covered from familiar view, but when she stoops or places herself in any other attitude this battery of Venus is not altogether impervious to the penetrating eye of the amorite. . . ." He paused a few moments to study that long sentence. He liked it. It seemed to him that he was becoming subtler in his description of intimate things.

The next morning, after the fog broke away, one of the men looking west let off a tremendous howl. He could see the ocean, he said. Instantly every man was on his feet, staring. It was the ocean, they cried: they could see it, they could hear it! Even the captains were stirred. The great Pacific Ocean, Clark was thinking, but it did not sound pacific: it was hurling its heavy dark waves upon dark shores and the whole world here seemed to be wet with it. Lewis wanted to look over at his friend, just to meet his eyes for a moment; or to say, "Over four thousand miles we have come from St. Louis, and at last here it is!" But he did not look over or speak. The men were spilling enough emotion for all of them. The men were hugging one another and dancing around like fools—slapping one another on the back, almost knocking one another down, making gestures at the heavens and kissing their bearded mouths at the universe. They were making more noise than the ducks and geese. . . .

"The ocean!" they shouted. "The OCEAN!"

31

But their wild outpouring of joy was not to last. Not a one of them had ever known such weather as this; the damp went through their clothes and right to their bones. It filled them with aches and miseries. For it was raining again. It had rained hard most of the night and it rained hard most of the next day; and even when rain did not fall, vast enveloping damps and fogs closed in and down, hiding the world and the sky and the sun, and shutting the men away in the small cold room of their wretchedness. Often when they knew it was daylight they could not see fifty feet. How were they ever to shoot game in this fogbound nightmare of ocean and river and sopping sky? When would they sleep again? They looked with astonishment at the slave-girl and her child: they were soaked to their skins too, they were dripping-wet, but when a man met her eyes she smiled, and the child turned his eyes everywhere, round-faced with wonder and the joy of life. The red people here, the men said, were probably like the sea otters—they could live in the water or out of it, it made no difference.

The next day after they were sure they saw the ocean the party went on down the river, and soon the river or the ocean—which was it, they asked, and were unable to tell—was rolling in such mountainous waves that half the men knelt hugging the edge of the dugouts, vomiting into the water. Such rain they had never known, nor such waves: this was simply a different world from New England, Virginia, Kentucky and Ohio: those who had never seen the Atlantic or the Gulf had not realized that there was such a world as this anywhere. They began to hate it. They heaved with pain that went down to old pains that were dormant but now came to life—the river-pains coming up the Jefferson; the hunger- and fatigue-pains crossing the mountains. "O God!" said one. "I've been praying to see the ocean, and now here it is and look at me!" Will Bratton was the sickest man of all: he just fell over to his back and heaved straight up, letting the boiled duck of his noon meal spill over him like the incessant and accursed rain. George Shannon was sick but was trying to be philosophic: he was in the dugout with the Indian girl: putting a hand to his face, he stared at her between fingers and saw that she was not sick at all. There she sat under a relentless downpour, soaked through and through; there her child stood in the cradle down her back; and both of them looked round as though they were warm and snug and well-fed, and had just had a good night's sleep! What Captain Lewis ought to put his mind to, George was thinking, was what comforts and luxuries were doing to make weaklings of the white race.

The captains at the moment were thinking that though they had the toughest group of men on earth half of them right now were puking—see what a spectacle Goodrich and Shields and York were in the other big dugout, and Hall and McNeal in another! George Shannon had stood up, ashamed of himself. He tried to summon enough will to drive the nausea away and make him a man but at that moment a great wave caught the dugout and rolled it half-over and then back, pitched it forward and then to the rear and rolled it again; and with a despairing willingness to be sick and weak and no more than he was George put his ghastly face over the boat's edge and heaved again.

It rained hard most of this night and a great wind drove in from the ocean. The tide came rolling and roaring in, and before the men knew it, one boat was sunk and the others were filled. It was only by using all their strength, only with the most desperate effort (and the girl toiling with them) that they saved the boats. They did it all in a hard driving rain, struggling in howling driven ocean water to their waists, sometimes to their chins, now and then over their heads. It did not matter. They had been soaked the night before and all day, and whether they were in the damned ocean or out of it did not matter now. They had the previous evening unloaded the boats, and the tide had not then come as high as their camp. The captains now realized that they would have to be more vigilant or this vast hungry ocean would drown and sweep them all away. Their task was not only to get a sunken canoe back to the surface and to empty the others of their salt water; after all this was done they had to go on struggling with the last of their strength to keep the boats from being crushed by monstrous floating trees. Great God, they had never seen such trees! They had never seen such torrential rains nor such ocean wrath nor such Indians. As for the trees, they were two hundred feet long, seven, eight or ten feet through. They were firs, the captains said. These great firs came up out of the ocean depths like long dark monsters with ten thousand tentacles, their enormous green branches heaving upward in lashing fury, and then crashing downward as the bole of the tree rolled and again sucked them under. One blow from a huge limb would have smashed a canoe to kindling—if a half-green waterlogged thing could be smashed.

Even as they struggled the men stared, fascinated, at the horrible heaving might of the inpouring ocean. They would not have been surprised if at any moment it had brought immense whales to the surface, or old ships dredged up from ocean bottoms; but the only thing it fetched up out of its darkness and depths were the trees. "There!" a voice would cry, as first a huge branch came up, rolling and rising, with water flung off it not in drops but in gallons. Then other limbs came up and increased in height, as the men struggled back from them, knowing that the monster itself, the great tree trunk, was getting ready to surface. When it came above water it rose in such amazing bulk and incredible length that every man trembled at the horror of it. Those more imaginative, like Shannon, began to wonder how many horrors the ocean hid in its depths, to fling to the surface now and then, and again to draw deep under.

During high tide their tiny campsite went entirely under water, and the members of the party then had to keep afloat on a number of logs that had been driven into the bank. As darkness settled down the night of November 8th it was raining hard and it rained hard all night. The heavens opened in a terrible drenching downpouring in which nothing could be kept dry, except the powder sealed away in lead canisters. All night they were as wet as water could make them. All night they shivered, chilled through. They had no fire, no warmth, no light, but sat huddled in darkness, seeing nothing but the dim immensity of heaving ocean and pouring sky; hearing only the ocean and the rain. Nobody even tried to sleep. The captains had pitched their tent and gone under it, taking the girl and her child with them; but the tent was getting rotten, the rain poured through.

Clark decided at last that it would be less unpleasant to sit out in the open storm, because under the tent were hissing trickles and sudden small deluges, so that a man never knew when a fresh burst of water would go down his back. Some of the men were deathly-sick. Unaware that salt water would make them ill, they had drunk it and it had worked on them as a purge. All night they slunk away, time after time, into the drenched darkness.

This campsite, Clark reflected, feeling the fingers of rain down his back, was like a spot out of hell. It was on a small point on the north side of the river: the men were unable to go back up, unable to go on down and, worst of all, unable to climb up out of the hole to higher ground. The seacoast behind them rose almost sheer; and above it the growth and undergrowth were such a dank tropical tangle of vines and ferns and shrub pines that a man could not penetrate it. There was nothing to do but to hope that the rain would stop, the ocean subside, when they would strike out to find a decent camping place. We'll have to catch rain water, Clark thought, raising his face to the storm and opening his mouth. They would have to eat sopped dried fish and roots in the morning, Lewis thought, groaning in his depths; for he had never liked rain and now abhorred it. He was worried about their maps and papers, now rolled into their heaviest leather. Clark was worrying about the guns, for they were already showing signs of rust.

The morning came as a barely perceptible warmness, as a dismal gloom in the darkness. The rain had not abated at all: it still poured almost straight down, but most of them by this time had got used to water running off their hair, down their throats and backs; down their rotting leather garments outside and inside; down their flanks and across their knees and into their sopping-wet moccasins. For several days now they had been wet. A few of them had caught colds but most of them grinned and with a jest flung water from their hair and beards. The ocean and the storm made such a din that they had to shout into ears to be heard; but some of them talked anyway, to keep up their drenched spirits. "Poor old Noah!" Bob Frazier said, shivering and wretched. "How many days and nights of this did he have, anyway?" He walked over and shouted into Joe Whitehouse's ear, "Cheer up, the squaws down here should be washed pretty clean but don't be surprised if their toes are webbed!"

The cooks were busy digging into the piles of soaked baggage. Each man and the girl were given a tin plate with three or four ounces of dried fish on it, and about that much dried roots. The men who had drunk salt water did not want breakfast; they sat apart in a small group, forearms hugging their bellies in, shoulders bent forward to the storm, long hair hanging in strands down over their foreheads. But most of the men ate, knowing that if they did not eat they would not last long in this enervating climate. They were utterly sick of this fare—the fish had a rancid taste and odor, the roots were flavorless and tough; but they chewed it and gagged it down and licked their plates clean. They could not smoke in such a soaker as this but they could chew; and so the tobacco-users sat in the storm and chewed and spit, looking from under wet brows at one another. It still rained but they could hear one another speak now.

"Noah had it worse," Frazier said. "Anyway, all the people did who were left out of the ark."

"My God," said Dick Windsor, "I'd never thought of that."

All the men then felt better, though the daytime was almost worse than the nighttime. Daytime was the time for moving and doing but here there was nothing to do, except move their baggage to floating logs when the tide came in, and back to the soaked earth after the tide had gone out. All forenoon and all afternoon the rain poured down. It would have to stop after a while, the men told themselves. It didn't rain all the time anywhere, did it? There was only so much water up there. The sun would come out, they would dry off, they would find a decent campground and shoot an elk and fill up. Such thoughts kept them cheerful, even though all day long they sat drenched, or walked around, wretched and full of hunger-cramps.

About four in the afternoon a wild insane wind came out of the southwest and bore in upon them with dreadful violence. For an hour or two it blew the storm away. Would it clear off now? the men asked, staring up at wind-driven clouds. It might be a cold night but that would be better than a drenched night. Some of them gazed round them, now that they could see better. George Shannon said, "God in heaven!" He had picked up his gun and found rust on it. Their clothes would rot and fall off, their guns would rust and foul up—and their knives and tomahawks; and naked, gaunt and frozen they would totter back and forth along the beach, uttering squeaking cries at any passing ship. Such were George's thoughts, grimly infused with his kind of humor. Frazier was saying to anyone who would listen that after a few more days of this they would all be web-footed and gilled and they would follow the sea-dogs into the sea.

As dusk approached, the cooks again came forward, bearing rancid fish which filthy squaws had prepared with God alone knew what seasoning; and the tough roots. With grimaces of distaste the men were inspecting their helpings when they became aware that it was raining again. Before deep darkness it was pouring. The wind had gone down, as though to allow the rain to find the party unhindered. This was Lewis's thought. It was another night like the last night, but when people were completely exhausted they could doze, Lewis told himself—yes, even if soaking-wet and chilled through. It was foolish to try to lie between blankets, for they were sopping-wet too; but Lewis made a big pillow of his and, lying on one side on the soaked earth, dozed off. The slave-girl slept sitting upright, and the child across her wet lap. All of the men got a little rest, but when another dismal morning came they were all a little weaker and Clark resolved to push on today if it could possibly be done.

It continued to rain after daylight but the wind and the swells had fallen. The boats were loaded and moved out to deep dark water, gently rolling. The party headed west past a deep bay and tried to look out to a broad rain-swept estuary. A wind rose suddenly from the northwest and the waves mounted to such heights that hurriedly the captains turned back. On their return they came to a tiny bay where a lot of driftwood had lodged, and here in a drizzling rain the men got a fire going and tried to dry their clothes and bedding. About midafternoon the captains thought the storm was breaking away and again in desperation the party set forth, seeking a better harbor and a better site; but again, as before, it soon encountered an ocean pouring up the river in great violence, and again turned back. Coming to a small eddy, where a stream of pure water came down the hill, the captains decided to anchor the canoes. The baggage they had piled on a stone ledge high above the water mark.

But where would they sleep here, if sleep were possible? Close to the water the stone rose almost sheer for five hundred feet. On the one stone ledge there was room only for the baggage. There was no beach at all. Studying the situation, Lewis decided that they would have to spend the night on the floating driftwood, though the logs lay only loosely together, and the underocean heaving might at any moment upend the logs and pitch men, woman and child into the sea. But there was nothing else to do. "At least," Frazier said, "we'll rise and fall with the tides, and I expect that's what Noah did."

They all moved gingerly around on the huge logs, trying to dry themselves and their bedding. They were not able to. The sky had been drizzling and now at dusk a steady rain set in and it rained hard all night. They had nothing left to eat but some rancid rain-soaked fish that had been brought all the way from the long narrows. A few of them were able to light their pipes and sat smoking, holding their hat or cap above the pipe bowl. Just how they were to manage to sleep on these enormous tree-logs, heaving and half-rolling, none of them could imagine. The captains were worried. They sat together on a log and talked. They knew that if a man stretched out in the rain, on a big log, and fell asleep, he might roll off into the water and be unable to fight his way out; or he might be thrown between two logs and crushed like a beetle, and then dropped into the black waters underneath. Clark said he guessed he would sit all night and smoke and watch. Lewis said he guessed he would too. He looked up at the stone shelf, to which with exhausting toil the men had borne what remained of the merchandise; and to the sky, but he could see nothing there; and then round him at the members of the party, sitting like huge grotesque bugs on this drift-wood platform, which gently heaved and rolled in the moving tide of the ocean. No exploring party in all history, he supposed, had ever made such a preposterous appearance—for look at them after four thousand miles, sopping-wet, half-naked, half-dead with hunger and want of sleep, the miserable captives of mountain ledge, river and ocean!

It was surprising, Clark was thinking, how much a man could endure. None of them had eaten well since the party left buffalo land; they were all underweight and some of them were positively emaciated. They had all nearly starved to death up over the mountain and down the Kooskooskee, and since then had lived chiefly on dog flesh, fish and roots. Still, only Charbonneau grumbled. The squaw-man sulked, scowled at his wife and child but did not dare to speak out loud, because he was too far from home and among Indians who would have loved to tomahawk him. The girl was unfailingly cheerful: not once during the long voyage had the men seen an ugly look on her face. Always when the captains met her eyes she smiled at them. Clark looked over at her now. She was only a few feet from him, on another log. She smiled, with water dripping from her black

eyelashes and the point of her nose, and from her fingers. She had
lost weight too and was now such a tiny thing that the men marveled at the ease with which she carried her child. They marveled
at the matter-of-fact sensible way she accepted things that white
women would find shocking—their nakedness when they towed the
canoes; the suggestive way some of them danced; their making water
in plain sight of her; and the crude way that some of them in her
presence relieved themselves of the gases of indigestion. She seemed
to keep her child clean, though none knew how.

O horrid weather! Clark was thinking, his gaze on the black wet
night. Would this rain never cease! He sat bent over, the storm beating upon him, trying to keep a cheerful frame of mind, though there
was nothing on earth, he decided now, so calculated to depress the
human spirit as continuous rain. A man would go insane in it after a
while. He would just run away shrieking, and die. How long could
the men endure it? Not more than ten days or two weeks surely. It
had been raining on them almost night and day for five days, and if
it rained another five days he was afraid that the morale of the party
would fall to pieces like their leather garments. They had to have
new clothing before much longer, he thought, looking round at the
men; but how were they to get clothing without the skins from
beasts? How ridiculous it would be if winter were to find them all
stark-naked!

Lewis was deliberately forcing his mind to other matters—at this
moment to the nasty verses that a tinhorn punk named Richard Alsop
had addressed to Jefferson when Tom was Vice-President—

> And reeling down the factious dance,
> Send Deborah's husband off to France,
> To tell the Frenchmen to their cost
> They reckon'd here without their host;
> Whilst thou, to smooth the ills of life,
> Held sweet communion with the wife.

How many persons had believed the vile calumny? Lewis hadn't
known Jefferson well at that time. After he got to know him well he
had realized what a slanderous lie it was. He had often wondered
about this man Alsop, and all men like him—what kind of dark little
minds they had, what small stunted souls. There was nothing the
Federalists hadn't stooped to in their efforts to besmirch, ridicule
and destroy a great man. Lewis again knew—how many times he had

thought of it!—that the biggest reason he had to return with all his men was right there: if he did not, if the Corps was to perish, the Federalists would make an unholy yelping crisis of it. Lord, all across the land newspaper headlines would scream that Jefferson's stupid expansionist ambitions had sent, deliberately and brutally, a group of men to die in a wilderness, the whole of which was not worth one of them. Oh, not worth the little finger of one of them! What yammering hypocrites! Yes, he had to go back and he would go back. He would shove the lie down their cowardly throats. He would endure anything and everything—even weeks or months of continuous storm, and as many black wet nights as the Devil could send. . . .

By turn this night, while some watched others slept, and the interminable time passed at last. Morning came, with rain still pouring. The captains sent two of their boldest men, even more, two of their most rugged men, Joe Fields and John Collins, upriver and then uphill into the tangled undergrowth to hunt. A little later a vast wave came rolling in, and, looking at it, the only word Clark could think of was tremendous. A moment later the captains were amazed to see five Indians in a canoe coming over the waves toward them. The waves were now so high that the canoe was visible to them only a part of the time: they would see it balanced on a crest and a moment later it was down and out of sight. When it drew alongside the driftwood the red men indicated that they had fish to sell, and held up what Clark took to be a species of salmon. For a few fish hooks he bought thirteen. The cooks got a fire going. These Indians, the men observed with surprise, were almost as ragged as they were, and just as wet and starved-looking. After bartering the thirteen fish they went back over the high seas, the best canoe navigators, Clark said to Lewis, he ever hoped to see. He would not have believed that a canoe could be taken across such waters.

In his Journal this day Clark wrote, "our situation is truly a disagreeable one our canoes in one place at the mercy of the waves our baggage in another and our selves & party scattered on drift trees of emence size . . ." Joe Fields came back to say that it was simply impossible to get through the undergrowth and fallen timber. The captains knew that if Joe couldn't do it, no man could.

In his damp Journal, with piles of leather tenting him, Clark wrote that it rained hard all night, it rained hard all day. A more utterly wretched group of people this earth, Lewis told himself, had never known. It took a constant dogged effort of will to keep going. The captains scanned the sky until they were sick of looking up, for there was only the dark of storm and wind to see. Was there a sun still shining somewhere? They had scanned the estuary of the ocean until they hated the sight of salt water. Some of the weaker men were getting weaker. The captains were afraid that most of their men would be flat on their backs with rain pelting them in their wan wet faces and green mold forming in the rot of their clothes. The thirteen boiled fish had appeased their hunger a little but there was not much strength in fish. Potts was almost too sick to move now. A dozen other men were only a little stronger.

The afternoon of November 12th a crashing thunderstorm burst over them and the gloomy sky-masses looked horribly menacing in the lightning's white flashes. The whole earth shook. When the tide fell the party moved to a small bottomland, with a creek flowing through it, and Drewyer led a few of the stronger men to the hunt. But they too were unable to penetrate the growth. Clark clawed his way up the creek a short distance and was able to kill two salmon. Some of the men brought in a dozen, and the party ate again. Then, covered over with sopping-wet leather, Clark wrote for a few minutes in his Journal, while his men wondered what could be worth writing down in such a world. They were so chilled they could not have held a pen, yet there he sat, wet through and through, recording something for his President! Clark was saying that they had all been wet for eight days and that all their clothing was rotten.

Toward night they were able to dry both clothes and bedding; and now that they were not on floating logs but on land they all sank and slept, so exhausted that neither pouring rains nor howling winds could disturb them. It rained all night. It poured the next morning and the winds still smote them, but a few of them recalled that for an hour or two during the night the rain had stopped. That was almost enough to make a man cheerful!

Clark set out, determined to climb to some eminence from which he could get a view of the country. He had to fight his way through drenched and almost impenetrable thickets of pine and fern, and in places the ascent was so sharp that he was forced to seize shrubs to pull himself forward. The struggle exhausted him. The view filled him with dismay. He could see nothing at all but rolling hills under their heavy blankets of timber. After a while he found the hoofprint of an elk and knelt to examine it. Then he looked round him again. Fog and rain shut out the river. Heavy sky-mists lay close and deep all around the horizon. Descending, he sent Colter, Willard and Shannon in one of the dugouts to explore down the estuary and find a better campsite. When night came and the men had not returned, Clark went to Lewis, sitting in rain and smoking his pipe.

He said he couldn't imagine what had happened to the men. In fact, he had been imagining it very well: the waves were so high and rough that he was afraid they had drowned.

Lewis had been looking out at the terrible ocean and wondering about the men. The canoe they had taken was a clumsy thing compared to that the five Indians had come in. He said he expected that maybe they had put in somewhere.

"Maybe they saw an elk or deer and went after it."

"I expect so," Lewis said.

"Or went farther than I thought they would. Surely they wouldn't be foolish enough to come back in the dark."

"I wouldn't think so," Lewis said. He looked up at Clark. He had never heard so much anxiety in his friend's voice. "Let's see, which men did you send?"

"Colter, Shannon and Willard."

"I expect Shannon got lost and the others are looking for him."

Clark was a little annoyed. Lewis would jest, he supposed, even in the face of death.

Lewis said, "They're three good men. I wouldn't worry about them."

"But they're so weak," Clark said.

"I expect," Lewis said, looking round at the storm, "that they found a place and decided to spend the night there. I hope they bring us fifty elk in the morning."

It rained all this night without a single letup, and an hour before daylight a great wind rose. At daylight the captains were aghast when they looked at their canoes: the wind had driven one of them with such force against stones that it lay shattered.

"Good God," said Lewis, "look. It's just one damned thing after another."

So depressed that their state of mind was plain in their faces the captains choked down a little of the rancid wet fish and scanned the heaving waters for sight of the three men. A few minutes later they saw a canoe approaching over the stupendous waves and knew by the way it was riding that it was not theirs. The five Indians had come again. With waving arms and gestures they indicated that the three white men were down the estuary. For just a moment the two captains exchanged glances.

An hour later Colter came in to tell them that he had found a good canoe harbor and campsite and two villages of Indians. He had seen no sign of white men or ships. Lewis decided to set off with Drewyer, Frazier and the Fields brothers, to explore beyond the spot where Shannon and Willard were waiting. He chose the large canoe and five other men to put him and his party around the point. The five with the canoe returned at dark to Clark's party, the canoe so nearly filled with water that it was sinking. All day it had been raining. Clark and his men had had only two small fish to eat.

In his Journal, Clark noted that for ten days now it had been raining and that bedding and clothes were rotting. If it were to turn cold before they could get skins and make new clothing the suffering of the men would be extreme. He hoped that Captain Lewis would find a good place to camp, and signs of game—yes, and signs of white traders, but in regard to the latter his hope was weak. This was not the season when they came.

It rained most of this night but the next morning for a change was fair. Clark had the baggage opened and found that most of it was soaked. Most of the dried fish had rotted. By late afternoon the wind went down, and Clark had the canoes loaded with such haste that the enfeebled men fell over one another. The canoes rounded the point safely and came to the sandy beach Colter had told them about, and to thirty-six lodges which Indians had abandoned to fleas. Shannon came up, with five Indians. Captain Lewis, he said, had gone on down. Then, while Clark and his men looked at him and listened intently, George told his story.

The previous night he and Willard had accepted an invitation to spend the night with the Indians. After he and Willard fell asleep the red devils had stolen their rifles from under their heads, and when, on waking and finding them gone, they demanded their return, the Indians at once put arrows to bows, intending to kill them. George thought that was the end of both of them but he bethought him of a stratagem: he told them in all the signs he could think of that a large party of white soldiers was coming down the river. These soldiers, he said, talking desperately in both signs and words, would shoot them and scalp them and feed them to the cormorants and crows. He would never know what would have happened then if Captain Lewis and his men had not at that moment come in sight.

He had no doubt that he and Alex would have been killed on the spot.

Pretty good for a youngster of eighteen! Will Clark thought, with anger rising in him. He turned to Labiche.

"Tell these red hypocrites to stay away from us or we'll shoot them down. Tell them that if they steal anything again I'll have them shot instantly. Be sure they understand it."

It was plain to the men watching that the five Indians understood it. When they first came up they had walked with an insolent swagger but as they understood what Labiche was saying all expression left their faces but that of fear. The white men looking at them saw five scrawny runts, ragged, filthy, disease-marked, half-starved. Two looked almost blind. Four of them were covered with open sores and scabs.

Clark said to Shannon, "Seen any sign of game?"

Deer tracks, George said.

"Well, let's find a good campground and some of us will go hunting. Private Shannon, keep your eye on these Indians. Don't take any monkey business." He turned to his black servant. "Here, lend Private Potts a hand." Private Potts had a bad cold, with fever, and was so weak he could barely sit up. They were all weak but their spirits were lifting, for the sun was shining again.

32

The next morning, Clark was to write, was "clear and butifull" and the next was "A fair cool morning." But when, the next day, he asked how many men wanted to push forward with him for a better view of the ocean only ten volunteered. "The ocean?" one of them muttered. "Doesn't he think I've seen enough ocean?" With ten men and his servant Clark went on, pausing after a few miles at a cabin to look in. He saw four women and three small children sitting in gloom and filth. The stinking creatures seemed almost covered over with scabs or with open sores. They were such a pathetic group of sick and dying people and the smell of them was so overpowering that he turned away. But at once he decided that it would be a good thing to have the men take a look. He told them to step up and look and smell and think. "You too," he said when York held back. "Get up there and see what you'll look like before you die."

This afternoon he and his men shot a number of geese and plover and dined well. Their spirits were rising. From an eminence they had what Ordway called a handsome view of the rolling ocean. They came to a tree on which the ebullient Lewis had carved his name, and most of them carved their names under his. It was not raining to-day. A feeble sun was visible through mists. Clark judged that this day he and his men walked about twenty miles down the coast, and for supper they again ate roasted goose. The men were feeling better but some of them were already expressing a wish to go back up the Columbia and winter at the falls. Anywhere on earth, they said, but here.

During these days the two captains explored from daylight till dark. They were looking for a site for a winter fort and for big game. All the party members were now eating goose and deer, and though they seemed to put on no weight they were getting a little stronger. They weren't doing much trading with the Indians. The red men here were crafty rascals because for years they had been dealing with white men. For either food or clothing they wanted ten or usually a hundred times as much as the captains would give.

Among the Chinooks, Lewis found two principal chiefs, one of whom he named Comcommoly, and the other, Chillarlawil. He gave to the first a flag and to each a medal. One day the captains saw a robe made of sea-otter skins, the most beautiful fur they had ever seen. They tried to purchase it with blankets, handkerchiefs, red beads, even a silver dollar—all these and more they offered and the owner of the robe sneered. In desperation Clark offered his watch. That was not enough either. As he looked round him, his gaze met the eyes of the slave-girl and she moved toward him, indicating the belt round her waist. It was studded with blue beads, the only beads the Chinooks cared for. She handed the belt to Clark, and when he offered it the robe was his.

"If only," moaned Lewis, brokenhearted, "we had brought a ton of blue beads!"

They were on the north side of the river. On the south side, the Chinooks said, were the Clatsops, whose great chief was Stillasha. Up north were the Chiltzes.

One evening a dozen squaws came to the white man's camp, and soon a dozen of the men were laughing their heads off. Stripping almost naked, the squaws were proudly showing them what white-man sailors had tattooed on their arms, legs and bellies. On a brave who had come with them, a young fellow with bright red hair and a freckled face, was the name

Jack Ramsay

"Look!" Bob Frazier howled. He seized the red-haired youth by an arm and pointed to the tattoo. "Here's one guy who knows his father!"

"Who at this moment," said George Shannon, "is probably in a Liverpool whorehouse."

Bill Bratton was snickering and choking. A fat young squaw had exposed herself and was asking all the men to look at the name or her belly. Shannon could not take his gaze off her monstrously swollen knees.

"The British have been here," said Frazier. "Don't anybody tell Captain Lewis."

The squaws now became ardent but the white men backed away from them. They simply couldn't stand their odor. They couldn't overlook the hideous swellings in their thighs and knees, caused, they all had learned, by binding thongs round their legs just above the ankles. Besides being swollen, the legs were so pricked over with images and names and the ears had so many blue beads threaded in their flesh and their hair was so matted and sticky with rain and grease that even York turned away from them. Frazier said that with some people the stink got under the skin.

An old fat wife of one of the chiefs came with six daughters and nieces and pitched camp near the white camp. When Lewis realized her purpose he went over to Clark. As usual, he was amused. "I perceive yonder," he said, "seven members of the fair and adorable sex, six ready to do business and one ready to take the money. How about our men?" When Clark was silent, Lewis said, "You think we need to tell them any more?"

He had warned the men, Clark said. The Corps would have to spend a winter here. If when spring came no ship were to pick them up they would have to return home by river and land. Men could not make that four-thousand-mile journey who had been weakened by the squaws.

"I agree," Lewis said. "The question is whether the men agree."

"Have any of them been with the squaws?"

"Not so far as I know. They're too much even for your black man."

Some of the more ardent men did go over to the old woman to have a look at her girls but they soon came back. It was the odor, Silas Goodrich said. It was their legs, Dick Windsor said. This whole country, Goodrich said, had a rain-soaked unwashed-squaw smell about it. The captains were eager to find a winter site and get their men as far from the squaws as they could. They would build a fort and shut the Indians out.

For a few days it was fair most of the time but the rain and wind came again, and with such violence that in despair Clark wrote in his Journal, "O! how horrible is the day waves brakeing with great violence against the Shore throwing the Water into our Camp &c all wet and confind to our Shelters, Several Indian men and women

crouding about the mens shelters to day. . . ." The captains decided
to find out where the men preferred to spend the winter.

In a pouring rain round a sputtering fire the whole party assembled, and Clark, standing, spoke to the men. There seemed little
likelihood, he said, that President Jefferson had sent a ship to pick
them up. They would have to go into winter quarters in a situation,
if it could be found, where elk or deer or some other form of meat
would be sufficient. They were all sick and tired of fish; and anyway,
the Corps no longer had the trinkets with which to buy fish or anything else, the prices demanded by the red people here being ex-
orbitant. So the first task was to find a situation in elk and timber
country. The Indians said the elk were more abundant on the south
side: he and Captain Lewis proposed that they cross over the estuary
and explore. There were many deer, the Indians said, at some distance up the Columbia, but in wintertime, when both beasts were
poor, elk was better. It was also easier to kill.

All of them were nearly naked, with such garments as they had
left falling apart from rot. It was necessary to get elk or deer or some
other suitable animal, not only for meat but for clothes and bedding.
He and Captain Lewis had discussed the matter, Clark went on, his
manner grave and quiet, and had concluded that a situation close
to the ocean would be best, for a number of reasons. For one thing,
they were badly in need of salt, and it was proposed that a small
party of them would boil a few bushels of salt out of ocean water.
For another thing, it would be well to remain within sight of the
ocean, for a trading vessel might put in, even though the red people
did not expect one before April. If the whole party had to return
overland next spring, it would be necessary to have a fresh supply of
beads, trinkets, knives and tomahawks, with which to trade for food
and horses. There were still other reasons why a coast situation
seemed best. The climate here was milder, as they all could tell by
the vegetation and Indian dress, than up the Columbia. If they
should not be able to get skins for new clothing it obviously would
be best to live in the mildest climate they could find, or they might
all freeze to death. The Indians here said that on the coast in wintertime there was little snow, but heavy snows upriver.

"I have tried to tell you," Clark concluded, "how Captain Lewis
and I view the matter but we want you all to feel perfectly free to
state your mind. The comfort and welfare of all of you is the first
concern of your commanders. Sergeant Ordway, what do you think?"

Ordway was sitting, with one of his half-rotted blankets tenting him. "Well, Captain Clark, I was thinking that if we went back up the river a ways we'd be that much nearer home when we set out."

Looking at the sergeant, Clark said that that was true, that much of it. He knew and Lewis knew that Ordway was expressing the view of those who, utterly sick of rain, wanted to get back to the mountains. "In that case, Sergeant, we'd never see a ship if it came in."

"I vote, Captain, to cross the estuary and explore the south side."

"Sergeant Pryor."

"I vote the same as Sergeant Ordway."

"Sergeant Gass."

"I vote the same, Captain Clark. We jist about have to have skins."

Clark put the question next to Joseph Shields, the wiry little Welsh blacksmith, without whose extraordinary skill in repairing guns the party might have perished long ago. Joe Shields wanted to get away from here—to get out of the rain and as far from the ocean as a man could walk in two lifetimes. But one after another—Shannon, Howard, Wiser, Joe Fields, Collins, Willard, Frazier—the men now voted to cross the river and examine the southern side, though some wondered aloud if it would not be best to go as far as the first mountains, if a fort was to be built. Charbonneau had no opinion. Shannon, Howard, Potts, Reuben Fields, Goodrich and Drewyer, though they all voted to cross and explore, suggested that the best winter site would be up the river at the falls.

After all the men had expressed their views Clark looked at the Shoshone slave-girl. Breathless, the men waited: was the captain going to ask *her* opinion? He was. And he called her by his pet name for her. "Jawey," he said, "what do you say?"

Sacajawea was so flustered that for a few moments she was not able to say anything. She took her son off her lap and stood him up in the rain, as though to get more freedom for thinking. She swept the circle of men with her lively black eyes and looked at Clark and away; and still every man waited. Then, with an impulsive movement that seemed self-effacing and apologetic, she said, "Where plen-tee potaits."

It took Clark a few moments to understand what she meant. Lewis's bearded face had parted in a grin. "Potaits?" Shannon had turned to the man at his side to tell him what the Indian woman had said. "You mean plenty of wild potatoes, Jawey?"

"*Oui*," she said.

Clark was looking at her with curious interest. He was thinking two things, and he thought they were related: not a man among them had stood the terrible rains of the past weeks as well as this frail girl: when plant food was available she ate much more of it than of meat. He recalled now that there had been days when she never touched buffalo flesh, but lived on roots. Like him, she had refused to eat dog.

"Wild potatoes will be fine if we can get them. We haven't much to trade for them, you know."

She glanced down at her waist, as though to see if her blue-beaded girdle was there. Then, like one abashed at having said too much, she returned the child to her lap and bowed her head.

It seemed the will of the majority, Clark now told the group, that the southern side of the river should be explored at once. Indeed, only one man had voted against it. If new reasons occurred to any of them for a coast site or an upriver site they were to bring them forward.

The men spent a wet miserable evening discussing the matter. Brooding and morose, Reuben Fields said, "Lord Jesus, I'd rather sleep in flea beds and eat dried fish till the cows come home than rot in this rain."

"Me too," another said.

"Still," Shannon said, "you have to admit the captains had good arguments. It's over four thousand miles home. What would we use to trade for food and horses?"

"We left horses," Goodrich said.

"Oh yeh. With the Indians. They might all be dead now, or hidden in a cove a hundred miles from the Kooskooskee."

"Walk," Reuben said. "We did before. What do we need anyway but guns and bedrolls?"

"There are all the instruments," George reminded him. "All the papers and maps—the heavy kettles to cook our meat in—all the traps and all the seeds and plants Captain Lewis has gathered. Bushels of salt."

"Salt, my grandpa. We can go home without salt. We haven't had any salt for weeks."

"No, Reuben, we have to have horses."

Bob Frazier said, "If we're smart we'll trust our captains. They've brought us a long way and nobody is dead yet."

"I guess we had something to do with that," Reuben said. He shrugged in the rain. He was a little homesick tonight. He was so sick of the rain that he wanted to run away screaming and kill an Indian. He looked round him, growling, "That's what I need. If they'd let me kill one of these stinking Indians I'd feel a lot better."

Silas Goodrich turned away to blow his nose hard. Like most of the men, he had a terrible cold, with fever. He said, "Damn it, if only these squaws was attractive a man might get warm again. All the way down this river they've been as ugly as sows."

"I figgered that was what would be on your mind," Reuben said.

"O form dee-vine," Frazier's baritone hummed softly, "wilt thou be mine? O lovely legs . . . like whisky kegs. O teeth like pearls . . ."

"Fleas!" Reuben muttered, reaching inside his rotted leather and digging. "From here on I'm going to ask every minister I meet why God made fleas. If he can't answer me I'll leave the church."

"O teeth like pearls——"

"Shut up!" Reuben roared, turning to Frazier.

"—in lovely girls, and holy Moses, a breath like roses!"

Reuben staggered up and went away. "I won't be at all surprised," George said, "if he does kill an Indian before we get home. I'd not want to be a redskin and swipe his gun."

The captains had hoped to cross the river early the next morning but another wild wind came in and waves as high as towers. There was again nothing to eat but half-decayed fish. The next day, and the next and the next, it was rain with high winds. The men made feeble and futile efforts to protect themselves from the storm but such tents as they had were rotten and full of holes, and their bedding was wet and rotting in its mildew. Hunters went out and found nothing, day after day. Day after day Indians came to sell pounded fish and roots but the price was so high that the captains bought only a little. Two handkerchiefs, Clark said, would now hold all the merchandise they had to trade with. Clearly enough something would have to be done soon or their bones would be found here by some trading ship. The wind now and then was so violent that the men were not surprised when huge trees were torn from the earth and flung down. In his Journal the indomitable Clark cried out, "O! how Tremendious is the day. . . . This dreadfull wind and rain . . ." But he and Lewis kept going and they kept their men going, knowing that if once they sat down in despair their spirits and wills would die within them. In pouring rain, and with an effort that most of the men would have believed the Corps wholly incapable of, they crossed the estuary to the south side.

And once there, Lewis called to him four of the most rugged and unconquerable men—Reuben Fields, Shannon, Drewyer and Colter —and Labiche, to talk in sign language if Indians were encountered, and set off down the south coast. It poured rain on them all day but they killed four deer, two geese, seven ducks and a goat. Leaving most of the meat for the larger party, which was following, the six men pushed on and spent the night in an old Indian lodge, wet and shivering but out of the rain. Before dozing off Lewis smiled grimly, remembering a few words he had read the previous evening in his friend's Journal: "O! how disagreeable is our Situation dureing this dreadfull weather."

The next day was cloudy and damp but with only a little rain. Lewis and his men pushed on mile after mile, exploring. Clark meanwhile had a dozen sick men on his hands, all convulsed by dreadful cramps because they had mixed ocean water with their rancid fish. This party had not yet found the flesh that Lewis and his men had left for them, and most of them were so weak that they could move only with a supreme effort of will. Clark was weak too, so weak that the girl, watching him, came shyly up for a moment when she found him alone and offered the small piece of camas-root bread.

Clark looked at it in his hand. "Why, Jawey," he said, "what is this?" He sniffed it. It smelled of mildew and mold.

"You eat," she said.

He tasted it. It had soured and it was hard but he ate it, reflecting that nothing else had tasted so good for months. He ate it, though he knew that all this while she had kept it for her son. When later in the day the hunters brought in three skinny hawks he tore off one of the largest legs and took it to the girl. "You eat," he said with a smile, and with a smile she took it. When other hunters brought in three mud hens he took her a wing from one of them and kept an eye on Charbonneau to see that he did not snatch it from her. It was a miracle, Clark thought, that for all these weeks she had been able to hide from her man the piece of bread.

Nothing in their captains so astonished the men as their sleepless interest, even when half-dead from hunger and cold, even when sick, in all the life around them. Both had given orders to bring in any new plants found, or any strange bird or animal they were able to capture or kill. One of the men with Lewis brought in a squirrel and the delighted captain wrote a description of it for his noble friend, Tom Jefferson: "about the size of the red squirrel of the lakes and eastern Atlantic States, their bellies are of a redish yellow, or tanners ooze colour the tale flat and as long as the body eyes black and moderately large back and sides of a greyish brown. . . ." A few moments later he was describing a briar.

Fifteen miles away Clark was wondering what had happened to him. He worried about him when after several days no word came in: he knew that Merne Lewis was imprudent, even reckless, in some moods; melancholy and unpredictable in others. The dreadful roaring sound of the ocean breaking upon the rocky shore was enough to make any man melancholy. It had so deeply affected Clark that he departed from the impersonal disciplined manner of his Journal to write, "Since we arrived in Sight of the Great Western; (for I cannot Say Pacific) Ocian as I have not Seen one pacific day Since my arrival. . . . rockey coasts, tempestous and horiable. I have no account of Capt. Lewis Since he left me."

It was December 1st. It was the twenty-fourth day since the party had come in sight of the great ocean, and in all that time it had found no food to speak of, nor a decent campsite. In all that time it had simply got wetter and weaker and gloomier. And where was Lewis? The weakest of Clark's men sat in the rain, feebly trying to patch their rotten clothes; the strongest went out daily to hunt, returning empty-handed or with no more than a coot or a hawk. Another miserable day passed and still no word from Lewis. Toward evening of December 2nd the rugged Joe Fields, whom neither hunger nor storms could subdue, came striding in with the thigh bones of an elk across his shoulder. The men gathered round him to hear if the news was good.

It was good. He had actually seen and killed an elk—the first elk to be killed by any man in the party since it left the Jefferson River. How far away was it? About six or seven miles, Joe said. Some of them were looking down at his feet: around each he had wrapped a piece of green elkskin and bound it with wet elkskin thongs. Most of his legs, a part of his back and belly and both of his arms were naked, or were hidden only by a few tatters of leather.

Had he seen much elk sign? Quite a lot, he said. He had seen other beasts but it had been raining so hard that he hadn't been able to get a shot.

Was it fat?

"Very nice," Joe said.

Clark sent Joe with six men to bring the meat in but the seven men did not return this night. That was not surprising, for it was a twelve-mile journey; and besides, they might have jumped a herd of elk. The next morning they came in with the meat and what was left of the hide and there was joy in Clark's camp, though he himself was too sick and feeble to eat. He tried a hot juicy morsel of boiled flesh but it gagged him. Later in the day Indians came with roots to sell and Clark bought a few pounds with one fish hook. He then ate a boiled root in elk broth. To keep his spirits up he went to a huge tree and there carved this legend:

CAPT WILLIAM CLARK DECEMBER 3RD 1805
BY LAND FROM THE U. STATES IN 1804–1805

When he returned to camp he found that the girl had broken some of the elk bones and boiled them, and extracted from them about a pint of marrow. She offered it to him, looking up hopefully. He tried to eat some of it spread on a boiled root but it sickened him. He drank a little broth and then, feeling worse than he had felt, save once, on the whole journey, he sat in a drizzling rain by the fire, wondering what had happened to his friend Lewis. He looked round in the camp at his men. It was not a cheerful sight. A few of them were lying on their backs in the storm, like men willing to die. But he knew that none was willing to die. They were wonderful men. They were so wonderful that he tried to hide from them the fact that he was weak and sick. Oh, he would be well soon—but where was Lewis? It was just like that reckless man to wander off fifty or a hundred miles and get himself and his party wiped out.

After dark two of the hunters came in and said they had killed six elk. The feeblest of the men sat up, the strongest got to their feet. Six elk? Father in heaven, this was good news!

"How far away?" Clark asked, looking up at Sergeant Pryor.

"Quite a ways, Captain. Seven or eight miles."

"A lot of sign?"

"Quite a lot, sir. It seems to be good elk country."

"No sign of Captain Lewis and his men?"

"None at all, sir."

Elk country! If only Lewis would come!

33

He did not come the next day and his sick and dispirited friend wrote in his Journal, "I fear Some accident has taken place in his craft or party." But the next day Lewis came in, and though his friend wanted to walk over and kick his lank hindend, for keeping him in a stew so long, instead he entered the good news: "Capt. Lewis's long delay below has been the cause of no little uneasiness on my part for him, a 1000 conjectures has crouded into my mind respecting his probable situation & safety." Lewis returned with good news: he and his men had killed six elk and five deer, and had found as fine a site for a winter camp as they could expect to find in a fogbound quagmire of earth where the rains never ceased.

Though it rained all this day and the wind blew like something out of hell, Clark began to feel better the moment his tall ungainly friend came in sight, and continued to improve all day long. Had he been a self-searching man he might have suspected that his illness had been caused less by want of food than by the absence of his friend, whom he now looked on as a brother. He drank a whole tin cup of elk broth, ate some boiled flesh and roots and was ready for work. On the rough elkskin cover of his fieldbook he drew a plan for their second winter fort: it would be a stockade about fifty feet square: on one side would be three cabins with a central fireplace; on the other side four cabins with two fireplaces. The inner part between the rows of cabins would be twenty feet wide.

They moved to the site as soon as the violent storm abated, and there, as at Mandan, Sergeant Gass was put in charge of the building of the fort, which was actually begun on December 10th. Some of the men were too ill to work or hunt: one had thrown a shoulder out of joint, another had a badly wrenched knee; a few had boils and tumors; a few were laid up with dysentery. The best of the hunters who were still able to go out were sent for meat and skins; the strongest of the other men, including York, were placed under Gass. Paddy reported to the captains that the timber here was a carpenter's dream of heaven: the huge trees could easily be split in puncheons only an inch and a half thick, yet ten feet long and two feet wide. Never in his life had he seen trees split so beautifully and true. He would be able to give the cabins good plank floors and rain-tight roofs. One cabin he built round a huge stump: he had the broad top leveled off and smoothed, so that it could serve as a table for Captain Clark's map-making.

Clark was touched but there was no emotion in his voice when he said, "Thank you, Sergeant. It is an excellent idea."

Joe Fields, the rugged one, whom the men had felt nothing on earth could subdue, fell sick with boils and running sores. George Gibson lay stretched out in the rain, trying to ease the cramps in his belly. William Werner, with the sprained knee, tried to limp around and help Gass but was no good for anything, except to bring a little wood for the fires. Bob Frazier's handsome face looked pretty ghastly but he never gave up trying to lift the spirits of the men: "Those Clatsop girls . . . with teeth like pearls! Those thighs, those knees . . . were made to please . . . !" He sang in a kind of mournful loping singsong way that convulsed some of the men.

It rained every day and every night. It was to rain every day and every night while the fort was being built but the men had good fat elk to eat now and nothing could dash their spirits. They would have a roof over their heads before long. They would have skins to make new clothing and bedding. Only three days after the fort was begun, Drewyer and Shannon came in to say that they had killed eighteen elk.

Lewis looked at them as he might have looked if they had said they had wiped out the whole Chinook nation. "How many did you say?"

"Eighteen, sir," said George.

"Great heavens, Private Shannon, are you trying to decimate all the game in this country?"

George smiled back in his soft fuzz. He had quite a vocabulary himself; he liked the way the captains flung big words around. "Extinguish, sir," he said. "Obliterate." Then, gravely, "We'll need a lot of hides, sir."

"And so we will. How far out are they?"

They were about six miles, George said.

The next day four men were sent to guard the meat, with instructions to wait until a larger party arrived; but by that time it was too late. Eighteen fat dead elk were already turning putrid, because of the incessant rain. It was Clark who led sixteen men in the second party, to bring the elk in, and before he saw it he could smell it. Just the same, he had most of it taken to camp. He thought it could be smoked and dried. They had lived on rancid fish for weeks, so half-decayed elk should not be too bad. He now realized that in the saturated atmosphere meat would spoil a lot faster than in a dry climate. So much rain had fallen on the piles of flesh that it looked as if it had lain for days in vats of water.

It rained hard all night, and five of the men bringing elk in missed their way and spent the night without fire or shelter, sitting in the downpour. The next morning, looking as if they had come out of a river, they rejoined the main party, cold and shivering but still cheerful. A wind rose, and it was so violent that, on looking round him, Clark saw trees falling in every direction. He had spent a miserable night trying in vain, with his men, to shelter himself under the green wet elkskins. When he lay down with a bloody elkskin over him as a blanket he soon felt water running under him and, speechless with disgust, he sat up, his rump sinking into the drenched sogginess of the forest mold, and considered his position. Some of his men were trying with elk hides to keep the storm off: they would hang two or three from a tripod of poles and crawl under, but in a few moments the wind would strip the hides away. They would lie on their right or left side with a hide pulled over them and try to sleep but none of them could sleep in such a nightmare of water and wind. The five who had got lost and who at daylight came in presented such a woebegone appearance that Clark and his men could only stare at them: naked in their tatters, blue with cold, their hair hanging in wet tangled strands, their teeth chattering, they were cheerful. They were grinning. These five were Ordway, Colter, Collins, Whitehouse and McNeal.

Ordway said, "Captain, we got lost. We're as bad as Shannon."

The five men stood together, grinning; looking down over their sopping-wet tatters or at the face of their captain. Clark liked their spirit. Nothing on earth, he was thinking, could dismay such men as these.

Clark said, "Sergeant, where's your meat?"

"Back a ways," Ordway said.

"You'd better bring it in."

The men managed to get a fire going, and then impaled hunks of flesh on green sticks, half-cooked them and ate. They could smell the decay in the meat. They could taste it. They would all be sick again, Clark supposed, for the captains had learned that putrid meat could cause horrible bellyaches. But the men had to eat and this was all they had. A part of the way to the main camp they had to carry the quarters and hides; a part of the way they would go by canoe down a small river which the captains had named Netul. Each man carried a quarter of elk. Because of the swampy nature of the earth, the fallen timber and the great weight of the burden, if it happened to be a shoulder of a bull, some of the men badly wrenched their backs and were grimacing with pain before they reached camp.

What, George Shannon asked himself while staggering along, kept the men going, anyway? He thought he knew what it was. It was the indomitable will, the perseverance, the unconquerable spirit and the unfailing politeness of their two captains. The men had talked about them many times when off hunting or gathering firewood, or when sitting by their fires. They were tough hand-picked men, every one of them except the squawman and York. They had all known hardship and privation. Those in military service had known leaders who never turned back or cried quits. But they admitted to one another that never had they known men of such quality as these two. Clark was carrying a quarter of elk right along with his men, and it was one of the largest quarters. The captains had never spared themselves. It was true that they spent a lot of time making maps and notes and taking observations, but when a real tough job had to be done, they pitched in and led, as Clark was leading now.

"They suit me," Reuben Fields had said one evening.

"If I had had a father like either one of them," the scowling Alex Willard said, "I reckon I wouldn't be here today."

A number of them had looked at Alex and considered his words. Then Bob Frazier, the glib one, the more sophisticated one, had said, "Well, we signed up for this journey and we did it blind. We didn't know a tinker's dam about either one of them but we'd all been around enough to know that our lives would depend on them. We're still all alive but Sergeant Floyd. We wouldn't be alive if we hadn't had such captains."

"That's true as murder," John Shields had said. "Just the same, I wish they'd lead us out of this damned rain."

"And back to some decent squaws," Silas Goodrich had said.

Frazier had then intoned, "These Chinook girls . . . with teeth like pearls! You know, I'm never going to be able to look a white woman in the face again. You fellows remember what horrible legs white girls have?"

"And their stink."

"And their breasts that stand up like this—instead of hanging away down in beauty like this."

"And their round heads."

"Oh, those round heads! What could be uglier than a roundheaded woman?"

Even more than the rain the men hated the wind. There was always a wind here at the fort site, or enough breeze to let the smoke take its capricious and tantalizing way. Wet and miserable, a man would carefully seat himself by a fire on the wind side, so that the smoke would be blown away from him; but after a few moments the wind would change and blow clouds of smoke into his face, from wet slow-burning wood, choking him, stinging his eyes, forcing him to change his position. Such a wind, the men said, seemed to have intelligence and will. They never heard Captain Lewis speak of it, but for Captain Clark it was such an intolerable nuisance, especially when he was trying to write or draw maps, that now and then he would exclaim with despair, while the fingers of both hands dug at his smarting eyes.

It was rain and wind and smoke every day, simply and unfailingly every day. Once in a while the storm would lift for an hour and they would catch a glimpse of a wan foolish sun; but every day during the building of the fort it rained. They had first built a meathouse. Some of the men tried to smoke and cure elk flesh but found that they were not able to smoke it enough to preserve it. They would smoke huge thin slices of it and hang these row on row in the meathouse, only to find a week later that it had spoiled. Five days after the men began to build the fort Clark happened to take hold of the leather tent which he and Lewis had used all the way from Mandan, and was startled when a huge patch of it came loose in his grasp. Curious, he examined the tent and found it so rotten that he could thrust a finger through any part of it. Some of the men had been put to the task of tanning the elk hides but they didn't have enough elk brains to tan in the Indian way, and there was so little lye in the pine ashes of their campfires that they weren't of much use either.

And week after week they were pestered by the hideous and foul-smelling squaws. It was the day before Christmas. The captains were not in a jovial mood: wind and rain had driven upon them all night and had not abated at all when daylight came. Over on the coast, near the spot where a few of the men were extracting salt, was a minor chief whose name Clark spelled as Cuscalah. Clark had accepted his hospitality one night, and on this day before Christmas the chief appeared in the gloom of the downpour with two young squaws. He laid before each captain a mat and a few edible roots, and then stood in the rain, watching and waiting, the two squaws standing behind him, with water pouring down their black hair and red faces.

Passing close to Lewis, Clark said, "I expect he'll stand there till judgment day if we don't give him something."

"I expect," Lewis said.

Hour after hour Cuscalah stood in the rain and waited but when evening came his patience was exhausted. He walked up to Clark and demanded two files. The captains had no files to give, and Clark asked Drewyer to tell him so. "Tell him to take his mats and potatoes and go home. We have nothing for him." Cuscalah was offended, as the captains had expected he would be; but he was a gallant man at that. He asked Drewyer to tell the captains that though he had to withdraw the mats and roots, because these things were of great value, he was happy to offer the girls, one to each chief. The captains had been expecting that too.

Clark said, "Thank him for us and tell him to take them home."

When Cuscalah understood that the strange white chiefs did not want the two squaws—whom he had personally chosen as the loveliest in his village—he was deeply and terribly offended. First, he turned and spoke to the women. Their response filled Lewis with droll mirth, Clark with weariness. They were unspeakably disgusted. They proceeded to show their disgust and their outraged vanity with facial grimaces, and by the way they looked at the captains, from one to the other. Cuscalah, apparently suspecting that the captains might change their minds, stood in the rain and waited. Each squaw now clasped to her belly a mat and a few roots. They waited too. Their disgust, their contempt, their unbelief were so plain and childlike that Lewis chuckled inside. The girls knew that they were just about the most attractive females in the whole village, and that when sailors came they would be eager to tattoo their names on their legs or bellies.

Working on the fort and watching the scene were Gass and his carpenters. Frazier and Silas Goodrich were on the roof. Looking over at the two girls, Frazier blew kisses at them and called out in his plaintive singsong, "O form dee-vine wilt thou be mine? You know," he said, "I think our captains are going to let those two beauties get away."

"They don't look bad at all," Silas said. "But it beats me how they can stink so when it rains on them all the time."

"A thing that lives on fish smells like fish."

"Then I should smell like elk."

"I smell like hell," Frazier said, raising a wet ragged sleeve to sniff. "Just the same, I like some of these Indian customs. Captain Clark gives the chief a fish hook and the chief brings his two daughters. I wish we had that custom back home, where fish hooks are cheap."

"A Chinook wife costs exactly the same as a tomahawk."

"They don't cost any more than that in New England. You think it is funny because the red men pay for their wives. Don't you think white men do? How much will Ordway's Betsy cost him?"

"I reckon he's lost her by this time."

"O form dee-vine!" sang Frazier, again blowing kisses. "What legs are these? O God, what knees! You know where those two beauties live? Right next to the village where Joe Fields and Bill Bratton and George Gibson are making salt."

"Poor George!" said Silas, staring hungrily at the girls. "He can't resist them at all."

"*He* can't! Just who in hell did the squaws get down over at the Snakes?"

"York," Silas said.

"Poor Yorick," Frazier said, and peered between pine planks down at the big black man. York was sick. When helping to fell trees he had shown off his strength and wrenched his back. Now he was lying in one of the cabins, groaning.

It was rain and wind, wind and rain, but most of the men kept themselves in good spirits. The cabin for the captains was completed first, and they moved in and sat in luxury on a plank floor before a blazing fire. Christmas morning they were awakened by the explosions of rifles and by great shouts under their window. A moment later a dozen male voices were singing. Lewis propped himself up on an elbow on his hard bed and looked over at Clark.

"Will, my friend," he said, "our men are singing a Christmas carol for us."

"That's right, it's Christmas again."

The captains left their beds and a little later the party was breakfasting on putrid elk meat. Except some soured fish, it was all the food they had. Some of them, like George Shannon, had trouble chewing it, the smell of it was so bad, but most of them smacked heartily. Frazier said he now understood the English, who wouldn't eat meat until it was decaying. When the breakfast was over, Lewis, his eyes alight with mischief, brought a Christmas present to his friend Clark—an undershirt, a pair of drawers, and a pair of socks. These things he had concealed in his personal baggage all this time. Some of the men caught the spirit. Joseph Whitehouse gave to each captain a pair of moccasins, and to the day of their death neither was to know where he got them. Silas Goodrich gave Clark a small Indian basket, and Lewis a handsome eagle feather, adorned with tiny sea shells. But the one who really astonished them was the girl: she came forward with two dozen pure white weasel tails, Indian-tanned and as soft as silk.

"Why, Jawey," said Clark, and Lewis thought the color in the florid face ran deeper. "They are very nice."

"You like?" she said.

"Thank you," Lewis said, with a courtly bow. "Captain Clark, these are exquisite."

"I had the same thought," Clark said. Where in the world, he wondered, did she get these tails! How long had she had them? What else in her generous womanly heart was she saving for them?

Lewis said, "Captain Clark, maybe we should see how much tobacco we have left. Not since the Fourth of July have we had any ardent spirits."

In the corner of the cabin which he shared with Clark, Lewis knelt before a large parcel wrapped in many folds of leather and brought to view twelve carrots of tobacco, which was all the party had left. Six carrots he divided equally among the men who used tobacco; and some, like Paddy Gass, who for days had been chewing bark, seized their portion and tucked a quid back into a cheek.

"To the seven who don't have the filthy habit what can we give? Oh, I know, Captain: we still have some handkerchiefs. Will a handkerchief seem equal to a fourth of a carrot of tobacco?"

Some of the men were grinning. Reuben Fields said, "A handkerchief will buy a wife."

"That much tobacco," Lewis said, "will buy a dozen wives. Anyway, we all catch colds in this beautiful pacific weather and a handkerchief is certainly more useful than a pipe or a cud."

He presented the handkerchiefs to the seven men and was turning away when his gaze fell on the girl, standing back, with her child in her arms. Lewis fetched out another handkerchief and, walking over to her in his ungainly but strangely courtly way, he presented it to her. She gave him just an instant of smile. She knew well in her shrewd Indian heart that Chief Long Knife did not care much about her—did not like her in the fatherly way of Chief Red Hair. And Chief Long Knife, in his shrewd white-man heart, suspected that the Indian girl's handkerchief would end up in the pocket of his friend.

The building went ahead and by the first of the year the fort was completed. The smallest room was given to the girl and her husband and child, and a part of the baggage was stored there. The other men shared five chambers, packed in five to the room, but they could keep dry now a part of the time, they didn't have to live day and night in the rain. They felt so luxurious that they pitied those over on the coast making salt. Still, they had their problems. Their only food was elk flesh, and though they kept a smoking fire under it day and night it spoiled, and not a man among them was ever entirely free of bellyache. Living on nothing but meat, they caught cold easily and suffered from more aches and pains than they had known existed. In spite of all they could do they were unable to get rid of the fleas. Indians came to visit them and were admitted to the fort, and when Indians came the fleas came. Bob Frazier said, "I figger they must get tired of red meat, for every damn flea jumps off and stays with us."

But there were lighter moments. The last day of the year a Clatsop buck came and he was a sight for tired eyes. He was the one who had Jack Ramsay tattooed on his arm—a gawky ill-shaped freckled fellow with coarse red hair. He did not speak a word of English, except a little jargon which he showed off. He pretended to be all white, for he was inordinately proud of his sailor father. "Blag phrasserds," he would say, grinning and showing bad teeth, though he was a young man. "Oh-uh son ov ah pitch." The men gathered round and stared at him as though he had come down out of the sky. They looked hard at the big murky brown freckles that splotched his forehead and nose. "God!" Bob Frazier said. "His father must have been a freckled son of a pitch. Ramsay. Isn't that Scotch? I didn't know the Scotch are freckled all over like a robin's egg."

"Wonder why they never flattened his head," Joe Whitehouse said.

Frazier asked the man about it. Grasping his own skull between palms, he made motions of elongating it, now and then breaking off to point at Ramsay's head or to separate his palms by eighteen inches and say, "Why are you a roundhead instead of a longhead?" The freckled red-haired half-breed only grinned, showing his black teeth, and with infinite pleasure said, "Blag phrasserd."

"Blackguard bastard yourself."

"Son ov ah pitch," the man said, grinning.

"You're right, your old man is a son of a pitch, but you know the name of your father and that's more than most of us can be sure of."

"Keckenbool."

"Cock and bull yourself, you freckled roundheaded phrasserd."

"Fook-a-luke."

"Holy Moses, listen to him now!"

Ramsay liked Bob Frazier. He thought Bob was more like white men than the others. He came over a number of times to show off his English. Bob jollied him along. After Ramsay had gone away Frazier would say, "I wonder how many over the wide world sailor boy Jack Ramsay has put his brand on."

34

The fort was completed January first and was put under strict military discipline, each night's guard consisting of a sergeant and three privates, relieved at sunrise. A sentinel was posted day and night on the parade before the officers' quarters. The orders issued by Lewis said, "It shall be the duty of the centinel also to announce the arrival of all parties of Indians to the Sergeant of the Guard, who shall immediately report the same to the Commanding officers."

The sentinel many times had to announce the approach of Indians. The red people were admitted to the parade but nearly always were dismissed from the fort by sunset, when both gates, one north and one south, were locked. It was the duty of the sergeant of the guard to keep the key to the meathouse, and to cause the guard to keep regular fires therein; to visit the canoes at least once every twenty-four hours to learn if they were all right; and every morning to report to his commanders. The captains felt safe in their fort against any conceivable Indian attack but as wise officers they knew that they had to keep their men under strict discipline, if they were ever to make the long journey home.

That they would have to return as they had come seemed more and more likely. The men making salt kept an eye out for ships, and from time to time one of the captains scanned the ocean with glasses. But no ship came. From the Indians they learned and wrote down in their own phonetic spelling the names of the traders and when each was expected—Youin in one moon; Mackey in one or two moons; Lemon, Washilton, Haley, Balch, Jackson and Swepeton in three moons. One-eyed Skellie had a large ship but had been gone a long time. The red man's favorite of all was Haley, the one they feared most was Fallawan, for he had killed a number of them. Twice a year the traders came, but only, the captains supposed, in late spring and early fall. Dared they wait until the middle of April? If they returned overland they would have to reclaim their horses before the pierced noses went over the mountains to buffalo land. It would be a struggle going up the Columbia in the high water of the spring runoff, with not much to eat, unless they were able to dry a few tons of elk meat and take it along. But dragging heavily loaded canoes upstream did not seem possible; and besides, there were all those portages.

Now and then in their snug shelter the captains would discuss the matters that worried them. No question stood as large in their minds as this: Why hadn't the President sent a ship?

"Absolutely the only reason I can think of," Lewis said, "is that he's afraid he'll offend the Spanish."

"I expect that's it," Clark said.

"Or is it the damned Federalists? Maybe Alexander Hamilton has made the whole country laugh at us."

The captains did not know that Hamilton had been killed in a duel.

Sitting by the big stump which he used as a table, Clark was working on a map. He said, without looking up, "They have all given us up as dead by this time. Maybe that's why no ship has come."

"Well, we don't know what has happened. We might be at war with the British again."

"That is possible."

"Or with Spain."

"Could it be that he's afraid he'll offend the English? I expect they claim all this country around us here."

"I just can't imagine what the reason is."

They were two worried captains but they did not let their worries get in the way of duty. During this winter they both wrote copiously in their journals, often copying from one another but not always exactly in the other's words. Lewis gave free rein to his love of moralizing and speculating, and Clark even copied some of the moralizing. Lewis described in great detail the roots, plants, animals, trees, berries, ferns and waterfowl in the area roundabout. He prepared *An Estimate of the Western Indians* and spent countless hours on his ethnological studies.

Observing that all the men seemed feebler on elk than they had on dog, the irrepressible Lewis observed, "it is worthy of remark that while we lived principally on the flesh of this anamal we were much more healthy strong and more fleshey than we had been since we left the Buffaloe country. for my own part I have become so perfectly reconciled to the dog that I think it an agreeable food and would prefer it vastly to lean Venison or Elk."

When the salt-makers brought over a gallon of salt Lewis was prompted to write, "this was a great treat to myself and most of the party, having not had any since the 20th Ult^{mo}; I say most of the party, for my friend Capt. Clark. declares it to be a mear matter of indifference with him whether he uses it or not; for myself I must confess I felt a considerable inconvenience from the want of it; the want of bread I consider as trivial provided, I get fat meat, for as to the species of meat I am not very particular, the flesh of the dog the horse and the wolf, having from habit become equally formiliar with any other, and I have learned to think that if the chord be sufficiently strong, which binds the soul and boddy together, it does not so much matter about the materials which compose it. . . ."

Clark read what his friend had written, and then set down his own confession: "I care but little whether I have any with my meat or not; provided the meat fat, haveing from habit become entirely cearless about my diat, and I have learned to think that if the cord be Sufficiently Strong which binds the Soul and boddy together, it does not so much matter about the materials which compose it."

Now and then when looking over one another's Journal, the captains were startled by their differences in spelling. Clark corrected the spelling of cord, then stared a long moment at boddy and decided that possibly it did have two *d*'s. Lewis's statement in his Journal and out of it that dog, horse, wolf, buffalo and beef were all the same to him made Clark shudder a little. His own prejudices ran deeper.

"I think," Lewis wrote January 6th, "it may be established as a general maxim that those nations treat their old people and women with most differrence and rispect where they subsist principally on such articles that these can participate with the men in obtaining them; and that, that part of the community are treated with least attention, when the act of procuring subsistence devolves entirely on the men in the vigor of life. It appears to me that nature has been much more deficient in her filial tie than in any other of the strong affections of the human heart, and therefore think, our old men equally with our women indebted to civilization for their ease and comfort. Among the Siouxs, Assinniboins and others on the Missouri who subsist by hunting it is a custom when a person of either sex becomes so old and infurm that they are unable to travel on foot from camp to camp as they rome in surch of subsistance, for the children or near relations of such person to leave them without compunction or remose; on those occasions they usually place within their reach a small peace of meat and a platter of water, telling the poor old superannuated wretch for his consolation, that he or she had lived long enough, that it was time they should dye and go to their relations who can afford to take care of them much better than they could."

Such a passage Clark would ponder for some time, and when his gaze again rested on his friend he would regard him with fresh interest.

Lewis's restless mind was forever thinking about things, in sleep or out of it. Only two days later he was writing, "The Clatsops Chinnooks and others inhabiting the coast and country in this neighbourhood, are excessively fond of smoking tobacco. in the act of smoking they appear to swallow it as they draw it from the pipe, and for many draughts together you will not perceive the smoke which they take from the pipe . . . in the same manner also they inhale it in their lungs untill they become surcharged with this vapour when they puff it out to a great distance through their nostils and mouth; I have no doubt the smoke of the tobacco in this manner becomes much more intoxicating and that they do possess themselves of all it's virtues in their fullest extent; they freequently give us sounding proofs of it's creating a dismorallity of order in the abdomen . . . nor are those light matters thought indelicate in either sex, but all take the liberty of obeying the dictates of nature without reserve. these people do not appear to know the uce of speritous liquors, they never having once asked us for it . . ."

Now and then he would interrupt his writing to sit with a droll expression on his face while he thought of droll matters. Some of his men seemed to have no capacity to learn the red man's ways. There was Hugh McNeal, who looked bright enough. Clark told Lewis that one evening he was smoking with the natives when he heard dreadful shrieks across the village and the sound of running feet. Going over, he learned that one of the young braves had invited McNeal to go with him to share some special pleasures. McNeal was being led away when a young squaw rushed up to him and, seizing his arm, tried to drag him back. When McNeal shook her off and again was marching away with the buck she uttered the terrible shrieks which Clark had heard.

"Can you guess what it was all about?"

"Well, let me think," said Lewis, pulling his brows down. "Looks like a triangle. The villain must be the young buck. I expect the squaw was warning McNeal."

"That's all right," said Clark, admiring his friend's powers of deduction.

"I expect that McNeal had been to bed with her."

"You are still right."

"I expect the red friend intended to kill him."

"To knife him for his blanket. McNeal had left his knife and gun with me."

"That's one thing about the red man, he'll kill as quick for a trinket as for a fortune. You suppose the incident taught McNeal anything?"

"I doubt it."

"Does the fool have a venereal?"

"He says not but I think he has."

"You know," Lewis said, "I sort of admire that squaw. She may get a knife through her, yet she saved the life of a man who had been with her, and who soon will see her no more. That is real gallantry. As for the stupid McNeal, it would have served him right. Did he seem grateful to her?"

"No, only astonished."

"I've observed that astonishment is a common emotion in the stupid."

Or Lewis would interrupt his writing to dwell on the problems facing the captains. The power to anticipate was, he believed, the chief mark of a good officer. According to the upriver Indians, they could not hope to pass the Rocky Mountain barrier before June 1st. According to the calculations he and Clark had made, the Corps would have to leave Fort Clatsop well before April 1st if it was to reach the horses before June 1st. If this were true it would be folly to wait until late April, hoping that a ship would come in. It would also be folly if a number of the men were down with venereal disease at about the time the party was ready to undertake the long journey home.

Both captains had talked to the men in plain words. Before the fort was built Lewis had called them together and had said, "We're going to have to spend a whole winter here in wet weather. We're not used to it. I observe that most of you have colds and you are nearly naked. All winter you'll be eating meat and nothing but meat. Early in the spring we'll probably set out for home. Going back may be a lot harder than coming out. We'll not have anything much to trade. Up the Columbia and the Kooskooskee we'll be fighting the high floodwaters of springtime."

He paused a few moments and looked from face to face. They looked at him, knowing what was coming.

"It's essential that we all be well and vigorous when we set out. You all know that Captain Clark and I have never set ourselves up as guardians of your moral behavior. We know that young men are full of vigor. I suppose you all know that white traders have come to these coast Indians year after year. Sailors from ships have put in. These Indians are a diseased and wretched lot. I don't see myself how any white man could stomach one of these filthy flatheaded squaws. Captain Clark and I are not going to give you orders to stay away from them. Such orders we couldn't enforce, even if we gave them. But we are going to say to you as I'm saying now that we want every man fit and ready when the time comes to go."

Well, they weren't all going to be fit and ready. The captains had known that even while Lewis was speaking, for he was then treating eight of them and suspected that others were infected but had not told him because of shame. A minor chief whose name they spelled as Delashelwilt had a fat wife whom the captains both spoke of and wrote of as the old bawd. By turn they came, the husband or wife, bringing six or seven young squaws, who all day long hung around the camp, and later the fort, until the captains were sick of the sight of them.

Lewis said one day to Clark that he himself preferred to return overland, even if Jefferson sent a ship, for he wanted to see more of the country north of the Missouri, and particularly those parts which the damned English were sure to lay claim to. He wanted to push up Maria's River. A ship, of course, would be a godsend, for the sick men could be returned in it.

It was an excellent idea, Clark said. Why didn't they let the men know how they were thinking?

"Threaten them, you mean?"

"Just tell them that those knocked out by the squaws will go home by boat. No real man would want to do that."

That might do some good, Lewis said, though even the men who were sickest, like the black man, had no doubt they'd be well when the time came to go.

Clark said, "We can't go up the Big River with sick men on our back."

"We certainly can't. How would we portage them?"

"I've told them all that."

"Who are the worst offenders, anyway?"

"Oh, such as Gibson and McNeal, Whitehouse, Goodrich. Aren't they?"

"Those have been some of the sickest," Lewis said. "If we have to leave some of them here we'll leave them. Maybe they'll get enough of squaws before they see their homes again."

It was not only the squaws. It was also the wet enervating weather, and the lean meat diet. By the middle of February, Bratton was so sick and feeble he could barely limp around. Lewis gave him huge doses of pills but they did not move him. Bratton complained of his back.

"Where does it hurt?" Lewis asked.

"All across," Bratton said, moving his hands back and forth across his lumbar area. "And all down my legs, here."

Lewis mixed together three medicines. Bratton gagged the concoction down and doubled over to vomit.

"Don't waste it," Lewis said. "We're running short."

"I'm sorry, Captain," Bratton muttered, wiping his wet mouth.

He did not improve. By the end of February there were more sick men than the Corps had ever had at one time. These men had terrible colds and fevers. Lewis diagnosed the illness as influenza. McNeal and Gibson were sick again, both having been weakened, the captains suspected, by too much consorting with the squaws. But even though sick all the men but Bratton were as busy as beavers making moccasins and leather clothing, because what a man wore on this journey depended solely on him. All together the men this winter made over four hundred pairs of moccasins, and clothing of all kinds from elk, deer, beaver and otter skins.

Bratton was the one who worried the captains most. While at the salt works he had become so weak that his companions had carried him to the fort on a litter. Lewis at first had thought it a combination of squaws and weather but Bratton swore to all the heavens that he had never touched a squaw.

Lewis enjoyed himself as physician, his interest in diseases being as insatiable as his interest in botany. He had written, "Goodrich has recovered from the Louis Veneri which he contracted from an amorous contact with a Chinnook damsel, I cured him as I did Gibson last winter by the uce of mercury. I cannot learn that the Indians have any simples which are sovereign specifics in the cure of this disease; and indeed I doubt very much wheter any of them have any means of effecting a perfect cure, when once this disorder is contracted by them it continues with them during life; but always ends in decipitude, death, or premature old age; tho' from the uce of certain simples together with their diet, they support this disorder with but little inconvenience for many years, and even enjoy a tolerable share of health; particularly so among the Chippeways who I believe to be better skilled in the use of those simples than any nation of Savages in North America. The Chippeways use a decoction of the Lobelia, and that of a species of sumac common to the Atlantic states and to this country, near and on the Western side of the Rocky Mountains. this is the smallest species of the sumac, readily distinguished by it's winged rib, or common footstalk, which supports it's oppositely pinnate leaves, these decoctions are drank freely and without limitation. the same decoctions are used in cases of the gonnaerea and are effecatious and sovereign. notwithstanding that this disorder dose exist among the Indians on the Columbia yet it is witnessed in but few individuals, at least the males who are always sufficiently exposed to the observations or inspection of the phisician. in my whole rout down this river I did not see more than two or three with the gonnaerea and about double that number with the pox."

When March came in and a number of the men were still sick, with the hour of departure imminent, the captains summoned all the men to a meeting and Lewis said, "Captain Clark and I have decided that our Corps will leave for home some time this month. In spite of the good advice we gave you, and repeated from time to time, some of you have the pox. Captain Clark and I feel a lively sense of responsibility for your health and safe return, but only when you treat us as fairly and show common sense. We cannot watch over you day and night. We cannot take sick men up the river, but will have to leave them here with the squaws, if they are sick with the pox, to find a boat and return in their own time, or to re-main here and become Flatheads. Those willing to pledge on their honor to Captain Clark and me that they will leave the squaws alone from now on I will do my best to cure, and have them in health and vigor by the time they leave. All others will be taking their own chances."

Every man gave the pledge. Did they mean it? The captains had no way of knowing that, but as the days passed they became con-vinced that the men were keeping their promise. Old Delashelwilt, sensing that the white men were getting ready to go, had come with his group of young women and pitched camp not far from the fort; and all day long every day the girls came over to pester and solicit the men. The captains watched their men closely but pretended not to watch them at all. By March 17th Lewis was pleased to be able to write, "I believe notwithstanding every effort of their win-ning graces, the men have preserved their constancy to the vow of celibacy . . ."

He thought he had cured the pox in those who had had it and that the men were in fair shape, except Bratton, who was now un-able to walk and barely able to move. He would be a dreadful bur-den. He would be five or ten times the trouble of his weight in salt or dried flesh but they would have to take him, for he was ill through no fault of his own. Both captains felt pride in the fact that so far they had lost only one man. Lewis told Gass and Shields to make a harness-litter of leather, so that Bratton could be handled speedily and with as little pain to him as possible. That he was in agony when moved no one could doubt, for his forehead burst with sweat. He was pathetic too, the captains thought: the poor fellow would look round at the preparations, as though wondering if he was to be left behind, as the Indians left their sick and old. He made heroic efforts to get to his feet.

Seeing his terrible anxiety, Lewis went over to him. "Private Brat-ton, are you worried?"

"Only a little, sir."

"Don't worry. We'll take you home and you'll be as good as new long before you get there."

"Thank you, Captain."

But Lewis was not sure that Bratton was going to get well. The man had been ill for nearly two months and he seemed to get not better but worse. Again Lewis studied the few medicines he had left, wondering if any combination of them would effect a cure. Was it rheumatism or a bad sprain?—or influenza of the spine?

The morning of March 18th Drewyer, the party's ablest hunter, was found groaning with a pain in his side. A half-dozen of the other men sat around looking forlorn and spiritless, and when Lewis asked them what the trouble was they said they didn't feel well. Damn it! Lewis thought. When we're about ready to go half our men get sick! He was so annoyed that when, a little later, he looked out and saw the squaws approaching he decided to give to Delashelwilt a certificate of good deportment and tell him to get his women out of sight. He would also give him a list of the names of those in the Corps.

After writing the list he decided to leave a second list, tacked to an inside wall of the fort, and with it these words:

> The object of this list is, that through the medium of some civilized person who may see the same, it may be made known to the informed world, that the party consisting of the persons whose names are hereunto annexed, and who were sent out by the government of the U'States in May 1804. to explore the interior of the Continent of North America, did penetrate the same by way of the Missouri and Columbia Rivers, to the discharge of the latter into the Pacific Ocean, where they arrived on the 14th of November 1805, and from whence they departed the day of March 1806 on their return to the United States by the same rout they had come out.

The day of the departure he would write in when it was known.

35

Drewyer improved but the other men did not, nor did the weather. It continued to rain and hail and there was nothing for the captains to do but write in their journals. Some days Lewis wrote nearly two thousand words, breaking off now and then to go out and look at the storm, or to the other cabins to look at the men. He took delight in describing the Killamucks, Clatsops, Chinooks, Cathlahmahs and Wackiacums, all of whom resembled one another in dress and habits —"they are low in statue reather diminutive, and illy shapen; possing thick broad flat feet, thick ankles, crooked legs wide mouths thick lips, nose moderately large, fleshey, wide at the extremity with large nostrils, black eyes and black coarse hair. their eyes are sometimes of a dark yellowish brown the puple black. . . ."

After another look at the storm he said to Clark, "Now that we're ready to go I expect the old infernal will pelt us day and night."

"Hail," said Clark, listening to the sound on the roof planks.

Lewis sat and resumed his writing: "I have observed the heads of many infants, after this singular bandage had been dismissed, or about the age of 10 or eleven months, that were not more than two inches thick about the upper edge of the forehead and reather thiner still higher. from the top of the head to the extremity of the nose is one streight line. this is done in order to give a greater width to the forehead, which they much admire. . . ." A thousand words and several hours later he was writing, ". . . the whole being of sufficient thickness when the female stands erect to conceal those parts usually covered from formiliar view, but when she stoops or places herself in many other attitudes, this battery of Venus is not . . ."

He looked over at his friend. "Will, I don't expect I'll ever be a very romantic man. These squaws——"

"I know what you mean."

"Garments are to mystify and enhance, not reveal."

"I don't expect," Clark said, "that the red men ever think much about romance."

"It's a Christian trait," Lewis said.

Clark was startled. He said he had never thought of it that way.

A few minutes later Lewis was writing, "The large or apparently sweled legs particularly observable in the women are obtained in a great measure by tying a cord Tight around the leg above the ancle bone. their method of squating or resting themselves on their hams which they seam from habit to prefer to sitting, no doubt contributes much to this deformity of the legs by preventing free circulation of the blood. . . ."

The next day the rain continued and a violent wind came in. The men just sat around and waited, even the hunters remaining inside. The following day, March 21st, the storm continued but a few of the hunters went out, for there was only enough meat on hand for one day. Bratton seemed to be worse and privately Lewis had given him up as lost. The captains had hoped to set out on the 22nd but the wild storm continued. Depressed and anxious, they sat by a small fire and listened to the howling of the wind.

Lewis said, "I expect in the morning we just as well be off."

"I expect so," Clark said. "How are Willard and Bratton?"

"Willard has a bad pain in his legs but he'll be able to walk. Bratton I despair of."

Word was sent out that the Corps would depart in the morning and most of the men howled with joy. "Did you hear?" Whitehouse cried, rushing up to Goodrich. "We leave in the morning!"

"We leave in the morning!" It was Hugh McNeal.

"We leave in the morning!" It was George Gibson.

After four and a half months of rain they would leave in the morning! Even Sacajawea caught the fever; and her child, more than a year old now, laughed with glee and clapped his hands. The sullen apathy seemed to fall away from the squawman. Bratton tried to sit up.

"I could just go walking right off on the air," Silas Goodrich said.

"What you'll be doing," Frazier said, "is wading over your head in spring floods." He seized a dried elk skin and, beating on its flesh side, softly intoned, "Mr. Jefferson, hear that drum! Here we come, sir, here we come. . . ."

Lewis said to Clark, "I never realized our men are homesick."

"Only a few of them," Clark said. "They're just sick of rain and spoiled meat. They want to get back to buffalo land."

"Or dog land," Lewis said, teasing him. "Ah, for a roast of dog again!"

The next morning the storm was still so violent that the captains stood in their doorway and hesitated. The tide was rising and they were afraid to risk their canoes in high tide. "But we can't tarry any longer," Lewis cried at last, and sent a sergeant to tell the men to hold themselves in readiness. And at one o'clock in wild storm the Corps loaded the canoes and set out. After they had gone a little way some of them turned to look back at their fort. Lewis looked back. He felt a great emotion of tenderness and a misting over of his eyes, as he stood off alone, looking back through falling rain, his mind teeming with memories. He was a sentimental man and he knew it. In him nostalgia ran deep. Well, it had been a good home in its way: over four thousand miles from family and friends, it had kept the Indians out and the storms out. He had written enough words there to make a book. He had lain many a night, dry and cozy, a low fire blazing, the cabin filled with wood smells, the rain singing on the plank roof. Still he looked intently, for half his soul was there where he had written and dreamed as never before, and the other half stood in his eyes ready to leave him. Was it that he did not want to return to the civilized life? He suspected that was part of it, as he gazed at the low range on the north, which hid the Columbia; at the higher and more distant mountains across the east and south; at the lower and nearer mountains across the west. Lord, how well he knew it all!—every turn of the river down there murmuring through its thickets; the impenetrable jungles of vines in which a man could stand and see nothing, not even the sky straight up, the vines being so tall, and arched over in dense ceilings. Yonder leading across the hills in the southwest was the trail to the camp of the salt-makers.

Might a ship from the President yet come in? He knew it was a foolish thought. They had made their return overland inevitable when they failed to send messengers from the Great Falls. They had left to the President only one possible conclusion, that the entire party had perished. This thought amused him. Back in the United

States the people had wagged their solemn heads, saying, "The Indians wiped them out, you know. It must have been the Blackfeet."
He could hear the Federalists chortle and snort, saying, "Jefferson's
folly! That freckled blockhead. That madman and wife-seducer, deliberately sacrificing that body of men to satisfy one of his insane
whims! The entire country out there isn't worth the little finger of
one soldier." That would be a little finger of prodigious size, Lewis
told himself, his mind ranging the vast expanses across which he had
come. Don't you worry, Mr. President. We'll all come back, even Private Bratton, even if we have to carry him on our backs. . . .

And still he lingered, taking a last look around. Farewell! he
thought, his gaze on the fort. Then he snapped out of his nostalgic
mood and was again the military man and the leader, with a tougher
job ahead of him, he had no doubt, than the one he had faced on
the journey west. He went to the path leading down off the small
tableland on which the fort stood. They had all gone down the river
and he was alone. Once again he looked back and once again he
murmured, "Farewell!" Then he stiffened and took the path in a
quick stride.

Just how difficult the return journey was to be Lewis learned before the party had gone far. It was not so much the rain that fell
day and night, until again they were all wet and miserable and their
bedding was soaked. It was not at first the scarcity of game, for they
were all used to hunger and lean rations. It was the terrible river,
now much higher—in some stretches twenty feet higher—than it had
been last fall when they came down. In the swollen and plunging
waters the men labored in vain to row the canoes, for all of them
were weakened men now. Not one of them, not even the huge Negro,
had half the strength he had had at Fort Mandan. Rain, cold and
hunger had sapped them. But not a man complained. They were
going home now, and at night when they lay in their wet bedding
under drenching rains and deep fogs they told themselves that they
were one day nearer. Before long they would be out of this God-
forsaken rain-soaked land where the deer were web-footed and the
waterfowl tasted like rain water. It was Frazier's fancy. He was composing rimes which he and some of the men sang to nursery tunes.

The first really terrible blow fell when they met canoes on their
way down the river. They had left their lodges, the red people said,
because there was nothing to eat up there. The captains looked at
one another. The men looked at one another and at their captains.

If there was nothing to eat in a distance of three or four hundred miles . . . But they would go on, the men said, looking over at their captains, who stood apart, talking. The captains decided to send all their best hunters on ahead to Deer Island, to kill all the game they could find and dry it and wait.

They would find something to eat, the men said. They had lived on berries . . . dogs . . . roots . . . fish. They could live on tree bark, if they had to.

When the Corps reached Deer Island the news was so shocking that the men would have been chilled had there been anything with power to chill them. The hunters said there was almost no game on the island. Then other Indians came canoeing down and they told the same story: there was nothing to eat up there, not in their nation or in any other nation. There was no game, not even a bird on the river, not even a root. All their dried fish was gone, their roots were gone.

Again the captains went apart from their men to discuss the problem. Should they push on? Above the rapids and narrows and across the plains that led to the pierced noses there would be no deer, elk or antelope. The Indians along there had—or had had—horses and dogs but these might now be only skin and bone. If there was nothing for men to eat what could there be for dogs to eat? Even if there were dogs and horses, what did the captains have to trade for them? They had a few elk and deer skins, some fish hooks and awls and needles.

The simple question, Lewis said, was whether to go back to the fort and wait till the fish went up ahead of them, or whether to go on. If they waited, the ice in the Missouri would catch them before they got home, and that would mean another winter at Mandan.

Clark was silent. It was a terrible decision which they now had to make.

Lewis went on: "We'll lose our horses if we wait. We could never get there before the Chopunnish go over the mountains to buffalo land. And we can never get over the mountains without horses."

Clark said at last, "I feel we must go on."

And so they went on, both knowing that they would be in greater peril than they had yet been on this journey. But once they made the decision they never reconsidered it or looked back. They would go on, they said; they would find something to eat, if no more than roots. If they came to the worst of it they would live on bark and roots and bones, and their own clothing, until they reached the Kooskooskee.

When the hunters came in to report that they had killed four elk and two deer the captains decided to linger here a few days, and kill and dry as much meat as they possibly could. They sent out three different hunting-parties; and Clark, having decided that on their downward journey they had missed a large river, which Indians called the Multnomah, went back down the Columbia to find it. That was the spirit Lewis liked to see! They might all die of starvation, but there was a job to be done and as long as they could walk they would do it. He saw his friend off and then enthusiastically set himself to the task of describing the life around him.

Hours later a hunting-party returned to say that they had killed two deer, but they were so skinny that all but their hides had been left behind.

Lewis was vexed. "After this bring it all in, all of it."

"But, Captain," George Shannon said, "there was almost no meat on the bones."

"In the bones there's marrow and our Indian girl can get grease out of bones."

Clark meanwhile was without food. When he came to an Indian village he tried to trade a fish hook for wappato roots but found the Indians hostile. They looked half-dead from hunger. They refused to talk in sign language or to have anything to do with him. Clark then decided to get by stratagem what he could not get by honest barter. He had with him a piece of what he called port fire match and he cut off about an inch of it and tossed it into the Indian fire. Then, sitting by the fire, he took out a pocket compass and a magnet and with the magnet he spun the compass needle round and round. The red people had been astonished and then alarmed by what he had done to their fire; when they saw the needle spinning their alarm mounted to terror. They begged him to put out the bad fire which he had blown up to terrifying size: since the piece of match-stick was almost burned out Clark affected to address himself to it and to prevail against it with mysterious powers. Suddenly the strange fire was gone. He put away the compass and magnet. A very old man who seemed blind began to shriek with great vehemence. Clark supposed that the old fellow was imploring his god. Squaws rushed away and came back to pile wappato roots at Clark's feet. The captain then filled his pipe and smoked with the men and gave two fish hooks to the women; and with an armful of wappato roots he went on his way. He did not like to practice deceptions, but necessity, Lewis had told him, was a stern master: before beginning their homeward journey they had stolen an Indian canoe, having no other way to get one. Looking down at his roots and hungrily sniffing, Clark reflected that they might have to take with magic a part of their food from a starving people.

The next day Gass and his party returned, bringing the flesh of a small bear and some venison. They had killed an elk and six deer but had thought the beasts too scrawny to bother with. Joe Fields and Drewyer returned to say that they had killed and dried the flesh of two deer but there were only a few pounds of it. Ordway and his men came in with the dried flesh of four elk, and there was not much of that. The game, the sergeant said, was so nearly dead from hunger it could barely move. Lewis sent four men up the river to hunt there and wait. Clark returned to report that the mouth of the Multnomah River was a hundred and forty-two miles up the Columbia from the ocean.

The hunters here, Lewis said, were killing no more than the Corps was eating. They might as well go on.

They went on up the river, with almost continuous rain above them, with winds lashing the river to furies. Day after day on short rations, they struggled upriver against the high waters of springtime, with the hunters coming in day after day to report that they found little that was worth shooting. The elk and deer had gone to the mountains. Most of the bears were still asleep. On one day all the hunters who went out killed only one scrawny duck; on the next they killed nothing, but Lewis was able to trade for a few roots and five skinny dogs. Day by day the captains were studying their men for signs of failing strength and spirits, and day after day the Indian girl caught their swift glance and smiled. Her imperturbable cheerfulness and her amazing endurance the men had given up trying to understand.

The party was now coming to the cascades, where the water drove down with such velocity that it took all the boatmen to drag one canoe forward. One boat was capsized and everything in it was lost. At the first portage every man had to pitch in, except Bratton, still too feeble to walk, and three with wrenched knees, and another who prepared the meals. The Indians along here were so hostile that when the men were in water to their armpits struggling to take a boat upstream, from above the red men would hurl stones and pieces of wood down upon them, until a furious Lewis rushed up to them and threatened to shoot them all. Indians now followed the party every day, hoping to steal something; and they did at last lure Lewis's scrawny dog into following them. Again Lewis lost his temper: he sent three of his boldest men after the dog, with orders to shoot if it was not surrendered at once. A half-dozen bucks caught John Shields alone with a dog that had been traded for and wrested it from him. He had had to draw his knife to recover it. The captains had to post guards every night. The men with short rifles were ordered to carry them in such a position that they could fire instantly. In three days, laboring from daylight till dark, the party advanced only seven miles.

The homeward journey had become a nightmare of fatigue and hunger, in the midst of hostile thieving Indians. They must push on, Lewis said, with all possible speed, until they came to the Indians with horses; and his men redoubled their efforts. Bratton felt so deeply ashamed of himself, being hauled up the river in a boat or carried over the portages by men not much stronger than himself, that he struggled desperately to stand up and walk, but always fell back, bursting with sweat and fainting. "Take it easy," Bob Frazier would say to him. "The time might come when you'll have to carry me."

When at last the party came to horse country the captains learned that the red men did not want to trade. Lewis would lay out all the merchandise he had for barter, and the Indians would look at it and turn away. They wanted tomahawks, war hatchets and guns. The red people came by the scores from villages up and down the river and all day long the captains tried to trade with them. Hoping to prevail over the childlike Indian mind, Lewis laid merchandise out in separate parcels and explained to the Indians that each parcel was intended for a horse. The red men looked and sneered and went away; returned to look again, again to show their contempt and go away. In his Journal the depressed and goaded Lewis confessed, "they tanterlised me the greater part of the day." A chief bargained to trade two horses and then withdrew the offer; bargained, next, to trade three, and brought forth three scarecrows, two with deep sores in their backs. When Lewis rejected these two, the chief, pretending to be shocked and wounded, withdrew the third. Other Indians came, to say that out on the plains they had many horses and would trade; and though they had deceived both captains again and again, over a period of days, Clark still had faith for each new day and on again being deceived would record in his Journal, "but to my estonishment not one would make the exchange to day."

"What on earth are we to do?" Lewis asked, despairing. It was Clark who saved the party. A chief with bad sores over him came to Clark for treatment, and Clark dressed the sores and gave the chief some salve and liniment. The chief then brought his wife, whom Clark thought of as a sulky bitch. She had pains in her back. Clark rubbed camphor into her back, her temples and neck, and bound a heated flannel over her kidneys. While doing his best for her it occurred to him that this was the moment to try for a horse-trade, and he was not astonished when his offer was accepted. He became the proud owner of two nags.

"Captain Lewis," he said to his friend, "we have two horses. If we both set up as physicians I think we can pretend to enough magic to see our way through."

"Whether we get more horses or not we have to leave the canoes. We're killing our men."

They tried to trade their boats but the Indians offered so little for them that the disgusted captains had them cut up for firewood. Discovering that for kettles they could get horses, they traded every kettle they had except a small one for each eight men. Their need of horses was so desperate, now that they were afoot, that Clark offered a blue robe, a calico shirt, a silk handkerchief, five parcels of paint, a knife, eight yards of ribbon, several pieces of brass, a moccasin awl and six braces of beads for one horse. He also offered a large blue blanket from his bedroll; his coat, his sword and his plume. All these things the red men rejected. While the captains were trying to get more horses thieves slipped around and made off with six tomahawks; and the next day when Clark saw a thief taking the iron socket from a canoe pole he rushed over in fury and after striking the fellow a solid blow in his face struck him twice again, and then ordered his men to throw him head over heels out of camp.

But one by one they got enough horses to take them forward, though most of them were scrawny and feeble, and some had backs so broken open with sores that not much baggage could be put on them. Both captains, hungry and weak and depressed, had reached the limit of their patience. Clark had Drewyer tell the Indians that he would shoot the first one caught stealing; and when a little later

Lewis found that a robe had been stolen he was in such a rage that he threatened to burn an entire village. Still, the captains felt pity too. These miserable stunted sickly half-dead-from-hunger Indians sat at this time of year in their stinking flea-ridden hovels waiting for the salmon to come. What a life it was, anyway! Half the year they spent drying fish; the other half they spent living on rancid fish and waiting for more fish to come. In hard winters like this one the feeblest of them starved and died, and desperation forced the others to risk their lives stealing, when there was anything to be stolen.

"It's true," Clark said, listening to his friend's compassion as they walked side by side. "You just have to feel sorry for them, but let's use some more magic, get a few more horses and go."

Clark's greatest success as a physician was with eye-water. Most of these people, even most of the young, had sore eyes, often pus-filled; he treated them and the Indians felt better and they were grateful. He treated Indians with fever, colds, chronic pains; and at last with enough horses to carry Bratton and the baggage, and with enough dogs to keep them alive a few days, the party went on and May 5th came to the mouth of the Kooskooskee. Lewis surveyed the junction of two great rivers and, again feeling ebullient and optimistic, told his friend that the worst was over.

"I see little trouble ahead of us," he said.

But he was wrong again.

36

The next morning, still feeling optimistic, Lewis cast a fatherly eye over his men and decided that never before in the world had there been such an ill-assorted and outlandish group. Their hair was long, tangled and filthy; most of them had beards. Because they had not been able to tan the hides well and had little skill in sewing, their garments looked even more preposterous than their heads: they had been rain-soaked so many days that they now creaked when they moved and looked as though at any moment they would fall off the gaunt frames. All the men had lost so much weight that to the critical Lewis eye they seemed positively emaciated.

The Corps moved up the river and at the first village tried in vain to buy something to eat; and in vain at the second; and only by offering ten times what they were worth were they able at the third to buy two scrawny dogs and a few roots. Clark had eaten no dog, nor had the girl and her child, all the way through dog land, and Lewis wondered how they kept going. In the third village a chief offered Clark a gray mare, which Clark thought elegant, asking in return only some eye-water. And so again Clark became physician to a host of ills and complaints: all around him in the pathetic creatures he saw rheumatism, scrofula, ulcers, sore eyes, swollen joints, sore mouths and tongues—and cheerfully with strong gentle hands he ministered to them all, rubbing liniment over swollen joints; opening abscesses on necks and thighs; giving purges or emetics; washing open sores with soap—all the while drily reflecting that two of his "cures" last fall had given him an immense reputation as a magician. He said in his Journal that he thought it pardonable to continue the deception, for otherwise the party could get no food. The Indians gave from their lean hoards in exchange for treatment but still looked with abhorrence on anyone who ate dog flesh; and the very first day on the Kooskooskee a brave came up with a puppy while Lewis was eating and with all his might hurled it into the captain's face. Outraged, with blood choking his face and almost bursting from the veins in his forehead and neck, Lewis seized the pup and with great violence smote the Indian across his face. When the poor dog gave off a yelp of pain and terror Lewis was twice as angry, because of shame for ill-treating a helpless beast: seizing his tomahawk, he rushed forward, and his astounded men, watching him, expected to see an Indian skull split open like a melon. But just in time Lewis got control of himself, and at the same moment the terrified Indian fled.

Meriwether Lewis almost fainted with embarrassment. Never before had his men seen him so completely lose that violent temper which nearly always he kept controlled and hidden. Nearly all of them were staring at him curiously, even the girl: here was a new vision of their captain. Lewis tried to go on with his eating but down in him was an ugly question asking itself over and over, Is it then so terrible to eat dog? His dreadful humiliation and shame fell away in him when a young squaw rushed up proudly to show off her new baby, an infant with negroid features and kinky hair. The men gathered round it whooping with glee, and the foolish proud mother thought they were praising her child. Now that all attention was withdrawn from him Lewis recovered his poise.

"God in heaven!" said Shannon. "No little Shannon?" Other men caught the spirit. "No little Goodrich?" asked Silas; and even more mournfully McNeal said, "No little McNeals around here?" In a voice so tragic that the men were startled Frazier cried, "O my God, no little Frazier?" On their way up the river the men learned that there were a few other half-breeds, just recently born, including two more tiny Yorks. It was the squaws with the half-Negro babies who were so inordinately proud—and the big black man himself, emaciated now and rather hideous as he grinned from ear to ear. Making a face of pain and heartbreak, Frazier called the attention of Goodrich, Whitehouse, McNeal and Gibson to another black infant, and intoned, "O how enviable is this man York, who has a secret agreement with the stork! I mean he knows his own ba-bees!" The men exploded. They began to search among the new infants for one that looked like them, and almost got into a fight over the matter, they were so ridiculous. "Looks like you!" one of them would cry, sneering. "It looks a hell of a lot more like me." And then he would look hard at the mother. A number of the men went round staring at the squaws and feeling frightfully silly because unable to tell whether this squaw, or another, had been their woman.

The captains were eager to find Chief Twisted Hair and their horses but some of their men were so weak that it was necessary to give them rest and a few rich meals. For the meals they wanted a couple of fat horses, though none of the beasts were fat. A small Indian girl, almost helpless with what the captains diagnosed as rheumatism, Clark bathed in hot water, and then rubbed her over with liniment and salves. She felt so much better that her father came forward with a young horse. Clark treated a squaw, who then slept for the first night in many moons, and received another horse. The captains then bought some root bread, and their enfeebled men feasted on bread with hot rich broth poured over it, and boiled horse flesh. A few good meals worked wonders in them, for they were a rugged crew, though Bratton was still unable to move. The Indians here, who would eat neither their dogs nor their horses, were in such a condition of famine that they were living on boiled moss that grew on pine trees. Again the captains were caught between necessity and pity: when, for some eye-water, a tearfully grateful Indian brought twelve small fish to Clark the captain declined them, knowing that these few dried fish were everything in the world this man, with his wife and four children, had to eat, except moss. So near death from starvation were some of these people that when the party's hunters brought in two does, each with a baby in its womb, the red people choked down paunch, guts, lungs, and even the foetus, without even bothering to wash anything, or to take the hair off. Looking on such ravening hunger, the captains found it difficult to eat anything at all.

When they came to Twisted Hair the captains found him cool and uncommunicative. It took them some time to discover the reason. Twisted Hair, Cut Nose and Broken Arm, three chiefs, had been feuding ever since the white men vanished down the river: Cut Nose and Broken Arm had been envious and put out because the captains had left their horses in the custody of Twisted Hair. To mollify them Twisted Hair had given them partial custody, and then had been humiliated and angered on learning that the two chiefs had ridden some of the horses almost to death. He had felt very bad about it, for how could he explain this to the white chiefs? On the other hand,

Cut Nose got the captains aside and told them that Twisted Hair wore two faces.

"I don't care how many faces he wears," Lewis cried, "if only he'll bring our horses in!" The chief had twenty-one of them brought, five of which had been so overridden that they were crippled. This night it began to snow, and by noon of the next day the snow lay eight inches deep on the plain. The mountains ahead of them looked white, and very high and cold. The red people kept coming by the scores to beg Clark to treat them; and while one captain doctored them, the other delighted them with the magnet, the spyglass, the compass, the watch and the airgun. The evening after the snowstorm an Indian was brought on a litter and laid before Clark: this was an important chief, the litter-bearers explained, who for years had not been able to move, though he ate heartily and had a clear mind. Clark treated the chief with various medicines, and soon the man sat up and said he felt much better.

The morning of May 12th, seven days after the Corps reached the Kooskooskee, Clark looked out of his small skin-tent and saw nearly forty Indians with sore eyes waiting for him. Cheerfully he doctored all of them, and Broken Arm was so grateful that he stripped off his leather jacket and handed it to Clark. In return Clark gave him the best of his shirts. The two captains again agreed that these pierced noses were the cleanest, most intelligent and most hospitable Indians they had found west of Illinois. These Indians lived in deadly fear of the Blackfeet and the Big Bellies of the Prairie, who killed them for the fun of it when they ventured over the mountains to buffalo land. Lewis had been trying to get guides to lead his party over the mountains but even Twisted Hair's sons seemed afraid to go. Twisted Hair said they could not cross the mountains now: the snow was twenty to thirty feet deep: they would have to wait two more moons. But the captains were determined to go on just as soon as they could find guides, and enough meat for short rations over the summit. With concern that had every mark of being genuine the chief begged them to delay; their horses, he said, would all die on the way over, for there was nothing for a horse to eat. There would be no sign of the trail, for the tree-blazings were now under the snow. The captains would stand for ten or fifteen minutes at a time, gazing at the mountains and thinking of the problem; and always their minds came back to the thought, If we wait much longer the Missouri ice will catch us for another winter.

They had to go now, even without guides. Still, what could they do about Bratton?—for he was too much of a burden to carry all the way across the mountains. What would they do for food? Sacajawea was gathering roots and making bread of them and hoarding the bread. All the best hunters were going out every day—north, south and east—but the few animals they found were starved to their hide and bones and always a long way from camp. Most of the men were sick now: some had what the captains called colic; others suffered with violent headaches; still others had boils and swollen joints. By May 21st the party had no meat of any kind, and only a few roots. The next day a colt was butchered for the sick members, among whom, Clark now learned, was the child. The boy's jaws and throat were so swollen that Clark concluded at once that he was dangerously ill: he applied a poultice of wild onions, and gave the child a big dose of cream of tartar.

The next day John Shields came to Lewis. He said he had known men with Bratton's disease, whatever it was—men who had eaten fairly well and had seemed to be in no pain, except when they moved. All these men had been cured with violent sweats. Lewis went to Clark and told him what Shields had said.

"You're the chief physician around here," Lewis said. "Shall we try it?"

"Does Shields know how it's done?"

"He says he does."

"Well, I expect it won't do any harm."

And so they told Shields to prepare the sweat-bath. He dug in the earth a hole about four feet deep and three feet across, and filled the hole with fire. He kept the fire blazing until the earth walls were heated to a considerable depth. He then scooped all the fire and embers out and at the bottom of the hole placed a flat stone for Bratton to sit on, and a piece of plank to rest his feet on. Green willows were placed like wagon bows over the hole, and over these a number of heavy blankets were laid. Bratton was then stripped naked and helped into the depth. Under the edge of the blankets he was handed a cupful of hot strong mint tea, and a kettle of hot water, which he was told to sprinkle over the hot earth all around him and to raise as much steam as he could bear. He was to drink all the tea he could. The captains, kneeling to listen, could hear the poor devil groaning in the depth. They told him to stand it as long as he possibly could and to keep drinking the hot tea. After twenty min-

utes Bratton begged to be taken out, and was swiftly dragged forth
and plunged into cold water. When he came up moaning and gasping, his eyes filled with horror, he was shoved under again. He was
then returned to the sweathole, where he drank more hot tea and
sat in hot steam for half an hour. He was then taken out and swad-
dled in blankets and allowed to cool gradually.

"That ought to kill or cure," Lewis said, looking at Bratton's pale
face flowing with sweat.

Though the paralyzed chief did not respond to cream of tartar,
sulphur and baths, the day after his ordeal in the sweathole Bratton
was up and around. He said he felt like a new man. The captains
then decided to give the steam treatment to the chief, and when he
proved too weak to sit up in the hole without toppling over, a relative went in with him. The Indian did not sweat with Bratton's ease
but the day after the treatment he said he felt better. He could move
one of his legs and wiggle its toes. They gave him another steaming,
and a third, and marveled that a man could endure so much: the
poor fellow looked utterly drained of moisture and more than half-
dead but he began to move his other leg. The child also continued
to improve, though a large abscess seemed to be forming under one
ear.

The captains wanted to be off but the red men talked them out of
it. Twisted Hair said they would all die, and their horses with them,
if they did not wait another moon. They would get up in the high
frozen mountains, on snow thirty feet deep with not a blazed tree
or a landmark in sight, nor a thing to eat for beast or man. Clark
stared at the mountains and this evening said in his Journal,
". . . where hungar and Cold in their most rigorous form assail the
waried traveller; not any of us have yet forgotten our sufferings in
those mountains in September last, I think it probable we never
shall. . . ."

And so June came and they still tarried.

Meanwhile every effort was being made to procure food for the
mountain passage. While trading a few trinkets for three or four
bushels of roots the men grimly reflected on the burial customs here:
a chief's wife had died and twenty-eight horses were to be sacrificed
upon her grave! The day this became known, Ordway and Frazier
returned from a long journey after fish, only to find that the fish were
spoiled by the time they reached camp.

"Twenty-eight horses for one squaw," Frazier said, "at a time when they're all starving to death. Where'd I ever get the idea I'm important?"

"It must have been from your mother," Ordway said. "But, remember, these Indians don't eat horses."

"But we do. I could eat two horses right now—two smaller ones, I mean."

"Did you know they're sending an express over the mountains?"

"To Travellers Rest?"

"So Captain Clark tells me. If they can go why can't we go?"

This was the question Clark had just put to Lewis. "We could follow their trail," he said.

They might, Lewis said, though Twisted Hair had told him that several of the streams would swim their horses. The ascents and descents for beasts would be slippery and dangerous. And what would the horses eat, or the men?

"I propose, just the same," Clark said, "that we go on up the river and see if we can lay in a stock of meat. Let's be ready by another week."

This they did, resolved to make a forced march from their next camp to Travellers Rest, just on the other side of the mountains. For five whole weeks they had dawdled along the Kooskooskee: it would have been better, they now realized, to have waited at the ocean for ships that might have come in.

Early June 15th the party set out in a rainstorm, without Indian guides or much sense of where the path lay; and at once the captains began to doubt that they could make it. The hillsides were slick with ice; the weakened horses would fall to their front knees and sometimes struggling to rise would sprawl on their bellies and then roll over. Trying to remain cheerful, Lewis on looking round him saw that honeysuckle, huckleberry and a small species of maple were coming into leaf, in those spots that were clear of snow. The middle of June and the earliest plants were just beginning to show leaf! What kind of country was this? If the party were to wait for a free passage the time might be July, or even August; and so, after a hasty noon meal of nothing but roots, they set out again, every one of them moved by a sense of desperation. By midafternoon they were walking on snow ten feet deep and there was no sign of path or trail, though Clark thought he recognized the spot where Drewyer had killed the stray horse. But it was not all gloom. The slave-girl, looking as if she wouldn't weigh eighty pounds with all her clothes on, always smiled when anyone looked at her, and carried her boy all day long. Bratton moved with the vigor of a man determined to erase the shame of having been carried. Frazier amused them with his drolleries and quips. "If I'd had a squaw to be my ma, then who, I wonder, would be my pa . . . !"

They spent a cold night and moved again at the first sign of morning, and after a difficult climb of three miles found themselves on snow twelve feet deep. Indians had peeled some of the trees here for food but there was no pattern in the blazings; and Clark, leading the way, could see only vast mountainous masses above him and could only choose the way that looked easiest. After another mile or two the party stood on snow from twelve to fifteen feet deep, in a cold wind that stung their faces and chilled them through. It was the middle of June but this was like deep winter.

The captains now consulted their most expert woodsmen but they were lost too. As nearly as anyone could figure it, they would need four days to reach Colt Creek, even if they were lucky enough to choose the right ridges. In those four days there would be no food for the horses. If they were to go on and lose their way, their beasts quite certainly would all starve to death, and the captains would risk the loss of all their maps and papers and possibly the lives of their men. How long could these gaunt beasts go without food? Not more than four days at the most. With luck! Lewis thought, but luck meant not a single miscalculation. The captains went off alone, and the men, watching them, thought that they seemed to be studying the faces of one another.

"Will, what do you think?" Lewis asked at last.

"I expect it would be madness to go on. We'd risk absolutely everything on a gamble."

"But if we go back?"

"We won't get home as soon but all our men might be alive when we get there."

"All right, we'll go back. But what about leaving most of our baggage here?"

They returned to their men and Lewis told them that they were going back. He could see the light go out of faces, the eagerness out of eyes. Lord, they had all been ready to take the risk! Anything but to go back down these dreadful mountains!

"Well, me," Frazier said, "I'm going over and camp right in the middle of those twenty-eight horses."

The captains had the men build scaffolds, and they then suspended from the scaffolds most of their roots, their instruments, even most of their papers, for the papers would be safer here, Lewis said, than on a feeble horse in a mountain stream. They soon discovered how right he was. They had not gone far before the beast Colter was riding fell under him in crossing Hungry Creek and both horse and rider were rolled over and over for a considerable distance before, miraculously, they emerged. Colter lost his bedroll but had hung on to his gun. The horse now had a bad limp. A little later John Potts severed a large vein on the inside of his leg, and it took Clark two hours to stanch the flow of blood. In all that time neither Clark nor Potts said a word. It was a dejected party that went back down the mountains; but now and then, seeing the disappointment in faces, Lewis would say, "Come, come, my men! In a day or two we'll have guides and be on our way."

The captains talked it over and decided to proceed on one of three plans: they would enlist dependable Indian guides and risk the four days, in a desperate attempt to get across; or they would send ahead of them their most expert woodsmen, with the three or four strongest horses, to blaze a path for the main party to follow; or they would swing south and then east, and try to force a passage to the Shoshone country. The mountains far in the southeast looked as if they could be crossed. Twisted Hair said they could not be. Meanwhile they sent Drewyer and Shannon, two of their strongest men, on ahead to find Indian guides; and on a small camas prairie the main party waited.

By June 25th a few Indians had come in, who this evening set huge pine and fir trees ablaze, making immense torches in the night. The Indians said the fires would bring luck and fair weather. The next morning the party set forth again, with Indian guides, though the captains expected them to desert at any moment. One of them was so ill and feeble that they gave him a small buffalo robe, for he had no covering at all but his moccasins and an elkskin dressed without hair; and no bedding. Lewis suspected that he was wasting the robe but he was praying that one guide at least would remain with them: if they had to turn back a second time. . . . Clark had resolved to turn back no more. The next day the Indians stuck with them and even urged them to hasten, saying that it was a long march to the campsite they had in mind for this night. So with all their strength they pushed forward, never pausing except when a horse or a man was down; and at dark came to the spot and found a little grass there. At daylight they were off again and by noon had reached the summit. The view now awed even those most accustomed to mountains.

Clear around the horizon they seemed to be confined by white frozen summits—so completely surrounded that one unfamiliar with the trails would have felt that there was no way out. On this lofty eminence the captains smoked a pipe with their guides, and set off again; and after three hours came to a campsite of last September, which they recognized. For what Clark judged to be almost thirty miles their horses had not grazed nor had their packs removed. They were weary beasts but Indian ponies were tough. There was nothing for supper this evening but boiled camas roots, mixed with a little hot bear grease. But they all felt cheerful, for the guides were confident and the end of this dangerous mountain passage was almost in sight.

The next day they marched from daylight till dark, as fast as weak legs would carry them, across snow that was often more than twenty feet deep; leaving a furrow of trail behind them, up over a crest, down through a ravine and up again; and the next day was like the one before it and the one before that, except that now they had reached the hot springs, and paused to refresh their cold aching limbs. The five Indians with them would plunge into the hot water and lie with all but their faces under, then dash to the icy creek and plunge in. They would frolic for several minutes in cold water, then lie again in the hot, to return still again to the cold. Their copper-colored bodies turned a deep red.

Where did they get all their energy? the men asked. "One thing I've learned at last," George Shannon said. "White people eat too much."

The next day, with a feeling of relief deeper than the captains had yet felt, the party came to Travellers Rest. The terrible mountain barrier had been crossed. Buffalo land was not far ahead of them. They felt safe at last.

They felt so safe, so flooded with relief, and in a deep prayerful way so triumphant that they decided to pause here three or four days, to let the party rest and to lay their plans. Though well aware of the grave risk they would take, the captains had decided to separate: with most of the men Clark would go south, upon the way they had come—down to Shoshone country, then over and down the Jefferson. At the three forks his party would be divided: some of his men would go down the Missouri, and the others, led by Clark, would go over to the Yellow Stone and down it. Lewis, with picked men, would cut across to the Great Falls on the Missouri. There a part of his men would raise the caches and make the long portage, using horses this time, while he cut across the mountains north and east to Maria's River and explored as far up it as time would allow. He hoped that Maria's River was deep enough in Canada to make a portage possible with the Saskatchewan. If this were so, Tom Jefferson's dream of bringing the Canadian furs down the Missouri might come true.

Their friendly Indian guides told them, talking in signs, that if they divided their party they would all die. The Blackfeet or the Big Bellies of the Prairie would ambush the smaller parties, one by one. The captains knew that they were taking that risk but for them risk was the first law of life. Nevertheless, they went away together to talk it over, sitting where they could look into the east, to the mountains and mists between them and the Missouri.

They were not much more than skin and bones, these two captains, Lewis quietly smoking a mixture that was chiefly bark, Clark picking at his teeth with a sliver of buffalo bush. Their hair was long, and tangled with leaves and small twigs; their beards hid their mouths; their faces were hollowed out, their cheekbones high; their hands were bony, bronzed and hairy. They looked like two men who had been a long time in unknown and dangerous lands.

Clark said he thought Lewis ought to take more than nine men with him, for Lewis would be in Blackfoot land, while he, with the main party, would be close to the Shoshones, even if he found a shortcut east of them, and then over at the three forks and down the rivers.

"But you'll have all the invalids," Lewis said. "You'll have the baggage and the boats and you'll need all the men you have, and more."

"I'll be going downstream all the time," Clark said.

"Yes, but you'll have the squaw and her child, and the squawman; and Bratton, who is still pretty feeble; and York and Gibson and Potts, all of them sick."

The captains knew that each was worrying about the other. Clark said, "But you'll be in Blackfoot country." He wanted to get that simple fact into the head of his reckless friend. He wanted him to understand that they'd be down on the Missouri by this time.

"Oh, I'll be careful," Lewis said.

Clark hid a smile. When under heaven had this man ever been careful! Coming over the mountains just now, Lewis and his horse had rolled down into a ravine. Indeed, Lewis had had the luck of an angel on this journey, in his friend's opinion, or he would have been dead a dozen times. Would that luck hold to the end? "What men do you plan to take?"

It was damned nice of him, Lewis thought, to give him his choice. That was just like Will Clark. He'd been wondering which men to take. He didn't for a moment intend to take only the best ones, or any of the best boatmen, or any but two or three of the best hunters.

"When I go up Maria's River——"

"You'll be going right into Blackfoot country."

"Yes, I know that. I'll take three good men with me."

"Only three?" asked Clark, staring.

"Three'll be enough if they're good ones. Three deadshots who are afraid of nothing. If it's all right with you I'll take Drewyer and the Fields brothers for that little excursion. You'll still have good hunters —Colter, Shannon, Collins, Ordway——"

"I'm not worrying about hunters."

"You don't have to, for you're the best of us all. As for the portage, I need a sergeant to take command there. Gass will do. I suggest I also take Werner, Thompson, Goodrich, McNeal and Frazier. That will leave you good hunters and good boatmen."

"You should take more than nine," Clark said, looking at the pale thin face of his friend and wondering why he was so reckless.

"Nine will be plenty. I expect six or seven would be enough, for three or four could make the portage."

For another long moment Clark looked at his friend's face, wondering if he would ever see him again after the tall ungainly form vanished some early morning into the mists. The girl had asked him not to let Lewis go into Blackfoot country. Clark knew that her terror of this Indian nation had grown beyond all reason because of the stories her people had told; but he was aware nevertheless that the Blackfeet were a fearsome tribe. The pierced noses were scared to death of them—as scared as the Shoshones. The five guides had found an Indian footprint in the Travellers Rest area and it had been all the captains could do to keep them from fleeing pellmell back over the mountains. What Indians who knew the Blackfeet were not afraid? What trader down from Canada but had told of their bold-

ness in battle and their fiendish atrocities? Yet Lewis proposed to
go up Maria's River with only three men, right into the heart of the
Blackfoot homeland. "Doan let heem go!" Sacajawea had begged
Clark; and Clark had said, "Captain Lewis usually does as he
pleases."

The five pierced noses tried to dissuade Lewis, and when they
failed the son of a chief bestowed on him the highest honor in his
power. He gave him his own name, White Bear-Skin Folded. When
Lewis realized that this meant the grizzly, and understood the full
significance of the honor, he was so deeply touched that he gave the
young Indian his name. Then, beaming on one another, they smoked
a pipe of bark. "Captain Meriwether Lewis," Lewis said, his tone
grave but his eyes full of mischief, "I want you to keep your people
friendly to my people." The Indian didn't understand a word of it,
but he smoked, and looked at Lewis with almost infinite friendliness.
Just the same, he was eager to be off. He hugely admired this strange
paleface who seemed determined to let the Blackfeet torture and
scalp him but he wanted none of it. A thousand times he looked into
the east.

Clark did not fully know just how reckless Lewis was being—for
Lewis had resolved to take with him both Goodrich and McNeal,
suffering from the pox. He figured that at the portage they could
lie around, dose themselves with mercury and get well. They would
be no good to Clark, so why should he be bothered with stupid men
who wouldn't leave the squaws alone?

"Tomorrow morning I'll be off," Lewis said to Clark one evening.

At daylight he and his men saddled and packed their horses, and
stood facing the sun that rested like a golden melon on the mountains in the northeast.

37

Lewis seemed gay enough but he was hiding a feeling of sadness, for he also doubted that he and Clark would ever meet again. In his Journal for this day, July 3rd, he was to write, "I took leave of my worthy friend and companion Capt. Clark and the party that accompanyed him. I could not avoid feeling much concern on this occasion although I hoped that this seperation was only momentary. . . ." All those going with Clark had crowded round Lewis and his nine men, to shout farewells, to make quips that hid their deeper feelings. Sacajawea made bold at last to push forward and to give a little salute of the kind she had seen the men make. "Goo-by, Cap-un Luis!" she said. "Goodbye," he said, and waved a hand to her. "Kiss little Pomp goodbye for me." The very last moment before turning away he looked over at Clark. Their gaze met a moment. Their beards parted in smiles.

Then Lewis and his men, together with the five Indians, were gone. He had persuaded the terrified red men to proceed with him at least a day or two, to point out the way. The chief's son had told him that he could not miss the river of the road to buffalo land or to the great falls of the river. Before this day was over the five Indians had become so frightened that they insisted on turning back. Lewis begged them to tarry until his hunters could bring them an elk or a few deer. As well as he could in sign language he said, "You have been wonderful friends to us, you guided us over the tremendous mountains, without you we might all have perished. I cannot let you leave us with nothing to eat."

But the hunters brought nothing in. When the Indians saw the fresh track of a horse their terror mounted. The next morning Lewis had to let them go. Again White Bear-Skin Folded begged Lewis to rejoin Clark and return by the southern route. If he went on this way he and his nine men would be killed, for ahead of them was a terrible canyon, stone-walled and gloomy, up which their path led: in this gorge the Blackfeet had ambushed and killed so many people that skulls lay everywhere. Did not the fresh horse track prove that the enemy was near? Probably the Blackfeet were looking at Lewis and his men at this moment. "I wouldn't be surprised," he said, smoking a pipe with the guides, while his own men stared round them. Then gaily he bade them farewell.

He was not so unconcerned as he seemed. When a day or two later he came to fresh Indian tracks he knelt on the earth to examine them, trying to make out which nation they belonged to. He decided to post a guard day and night, in watches of four hours each. As he rode on, looking round him at wild mountain country, he considered his problems: because the men he intended to leave at the falls were not hunters he and his three men would have to delay there and kill a lot of buffalo beef for them. Another problem was the portage: without the help of McNeal and Goodrich would Gass be able to get the baggage around? The worst problem of all was this, that he would be leaving on the river men who were not expert in the handling of firearms. What if the Blackfeet came? *Had* Clark been right? Was he too reckless? It was pretty late to think about that now.

By the tenth they were in buffalo land, and they saw around them larger herds than they had ever seen. Because this was the mating season the men found it almost impossible to sleep: an infernal and earth-shaking bellowing and blowing and snorting kept up all night. "It makes a man ashamed," Frazier said, "to be a male." Slyly he looked over at Goodrich and McNeal. They also saw thousands of wolves and large herds of elk. How strange it was, they thought, looking back: yonder, just over the mountains, Indians were starving to death, while here there was more beef than ten worlds could eat. Frazier reckoned that Captain Lewis was right: the Blackfeet were so ornery because they had so much to eat. And the white men too, Frazier said: in all times past hadn't those nations waged the most incessant war who were best fed? For ten or fifteen miles before the first buffalo came in sight the men had heard the roaring thunder of the bulls and, grinning all over, had said to one another, "Beefsteak again!" No more rancid fish. No more dogs and roots. It would now be elk roast and buffalo hump. They had forgotten how vast the herds were. Looking into the east and the south and remembering their months of famine, they realized that it was buffalo land not only farther than they could see but farther than they could think.

They had moved warily up the narrow canyon and its river, and though they saw fresh Indian sign every day they never saw Indians. They supposed that the Indians were hiding and watching. The red rascals knew how many there had been in the party when it went down and no doubt imagined that the main party was now somewhere behind. By the 11th of July they came to the campsite at the downriver end of the long portage, which the Corps had left the last July 13th. Now the bellowing of the bulls so filled the earth that it was one continuous roaring. The horses, which had never before seen the enormous shaggy beasts, trembled with fright. The men were so delighted that they just grinned and stared. Lewis told them that if they overate they would be sick, having lived so long on rancid fish and roots, but the men after devouring a huge helping would look at him, their eyes luminous with hope and hunger, and say, "Captain Lewis, I think I can stand one more." After eating they stretched out on their backs, groaning with gluttony but with happiness too, knowing that never again on this journey would they go hungry.

It was while the party was encamped here that Hugh McNeal went off alone to hunt. Lewis had reminded the men that they were again in grizzly bear country, and the day before McNeal set out had given Drewyer up as dead, when that intrepid man vanished for a day and a night. "I expect a white bear got him," Lewis said. Then McNeal went hunting, to return hours later with his hair standing up, his eyes bulging and his gun broken. He told a story that astounded them.

Without knowing it he had ridden within ten feet of a monstrous grizzly, hidden by a thicket; and when his horse smelled it or saw it the bear suddenly rushed out and the horse swung, unseating McNeal and hurling him to the earth. He was thrown right under the bear's teeth and talons, and for a moment was stunned. Instead of taking his head into its mouth or gutting him with a blow of its claws the bear slowly rose to his hind legs as a sign that he was getting ready to make a fight of it. This deliberate preparation on the beast's part saved McNeal's life. It gave him a chance to leap to his feet and seize his rifle, which lay only a few feet from him.

He now paused in telling the story. The men looked at him and waited, knowing that he was deeply agitated, for he still breathed hard and his voice shook when he talked.

Bob Frazier said, "I suppose you're now going to tell us that you mounted him and rode away."

McNeal said he seized the rifle and waited for the bear to come down. Then with all his might he struck the monster across the skull with his gun. He hit him so hard that he broke the gun in two. The blow stunned the bear and gave McNeal time to dash to the tallest tree he could see anywhere and go up it like a squirrel. He had never known how well and how fast he could climb a tree: he had felt as though his hands were full of lightning. He shinned up to a limb about thirty feet above the earth and on looking down saw the bear scratching its skull and acting confused. In a few moments it came over to the tree and sat, and for hours it just sat there and looked up at him.

Lewis had been looking hard at this young man. He now said, "I hope he scared the pox out of you."

"He scared something out of me," McNeal said.

A few days later Lewis with Drewyer and the Fields brothers headed for the country up Maria's River. They soon came to lodges that had recently been lived in. Then they found Indian campfires only a few days old. Suspecting that the red men were watching him, Lewis and his men took turn standing guard every night. But even though he knew that hostile Indians were all around him, and had no doubt that they were spying on him, he went on up the river, until convinced that its headwaters were not close to the Saskatchewan. His northernmost camp he called Camp Disappointment. Instead of turning back at once, as his more prudent friend would have done, he lingered here for several days, observing the plant life and searching the area for sign of mineral wealth. The Indians still kept out of sight. He thought their reluctance to show themselves more than strange. He thought it incredible. Every day he and his men had been firing their guns to kill fresh meat. They had built big fires. Standing on a hill and gazing round him, he said, "Damn it, they must know we're here. Why don't they show themselves?" Though he chose campsites that could not be easily surprised, even the Fields brothers, as bold as any men in the Corps, wondered if he was inviting a showdown.

The day the four men left Camp Disappointment and turned south the Indians came in sight. After looking at them a few moments Lewis climbed to an eminence for a better view. He then saw about thirty horses. Looking through his spyglass, he could make out several Indians, all of whom seemed to be looking down the river, where at the moment Drewyer was hunting. "I guess they're watching Drewyer," he said, still looking through the glass. "About thirty horses, most of them saddled. I can't tell how many men." He turned to the Fields brothers. "This looks bad. I expect the only thing to do is to approach them as friends. You," he said, speaking to Joe, "hoist the flag." Joe Fields took from his roll a small United States flag and held it aloft. Now the Indians seemed for the first time to see the three men. They began to rush around like ants in a disturbed hill. Moving forward with his two men, Lewis said, "I calculate there must be as many warriors as horses. If we flee they'll pursue us and their horses are stronger than ours. The only thing to do is to advance. Be sure all your weapons are in order."

When the three men were four or five hundred yards from the Indians one of them rode toward them at full speed. Lewis then dismounted from his horse and advanced alone, making signs of friendship. About a hundred yards from him the Indian stopped, looked at him a few moments, and then raced back to his companions. Then they all came toward Lewis. Turning his head, he called to the brothers, "Advance—and be alert. I can see only eight but I expect others are hidden. Be prepared for trouble."

"This," said Reuben, "is where I get myself an Indian. I'm going to shoot the biggest bastard I can see."

"You'd better wait for orders," said his more disciplined brother.

Within a hundred paces all the Indians but one halted and the one came forward. Telling his men to stand with their guns ready, Lewis advanced and shook the red man's hand and looked into inscrutable black eyes. Was this a Blackfoot or a Big Belly? He advanced to the group and shook hands with the other seven, and the lone Indian went to the Fields brothers to shake their hands. All the men then dismounted, and with signs the red men asked the white men to smoke. At this moment Lewis had a happy thought. In sign language he said that his man over on the river had his pipe, and asked one of them to go with Reuben Fields to find him.

Joe said, "Don't shoot him, you damn fool. He's your red brother."

Lewis looked at Joe and said, "Private Fields, what do you mean?"

Joe waited a moment until Reuben was out of hearing. He then said, "Just a joke, Captain. My brother has an itch to shoot a redskin."

"I expect maybe he'll be scratching that itch before we are out of this."

Lewis now gave one Indian a flag, another a medal, a third a handkerchief, all the time watching their eyes and gestures. These were bold sturdy warriors. He knew there would be trouble. As long as it was four against eight he was not worried but he suspected that there were other warriors concealed in the riverbrush. In a low voice he said, "Watch the river thicket for signs," and Joe answered, "Yes, Captain, I am."

When Drewyer and the two men came up, Lewis said, "Any sign of red men along the river?" Drewyer said he had seen none. The four white men and the eight red men stood a few moments looking at one another. Lewis then proposed that they should all camp together for the night and the twelve of them, mounting their horses, headed for the river bottom. With buffalo skins the red men set up a lodge and invited the white men to share it. Lewis accepted, though he suspected that this was an ambush. He took Drewyer with him into the lodge to interpret but told the Fields brothers to remain apart by their own fire and to be on the alert.

When the brothers were alone by their fire Joe said, "Does our captain know what's in the red man's mind?"

"I wonder," Reuben said. "If I was the captain we'd shoot them all now. That would be eight we wouldn't have to shoot tomorrow."

"Captain Clark knows Indians better."

"A lot better," Reuben said. "He ain't so damned trusting."

"Still," Joe said, "he might have something up his sleeve we don't know about."

The irrepressible Lewis was telling the red men who he was, where he had come from, where he had been. He asked them to live in peace with all other Indian nations, and to pledge their allegiance to the Great Father in Washington. When he told them that he had a large group of armed men near the mouth of this river, the Indian spokesman was quick to say that only a half-day march from where he sat was a mighty band of his people, ready to move south. Wondering if this was true, Lewis chided the spokesman for his warlike attitude, knowing that he might as well throw his words on water. The red man said there was a white man with the big party up north. Lewis told him to send a messenger to bring the white man down, and to invite all the chiefs to come and be his guests. He said he was eager to meet all the chiefs, for he had heard that they were very brave men. To this the red man made no reply and his eyes revealed nothing.

Knowing that these rascals intended no good, Lewis took the first watch and sat up till almost midnight. By this time the Indians were all asleep, or seemed to be. Lewis then aroused Reuben and told him to take the next watch. In firelight he looked at Reuben's sleep-filled face and said, "Keep alert, Private Fields. I expect they intend to steal our horses. If you see anything suspicious, fire your gun and wake us at once."

"Yes, Captain."

Lewis then lay down and almost at once fell asleep. He knew afterward that he should have known better. Indeed, he did know better, even then, but he was a reckless man who seasoned life by deliberately taking risks. At the break of day or a little before, all the red men came to the fire where Lewis lay in sleep with Reuben and Drewyer. Joe stood guard. Joe had laid his gun on the earth close by his brother. An Indian slipped up in the dusk and seized Joe's gun, and Reuben's, and a moment later two other red men took Drewyer's gun and Lewis's. It happened that at this moment Joe Fields glanced behind him to see if his gun was safe, and saw the Indian running off with it. He gave a yell that would have aroused the dead.

The next instant Reuben was on his feet and though filled with sleep he raced away, following his brother and then overtaking him, and running on ahead, a dagger blade flashing in his hand. He overtook the Indian, and with one violent sweep of his powerful arms tore the rifles from his grasp. In the next instant he drove the dagger blade through the red man's ribs and deep into his heart. He yanked the blade out and shook it, and like an infuriated buffalo bull glared round him. The Indian sucked his breath in once, staggered, and fell dead.

"That's one," Reuben said to his brother. "Where are the others?" He now had his rifle in his hands.

Lewis had been awakened by Joe's shout. Drewyer had seen the Indian steal up and take hold of his gun. Leaping up, he had seized his gun and cried, "Damn you, let go my gun!" Lewis heard his cry. He then leapt up, saying, "Drewyer, what's the trouble?" The next moment he saw Drewyer struggling with the Indian, and, turning to seize his own rifle, found that it was gone. Glancing round him, he saw an Indian making off with it and, drawing his pistol, he ran after him, shouting, "Damn you, lay my gun down! Put my gun down, you red thief, or I'll shoot you dead!" Reuben was to say afterward that if Captain Lewis had only a moment of life left his talk would still be highfalutin. "I'll shoot you dead!" Lewis was shouting. "You red rascal you!" At this moment the Fields brothers ran up and the next moment would have shot the Indian down if Lewis had not yelled at them. "Don't shoot him!" he said.

The red man had laid Lewis's gun down and was now walking away. Lewis advanced and picked up his rifle. Hearing running feet in the direction of the camp, he turned. It was Drewyer.

Pointing to a fleeing Indian, Drewyer said the man had stolen his gun. Did the captain give him permission to shoot him?

"What with?" Lewis asked, amused.

"Look!" cried Reuben, pointing. "And there!" Lewis looked one way and saw three Indians driving off the main body of horses; and the other way and saw the man who had stolen his gun, with a companion, driving off still another band of horses.

"Pursue them!" he cried, indicating the main band. "If they refuse to halt, then fire." Drewyer and the Fields brothers were off at a dead-run. Lewis shouted after them, "Don't shoot if you don't have to, but be sure you bring horses back!"

He himself took after the two men driving the smaller band but after running a few hundred yards he was winded. He had been shouting to them to stop but either they did not hear or did not care. Breathing hard, with his heart roaring in his ears, and feeling that he could not run another fifty feet to save his life, he again called to them, his voice hoarse with rage, "Bring my horses back or I'll shoot you!" He then raised his gun and at this moment one of the Indians looked back. The two of them were hardly more than a hundred feet beyond Lewis; he held his gun steadily on the larger one. This man jumped behind a huge stone and shouted something to his companion, who then turned broadside to Lewis. Shifting the sight to him, Lewis aimed at his belly and fired. The man dropped to his knees. He then rolled to his right elbow, took swift aim and fired: Lewis felt the wind from the bullet fan his hair.

Unable to reload because he had left his shot pouch in camp, Lewis retreated, expecting at any moment to feel the shock of a bullet in his spine. The two Indians had only the one gun. Why the one behind the stone did not rush out and reload and fire he was never to know, and right now he was not thinking about it, for he was ashamed of himself. He had shot an Indian and that was bad. That might cost him his life. True, the Indian had been armed but he had not yet raised his gun. Lewis was thinking that he could have held the sight on him and advanced and disarmed him. Why hadn't he? He was just too damned impulsive for any good at all. While angrily chiding himself he met Drewyer, who, having heard the shot, had rushed to his aid. Drewyer now told him that one of the Fields brothers had stabbed an Indian dead.

"Then that's two," said Lewis softly. In his mind was a picture of the Blackfoot camp only three or four hours away—and a picture of the incredible tortures he and his men would have to endure, if captured. He had no doubt that an Indian was already riding toward the camp at full speed. "Where are the Fields boys?"

"Still chasing them."

"O good God, we have no time for that now!" That was the trouble with such men as the Fields brothers: they never knew when to quit. They might chase them right into the big camp! "Come," he said. "We must get our saddles and be ready to go."

He and Drewyer caught four of the strongest Indian ponies and had them saddled when at a wild gallop the Fields brothers rode in, with four of the horses belonging to the white men. Lewis had been looking round at the camp. The eight Indians had had only two guns and they had left one of them. They had left their bows and arrows, their robes, their buffalo meat. "Be quick now!" Lewis said. "Grab some of the meat and the gun. It's a ride for our lives now." A few moments later the four men were riding south. Lewis asked Joe how many Indians had been in the party he pursued. Five, Joe said. Lewis had pursued two. Reuben had slain one. Well, that much was good: he had been wondering if one of them had left camp in the night to alert the main band.

He decided that they would have to ride long and hard, straight for the mouth of Maria's River, and pray that some of the men would be there with canoes. He supposed that the three men with him knew that they were in grave danger and riding for their lives. They had stupidly killed two Indians and left them to the wolves: the whole

Blackfoot nation would be out for vengeance, and in pursuit they would ride their horses to death. A pursuing party might even at this moment be only a few miles behind. He kept this thought before him, and if one of the riders fell back he would turn and shout, "Get up here, Drewyer! Don't any of you fall back out of sight!"

At first he had thought to take eight horses, riding four and leading four, but abandoned four of the beasts when he saw that they slowed him up. Riding for their lives, they had no time to fool with extra horses. They were on the four that had looked strongest, all Indian ponies, and they were riding them hard. By the middle of the afternoon Lewis figured that they had covered about sixty miles.

By a small stream they halted to let their horses drink and graze, and themselves eat raw meat. The Fields brothers were looking at their captain.

Reuben said, "I guess, Captain, you figger they're pretty close behind us."

"They could be."

"Drewyer thinks maybe they bluffed about the big camp."

"Maybe. We can't afford to speculate. Are you sure there were five, or did one of them leave in the night to go to the main camp?"

"Oh yes, Captain, there was five."

"Well, we should have several hours the lead then. If only none of our horses fail!"

The men looked at the ponies. "They're tough," Reuben said. "Still, one might fall and break a leg. Then someone would have to walk."

"A hell of a chance he'd have walking," Joe said.

Drewyer, an expert tracker, was looking round him. He gestured at the wet earth. It had been raining and even a blind Indian could follow their trail. As the horses moved while feeding, the men moved with them, so that they could reach them for instant flight. After an hour they mounted the beasts, lathered white with foam, and rode again. By the time darkness fell, Lewis calculated that they had ridden another seventeen miles. Again they halted, not for themselves but for their tired mounts. Lewis sent Drewyer to a herd within sight to kill a fat buffalo, figuring that a rifle shot would not matter much, for if the Indians were close to them and gaining they were lost anyhow, and if they were not pursuing then they were safe enough. Building a fire, they roasted hump and tongue, letting their horses feed and rest; and after two hours they rode again. By moonlight they rode until two in the morning, and were now, Lewis figured, about a hundred miles from the two dead Indians. They hobbled their horses and sank into sleep.

At daylight they were up, and so stiff and sore that it was painful merely to move, let alone to sit astride a horse. The men had been slow to leave their beds, and on their feet stood as though they would never move again. A little sharply Lewis told them that not only their own lives, but possibly the life of every man in the party, depended on them—on their coolness and speed, for this flight was not over. "They might be almost on us now," he said. "If they overtake us we'll tie the bridles together and stand behind our horses and sell our lives for as many red men as we can."

"Ten for me," Reuben said.

Joe said, "If we kill ten or fifteen the others will run."

"Oh no," Lewis said. "I think these are Blackfeet. If the main party overtakes us that will be the end of us but we'll die like men. All right, let's be off."

And again they rode. After about fifteen or twenty miles they knew they were close to the Missouri and they thought they heard the sound of a gun. A few miles farther they had no doubt of it. They heard the report of several rifles and, knowing that it was their own men firing, they relaxed a little. But they still rode hard for the river, and on gaining the bank saw a canoe coming down: it was as if the men with the boats had known Lewis and his men were racing for their lives, and had determined to be here at just this moment! Lewis glowed all over inside, as from hot wine. These men were from Clark's party. Ordway was so overjoyed when he recognized Lewis, whom he had hardly expected ever to see again, that he fired off a salute of small arms, and followed this with the swivel gun. Lewis and his men were busy unsaddling and tossing the useless saddles into the river. Turning the half-dead horses back to forage, they tumbled headlong into the first canoe that came up, Lewis saying to Ordway, "I think half the Blackfoot nation is after us. Get going as fast as you can!" He and his three men had, he figured, covered a hundred and twenty miles in just twenty-four hours and, like their beasts, they were more dead than alive.

38

The oarsmen went downstream at a speed that Lewis found astonishing. Lying back against his bedroll, he asked Ordway for a report on Clark's part of the journey. They had not encountered many difficulties, Ordway said. They had been able to find the other pass across the divide, and so had saved many miles; and by July 8th, with Sacajawea's guidance, they had reached the sunken dugouts. In these most of the party had taken off down the swift Jefferson River, leaving Ordway and a few of the men to take the horses overland. The boatmen made a hundred miles the first day.

"That's a lot faster than we went up it," Lewis said.

"They gave it the heave-ho," Ordway said. "They don't care much for Mr. Jefferson's river."

"They forget," said Lewis, "that the river is just as anxious to get out of the mountains as they are."

Ordway turned a smile on the dry witticism and went on with his story. At three forks Clark had taken eight men, plus the squawman and his wife and child, and with about fifty horses had headed for the Yellow Stone. He had sent Ordway and the other men down the Missouri to the falls. In six days they were at White Bear Island.

Lewis now had nineteen men in his party. He felt secure enough to pause to dig up the largest cache they had made on the westward journey, but found it caved in and most of the things ruined. Sergeant Gass and Willard joined them here. The party then went to the island at the mouth of Maria's River and found the red pirogue so decayed it was worthless. They went on down the Missouri in the white pirogue and five small dugouts. Lewis was eager to rejoin Clark, whom he was to meet at the mouth of the Yellow Stone, many hundreds of miles on down. Traveling at a speed that surprised all of them, the party passed the Mussel Shell River on August 1st, the Milk River on August 4th, and reached the Yellow Stone on the 7th. Landing, Lewis perceived that Clark had been camped here but had been gone for a week or more. On a pole he found a slip of paper on which Clark had written Lewis's name; and in the campground a note attached to an elk horn. The note said that because game was scarce here, and the mosquitoes worse than the Egyptian plagues, he was going down to some convenient spot and wait.

More eager than ever to see his friend, Lewis ordered his men to the boats and again they were off. He hoped to overtake Clark before dark. After an hour or so the men saw a small fire blazing on the shore and a piece of meat hanging from a pole. Ordway examined the spot and reported that two men had recently been here. He brought with him a piece of a Chinook hat, which McNeal was sure had belonged to Gibson.

"They can't be far off," Lewis said. "Let's go."

But they did not overtake Clark's party this day. The next day, observing that some of his men were almost naked, and that a herd of buffalo was near, Lewis decided to pause a few days to let his men dress skins and make clothing. They would also dry some meat. He thought it a little strange that Clark had not waited for him at this point, where game was abundant and the mosquitoes were less troublesome. He was a little put out, but chided himself, saying that Will Clark always had a good reason for what he did.

August 11th, Lewis and his party set off again. When they saw a large herd of elk not far distant he sent most of the men ashore, and in the pirogue with a half-dozen men he went on. In a little while he saw another herd of elk and after beaching the pirogue he told Cruzatte to come with him. The two men slipped away and a few moments later they fired simultaneously. Lewis saw his beast fall and he knew that Cruzatte had wounded his. Reloading, they set off through river bottom willows after the wounded elk, and Lewis was on the point of firing again when a blow spun him and almost knocked him down.

He knew instantly that he had been shot, yet doubted his senses. In a voice that expressed no anger, almost no emotion of any kind, he said, "Damn it, you've shot me." He looked over in the direction

Cruzatte had taken but could see nothing. He looked down at his rump and saw the blood gushing. He put a hand down. Aware now that he actually had been shot, and perhaps fatally, he began to yell at Cruzatte, "Damn you, come here, you have shot me! Cruzatte . . . !" But there was no reply. Lewis now decided that it was an Indian who had shot him. The report of the gun had been only thirty or forty paces away, and surely, he reasoned, if Cruzatte were no farther than that he would hear him shouting. Besides, he'd be coming forward to learn what he had shot at.

Convinced that he was in mortal danger, and his men with him, Lewis let the blood gush, while looking round him, trying to figure out what to do. He concluded that it would be best to get to the pirogue, if he could; and so he began to run, feeling the blood pump out of him at every leap, and all the while shouting to Cruzatte. "Back to the boat, Cruzatte! There are Indians around us and I'm shot! Cruzatte, do you hear me . . . ?" In spite of the pain and the spurting of blood Lewis kept running until he came in sight of the boat. He then shouted to the men there to seize their arms, which they did instantly. He went staggering up, out of breath, faint from pain and loss of blood, saying, "I've been shot, but not mortally, I hope. Indians have attacked and Cruzatte may already be dead. Come, follow me." But he was not able to lead. After he had gone only a little way, dizziness seized him and he had to stop. To his anxious men, staring at him, he said, "Go rescue Cruzatte if you can. If you find too many against you, retreat to the boat, keeping close together and holding them off with your fire. Be off now."

He then turned, gasping with agony, and made his way to the pirogue. He figured that this was the end of him, and as always, in a situation of danger, his first thought was to sell his life for all he could get. On reaching the boat he first placed his pistol, rifle and the airgun within easy reach, intending to empty them one after the other if the Indians came in sight. He then tried to examine the wound. It seemed to him that the bullet had struck his left thigh an inch or so below the hip joint, and after going clear through his left buttock had cut a deep furrow across the right rump. Spent, it had dropped within his leather trousers, and feeling around, he found it there. He drew his hand out with the bullet clasped inside it. He looked at the bullet. Then he knew. He knew bullets. This was the kind fired from a short rifle such as Cruzatte carried. He looked over toward the thicket of willows but saw no one and could hear nothing.

A little later the men returned, their eyes fixed on their captain, their faces extremely grave. Lewis looked at Cruzatte.

The poor half-blind fellow seemed about to burst into tears. "Captain, if I shot you I did not intend to!"

"I expect you didn't," Lewis said sharply. "Why didn't you answer me?"

"I didn't hear you."

"You didn't hear me. You couldn't have been more than fifty paces away and I shouted as loud as I could. But you didn't hear me?"

"No, Captain."

Lewis looked at the man a few moments. He thought he was lying. Cruzatte had heard him, he knew that he had shot him, and so to hide his folly had rushed away, pretending not to hear.

Lewis turned to Gass. "Sergeant, help me undress."

With the aid of Gass, Lewis took off all his clothes and examined the wounds. So far as he could tell, the bullet had missed both bones and arteries, though there was still a good deal of bleeding. He had Gass bring him the roll of medicines, and then stuffed lint into the wounds, plugging the holes and trying to stanch the flow of blood. He then sent the men to dress the two elk and bring the flesh in, and while he waited for them he thought with grim humor, What folly it is that I should go safely for thousands of miles and at last, when the journey is almost over, should first be almost scalped by Blackfeet, and then shot by one of my own men! He wanted a drink of brandy but there was none. There was tobacco, taken from a cache: when the men returned he would have them fill his pipe.

The men came with the meat, and the five small canoes upstream came down. Gass went over to tell the men their captain had been shot, and not a one of them said a word. They were too shocked to speak. Again the party set off, with Lewis lying back against bed-rolls and puffing his pipe. He was touched to see how anxious the men were: if he glanced round him he surprised, in the pirogue or in the dugouts close by, sober eyes fixed on him, eyes that instantly looked away. He would be all right in a few days, he thought, puffing smoke out or grimacing at the stabs of pain. He didn't know whether he would ever forgive Cruzatte. Still, the brown color of his britches was about that of an elk; and besides, he should have known better than to take a nearsighted man with him. Why had he done that?—when he could have chosen one of the best hunters! He did the damnedest things. Anyway, it was done now and it was folly to think about it. How far ahead was Will Clark?

When dark came he told his men he would remain in the pirogue. It was simply too painful to move. He had a high fever and he spent a miserable night. There was no sleep for him. He studied the nature of the stabbing pains in his wounds, looked at the stars and waited for morning. At the first sign of daylight some of his men were looking at him and asking what they could do for him. "Some soup," he said, "and a little meat." Gass brought him hot broth and morsels of meat, and Lewis could tell that he had searched the kettles for the best of both.

This afternoon they passed a camp that Clark and his party had left only that morning. The men found a letter Clark had left and brought it to Lewis. Clark wrote that at the mouth of the Yellow Stone he had left a letter for his friend but that Sergeant Pryor had come along and taken it. Pryor and his men, the present note said, had been robbed of all their horses by the Crow Indians and had had to make bullboats and come down by water. This was bad news. The captains had hoped to take most of the horses to the Mandan villages, there to buy the good will of the Sioux and persuade some of their chiefs to go to Washington.

Lewis read the note twice and put it away. "They're not far," he said. "Let's catch them."

In only a few minutes they saw a canoe and a campfire on the north shore, and on rowing over found two trappers. Captain Clark, they said, had passed them about noon the previous day. The men with Lewis were staring at the two bearded fellows as though they had never seen white men before. Lewis gave the trappers information about the water courses upriver and told them where to find the most beaver. He then went on, suspecting that Clark was waiting for him.

And so Clark was. It was noon when Clark heard wild shouts up the river, and answering cries from his own men. He heard a voice say, "They have come!" He saw Sacajawea clapping her hands and making sounds of joy. Going to the bank for a better view, he saw sweeping toward him the pirogue and the dugouts behind it. All the men seemed to be standing and shouting but Clark could see no sign of the tall ungainly figure, whose presence he sought, his eyes glancing from boat to boat. Where was Lewis? His heart sank a little. He had had the feeling that his reckless friend would go too far up

Maria's River ever to come back. One of the dugouts was outdistancing the others. Clark went quickly upstream and motioned to it to put in. It came in with great spirit and dash, its men shouting greetings to the captain and to the men on the shore.

In the hubbub Clark commanded silence and asked, "Where is Captain Lewis?"

Joe Fields turned and waved at the pirogue. "Back there."

"In the pirogue?" said Clark. "I can't see him."

"He was shot," Joe said.

"Captain Lewis was shot? Private Fields, what are you telling me?"

"Cruzatte shot him. It was a mistake."

Clark said no more. He looked at the pirogue and waited, and the moment it touched land he was there, looking into it. Seeing Lewis stretched out, he climbed into the boat and went stumbling over the baggage to his friend. He sank by his side and looked into his eyes.

"Captain Lewis, is it true you were shot?"

"Yes, damn it. That half-blind Cruzatte took me for an elk. Do I look like an elk?"

"More like a moose," Clark said. "Where is it? Is it bad?"

"It's nothing," Lewis said. "Just a scratch."

Clark knew better. The Lewis face was haggard and drawn. He was obviously in pain but was the sort who would pretend that a serious wound was a scratch. "I'd better have a look at it," Clark said. But first his right hand found Lewis's right hand and clasped it and for a few moments held it.

When he examined the wound he thought it looked pretty bad. He smelled it. It seemed to be clean. He could tell that Lewis was in great pain when he moved or when the wound was touched.

"This is going to hurt like hell," Clark said. "You went and stuffed the hole full of cotton and now I have to pull it all out."

"You're the doctor," Lewis said.

"What have you been putting on it?"

"Peruvian bark."

When Clark began to pull the lint out Lewis fainted dead away. It was an ugly ragged hole where the bullet had entered, and where it had come out. The wound in the right cheek was only about three or four inches long, and as deep as the bullet, but in the left ham the ball had gone clear through. With hands as gentle as his large rough hands could be Clark dressed the wounds with such medicines as he had, and then put flannel wraps over the bandage. Lewis said he felt a lot better.

"That'll fix me up," he said. "I'll be well in no time."

"You'll be lucky if you're walking by the time we get home."

"I guess you better keep the Journal now," Lewis said. His face had drained white but his gray eyes were twinkling. "But if you don't mind there's one thing I must do. There's a strange cherry——"

"Shall I fill your pipe?"

"Thank you," Lewis said, and took up his pen. He had made the record relating to the two trappers, and the return to the party of Colter and Collins, who for several days had fallen behind. He now wrote, "at 1 P.M. I overtook Capt. Clark and party and had the pleasure of finding them all well. as wrighting in my present situation is extreemly painfull to me I shall desist until I recover and leave to my frind Capt. C. the continuation of our journal. however I must notice a singular Cherry——" Feeling Clark's grave eyes on him, Lewis looked at him and said, "I want to make just one note about a strange cherry I saw, then I'll desist." His note stretched out to over two hundred words, and all the while Clark watched him, thinking, What a man he is! If he were dying, if he had only ten minutes left, he would describe still another strange botanical specimen for his President!

This evening and night Lewis remained in the pirogue, for it was too painful to move. The persons who had been with Clark, including the squawman, came to the boat to pay their respects to Lewis, Sacajawea coming last, her big husky boy in her arms. Clark was sitting with Lewis when she came. Lewis was startled to hear him say:

"There's my boy Pomp. Hasn't he grown?"

Lewis looked over at the child. He was a big boy all right, for eighteen months, with a round happy face and bright black eyes. Clark said his boy Pomp had learned to dance; round the fire when the fiddle was played and the men capered, he would clasp the middle finger of a man and with cries of joy hop up and down or try to prance as the men pranced. Or he would try to turn round and round and would then fall over. He was a bright child, Clark said.

The girl in her shy Indian way had come up and said, "Haylow, Cap-un Luis." With her child she had returned to the main fire.

In fireglow the two captains sat in the pirogue and talked. Clark and his group had had a rather uneventful journey, though not without difficulties. Gibson one day, trying to mount his horse, had slipped and fallen, driving a jagged piece of dry wood two inches deep into one thigh. He had suffered most dreadfully and for a while they had had to carry him in a litter. The wolves in places had been so thick that they had come right into camp and taken the drying meat off the scaffolds; and one night a wolf had sunk his long sharp teeth clear through the hand of Sergeant Pryor while he slept, and was so vicious that he had then attacked Windsor.

Lewis said, "I expect we'd be minus a sergeant if the wolf had seized his throat."

"I expect so," Clark said. Shannon had leapt from his bed and killed the wolf.

The Crow Indians—he supposed it had been the Crows—had stolen more than half their horses almost before they knew it. He had then sent Pryor overland, with three men and the remaining horses, and in just one night the Indians made off with the whole bunch. Clark said he doubted that Pryor could have driven the beasts to Mandan anyway; every time they came to a buffalo herd the horses that were free and unridden went headlong after the buffalo, exactly as they might have if on their backs had been Indians with bow and arrow. Pryor said he and his men had an awful time trying to overtake the ponies and manage them.

Lewis chuckled and then groaned. Even a deeper breath shot stabs like knife blades through his rump.

They had seen, Clark said, the most immense herds of buffalo. Actually in places on the Yellow Stone so many of them were swimming the river for so many miles up and down that the party was unable to proceed in the dugouts. Again and again they had to beach the canoes and wait.

"That was hundreds of miles from where I was," Lewis said. "There were such immense herds around us that we couldn't sleep. To think that they are just as thick all over the hundreds of miles between us, and down south and southwest other hundreds of miles. How many millions are there? Did you have any trouble with the grizzly?" he asked, and told of McNeal's experience.

O Lord, the grizzlies, Clark said. They saw grizzlies larger than any they had seen when going up the river last year. One of them was shot six times and kept on going as though it had never been shot at all. Their most amusing experience with one happened in the river. A huge monster on the bank plunged in after them, supposing, no doubt, that they were a swimming buffalo. "I expect about the only way they can catch a buffalo is when it's swimming."

"I expect so."

Well, this monster, the largest they had ever seen, came straight at them, swimming fast. Clark had told his men to be ready to fire but to wait for the command. About a hundred feet from the grizzly they all fired and every ball went home.

"How many?"

"Besides myself I had Shields, Bratton, Gibson, Labiche, Shabono and my man York."

"Seven bullets into him at one crack. What did the bear do?"

"Swam away so fast we couldn't catch him."

Again Lewis chuckled, and groaned. "He must have thought that was quite a bull."

"I expect he did," Clark said. "He was bleeding so bad he left a red trail all the way across the river."

The worst curse of all had been the mosquitoes. The pests they saw on the outward journey had been only feeble ineffectual little females compared to those on the Yellow Stone. Lewis's dog had howled all night. The baby Pomp in spite of all his mother could do had his eyes swollen shut, his ears puffed up like big overripe slices of tomato, and his whole face so enlarged that it looked like a round dull-red half-decayed vegetable. In places the mosquitoes had been so dense that a man could not fire his gun. He would be walking along, Clark said, and he would see a mountain sheep on a bluff or a fat elk on the plain and he would raise his gun to fire, but before he could sight along the barrel it was simply covered with huge mosquitoes. He had said a fat elk but that wasn't true: elk, deer and buffalo had all been scrawny because eaten alive by mosquitoes.

Clark returned to the child and told again of Pomp's delight in dancing with the men; of his eagerness to ride a horse alone, with no one holding him; of his hardly giving off a whimper after the mosquitoes had sealed his eyes and covered his whole face with sting-bloat. He's pretty fond of that boy, Lewis was thinking. Then Clark was telling how day after day Sacajawea had brought him roots, plants, berries and curious objects which she thought might interest him. One day she had brought him a double handful of very large and wonderfully flavored gooseberries, with a rich crimson color; and on another, the largest purple currants he had ever seen.

She had seemed to know where to find the choicest prairie potato and bread root, and the tenderest watercress. . . .

Lewis would have talked all night, for he was in too much pain to sleep anyway; but Clark again clasped his hand and said, "My friend, you better rest now."

Returning the strong pressure Lewis said, "I expect I had."

"I'll see you in the morning. Goodnight."

"Goodnight."

39

Left alone, Lewis lay in thought. He was a wonderful man, Will Clark was: so sensible, so dependable, so resourceful, and so brave without being foolish and reckless, so persevering without being impulsive and romantic, so levelheaded in all that he did. Lewis sighed, for he would have wished to be more like him. Clark was woman-lonely, he had decided: he had a Judy or Julie or Judith or somesuch waiting for him but there was no woman waiting for Merne Lewis. No woman but his mother.

Well, it was about over now. The dangers were passed, the triumph had been won. It was still a long way to St. Louis but it would be an easy downstream journey, with eager men looking ahead around every bend. Most of them wanted to be home. They had loved it, they said; not for ten worlds would they have missed it but they wanted to be home now. Most of them but not all of them. Not John Colter.

Yes, it was almost over now, Lewis reflected, looking up at the sky. He felt a strange tearful nostalgia. He would have given a great deal to look in again at Fort Clatsop; he felt a pang of sorrow on thinking that never again would he see the spot they had called Travellers Rest—or so many other spots, at the time a curse and an impatience but now, in memory, something haloed in its own special glory. Perhaps never again would he see such incredible herds of buffalo; such immense gangs of elk; such millions of waterfowl or such millions of beaver; or such magnificent mountains as those which had almost been the death of them. It was all magnificent, the whole vast reach of it, with its great rivers and summits, its prairies and valleys, and all its buried and barely suspected wealth. He hoped Mr. Jefferson would be pleased. He would write to him. He might say, "Mr. President, you assigned me to a mission which to the best of my ability I have after two years fulfilled. We found no mountain of salt and no eagle of salt to please the Federalists but we found an immense country that simply must be a part of the United States, if our nation is to be what it should be. I suggest, Mr. President, that the southwest portion should now be explored, with the view of annexing it, so that before too long our nation will fill out to its logical borders, before the Spanish and British can lay claim to what they have no right to. . . ." He would write to the President, but not that way. In fancy he could see Tom Jefferson smiling, with the big freckles rising on ridges of flesh and his large luminous eyes filling with wonderful things. He could see in his eyes the vision of a great nation stretching from the Gulf to northern Canada and from ocean to ocean. He was sure that Mr. Jefferson would be pleased, and on this thought he closed his eyes at last and tried to sleep.

It would soon be over now. Two days later they were opposite the principal Minnetaree village, and Indians swarming down seemed pleased to see them. And surprised, too. A chief was wailing his heart out; never had Clark seen a man, white or red, weep with such wild abandon. He asked the trouble and was told that the Blackfeet had killed his son. Here and there on the way downriver Clark paused to smoke a pipe of peace and to invite one chief after another to go with him to Washington. But they were all afraid of the Sioux.

The two trappers had come back down, and now John Colter went to Clark and said he wished to have a word with him. John was a sinewy powerful young man whose eyes looked straight and deep into your eyes. He said he wanted to go back. The civilized world was not for him. The two trappers had made him an offer and he wanted to go with them, back deep into the unknown.

"You don't want to go home?" asked Clark, astonished.

"No, Captain."

Clark felt sudden warmth in his heart. This was his kind of man. But his voice was toneless when he said, "I'll have to take it up with Captain Lewis."

"Wants to go back?" said Lewis, so astonished that he tried to sit up. Still, he was not astonished at all. Something had awakened and stirred in him, as it had in Clark. In his whimsical way he said, "Why don't we all go back?"

The captains decided to let Colter go back, if no other man wanted to: they would have to keep hunters and boat-crews for the long journey to St. Louis. They polled the men and they all said they were willing to go home. But Clark saw them this evening gathered round Colter, asking him questions and looking back up the river. In their hearts a few of them wanted to go with John, for it was a man's world, that great unknown back there.

Clark gave Colter powder, lead and some clothing. Some of the men gave him a few things that they thought he might need. They all said goodbye to him and stared at his broad muscular form as he turned away.

"Going back to Blackfoot country," Silas Goodrich said. "Who would believe it?"

"Back to a man's world," Alex Willard said.

There now came the parting, poignant for Clark, and moving in less degree for a few of the other men, from Sacajawea and her child. Clark had offered to take the boy—whom this day in his Journal he called "a butifull promising child"—to St. Louis with him, there to raise and educate him. Jawey thought him too young to leave his mother. Clark then offered to take husband, wife and child down the river with him, and to find work for Charbonneau, but the squaw-man said there would be no work for him, that this was the only life he knew. He preferred to stay here. The mother said that in another year Clark could take her son, if he still wished to, and educate him.

"You know how far it is to St. Louis?" he asked her.

She shook her head no.

He told her it was a thousand miles, fifteen hundred miles, even more miles than that. It was as far as from where she stood to her own people. Did she realize what a long journey it would be, and what a great bother, to come all this long way to pick the child up a year from now?

"Trader," she said. She meant she could send the child downriver by some trader.

"Will you do that?" he asked, looking into her eyes.

"*Oui, Cap-un.*"

Charbonneau had turned away. He had never cared for the child and suspected Clark of some evil design.

"That will be a year from now, Jawey?"

"*Oui,*" she said, nodding her head yes.

Clark sensed that emotion was threatening to strip away that stern military discipline by which his life was ruled. He was a little abrupt. He took Pomp and put his cheek against the boy's cheek and for a moment looked into the black intelligent eyes. "Goodbye, my boy Pomp!" he said. He set the child down, then touched the mother on her shoulder, gently, turned away and was gone.

"Goobye," she said, looking after him.

Three days after saying goodbye to the squawman, his squaw and child, Clark wanted to see them again. He wanted to see the child, for he deeply missed his bright alert face. Possibly he wanted to see the mother too. He decided to write a letter and send it upriver by the first trader he met.

> On Board the Perogue Near the Ricara Village
> August 20th 1806.

Charbono

Sir: Your present Situation with the Indians givs me Some concern—I wish now I had advised you to come on with me to the Illinois where it most probably would be in my power to put you in Some way to do Something for your Self—I was so engaged after the *Big White* had concluded to go down with Jessomme as his Interpreter, that I had not time to talk with you as much as I intended to have done. You have been a long time with me and have conducted your Self in Such a manner as to gain my friendship, your woman who accompanied you that long dangerour and fatigueing rout to the Pacific Ocean and back, diserved a greater reward for her attention and Services on that rout than we had in our power to give her at the Mandans. As to your little Son (my boy *Pomp*) you well know my fondness for him and my anxiety to take and raise him as my own child. I once more tell you if you will bring your son Baptiest to me I will educate him and treat him as my own child—I do not forget the promis which I made to you and Shall now repeat them that you may be certain—Charbono, if you wish to live with the white people, and will come to me I will give you a piece of land and furnish you with horses cows & hogs—If you wish to visit your friends in *Montreall* I will let you have a horse, and your family Shall be taken care of untill your return—if you wish to return as an Interpreter for the Menetarras when the troops come up to form the establishment, you will be with me ready and I will procure you the place— or if you wish to return to, trade with the Indians and will leave your little *Son Pomp* with me, I will assist you with merchendize for that purpose and become my self conserned with you in trade on a Small scale that is to say not exceeding a perogue load at one time—. If you are desposed to accept either of my offers to you and will bring down your *Son* your famn Janey had best come along with you to take care of the boy untill I get him—let me advise you to keep your Bill of Exchange and what furs and pelteries you have in possession, and get as much more as you can—,and get as many robes, and big horn and Cabbra Skins as you can collect in the course of this winter. and take them down to St. Louis enquire of the Govorner of that place for a letter which I shall leave with him for you—in the letter which I shall leave with the governer I shall inform you what you had best do with your firs pelterees and robes &c and derect you where to find me—If you should meet with any misfortune on the river &c. when you get to St Louis write a letter to me by the post and let me know your Situation—If you do not intend to go down either this fall or in the Spring, write a letter to me by the first oppertunity and inform me what you intend to do that I may know if I may expect you or not. If you ever intend to come down this fall or the next Spring will be the best time—this fall would be best if you could get down before the winter—. I shall be found either in St Louis or in Clarksville at the Falls of the Ohio.

Wishing you and your family great suckcess & with anxious expectations of seeing my little dancing boy Baptiest I shall remain your friend

William Clark

Keep this letter and let not more than one or 2 persons see it, and when you write to me Seal your letter. I think you best not determine which of my offers to accept untill you see me. Come prepared to accept of either which you may chuse after you get down.

Mr Teousant Charbono, Menetarras Village

He read the letter over and sighed, for he doubted that he would ever see his boy Pomp again.

Clark had found only one chief who would go down the river with the Corps, Big White, the fat and garrulous fellow, whom the other chiefs held in contempt. And to get Big White to go Clark had had to agree to take his wife and children.

August 24th, twelve days after the two parties had come together, the entire Corps was swiftly on its way. Examining Lewis's wounds, Clark found that the hole where the ball had come out was healing over nicely, and where it had entered was freely discharging pus. Two days later Lewis was walking a little but in his eagerness again to feel like a man he overdid it and in severe pain took to his bed.

They were on their way now, down the home stretch; and day after day lying back in the big pirogue Lewis was amused by the antics and clowning of some of the men. Bob Frazier, Shannon, Bratton, Goodrich were simply overflowing with nonsense, with Frazier acting as leader. He improvised ditties or sang old ones, that he had created away back yonder:

> "Tell our mas and tell our pas
> We're in love with the lovely squaws!

> "Tell the girl who waited for me
> I've got a girl who's a Minnetaree . . . !"

The captains had expected trouble from the Sioux, and when one day the party was hailed from the bank by a band of warriors Clark paid no attention to them. This angered the Indians, who began to call insults across the water. As nearly as Drewyer could interpret, they were shouting, "Come over here and we'll kill all of you! You're cowards and dogs and we're not afraid of you . . . !" How like small children they were! Lewis reflected. They were full of wind and brag and bluff. Would they have dared, four of them, to go up Maria's River into Blackfoot country? Not a one of them—not even a hundred of them in one pack, all armed to the teeth. There they were, the silly fellows, on a bluff above the river, making menacing gestures and shouting insults. If white men were to put over they would all run. . . .

Frazier was looking at a group of squaws on the bank. He now sang a ditty in which other men joined:

"O form dee-vine—wilt thou be mine?
My Teton Sioux, my valentine . . . !"

After the Sioux were passed there was no more danger of any kind but they still had three weeks to go, even though the oarsmen bent to their oars all day long. In a small canoe the best hunters were sent on ahead to kill deer and elk, prairie chickens, geese, ducks and now and then a beaver. By early September they were meeting white men and hearing news: General Wilkinson was now the Governor of Louisiana; the Spanish had seized an American frigate in the Mediterranean; two British ships had fired on an American ship in New York harbor and killed the captain's brother. Two Indians had been hanged in St. Louis for murder; a score were in jail; Aaron Burr had killed Alexander Hamilton in a duel. . . .

It was another kind of news that most amazed them: "Why, good God, everybody has given you up for dead long ago!" "Everyone?" asked Lewis, raising his brows. "Even the President?" "Yes, even the President. Maybe he was the last but he gave you up too." The white people they met could not take their eyes off the party's members, because of their long tousled hair and beards, their deeply bronzed faces, their outlandish clothing.

The Corps paused at the grave of Sergeant Floyd and, finding it open, covered it deep and paid their respects to it. Three days later they met a trader from whom they bought a gallon of whisky, and, full of ardent spirits, the men sang twice as loud and long:

"Mr. Jefferson, hear that drum!
Here we come, sir, here we come . . . !"

Far up the river John Shields had made a drum of buffalo hide, and on this, Goodrich smote with a huge baton, sending a great booming across the waters. And the men sang:

"Out in that vast unknown, they said,
They're dead, oh hell, I know they're dead!

"Mr. President, hear that drum,
Here we come, sir, here we come . . . !"

Lewis had to smile, listening to them. They were now all overflowing with gallantry and good spirits, and the men bending over oars sang as loud as any across the Missouri's wide waters:

"Here we come, sir, here we come . . . !"

Big White didn't like the singing or the boat or the white man's cooking. He sulked and growled; his squaw glared round her at strange country; his children cried most of the night. Frazier would look over at them when they interrupted his singing and snarl, "Shut up, you sniveling little redskins, or I'll peel your scalps off!" Big White would look up at Frazier and then drop his broad fat face and mutter.

By September 9th, Lewis was up and around and almost entirely well. Three days later the party met Gravelines and Dorion, and if these two men had been looking at men from graves they could not have stared harder or with more unfeigned astonishment.

"Lord God Almighty!" Gravelines said to Clark. "We gave you all up for dead long ago."

"Even the President?" asked Lewis.

"Even the President, though he did instruct us to inquire about you."

Four days later the party met one John McClallan, a captain of artillery whom Lewis had known before. McClallan showed the same undisguised astonishment that Gravelines had shown. The whole nation, he said, had long ago given the party up as dead, some believing they had all been slain by the Blackfeet; some, that they had been captured by the Spanish and taken south to the copper mines. Most of their countrymen, McClallan said, had even forgotten that they had set out in the spring of 1804, two and a half years ago. He gave the captains biscuits, sugar, chocolate, whisky and talked to them until midnight.

By the 18th their food was gone and there was almost no game along the river, but the men begged their captains not to pause. How far was it? they asked, and on being told that to St. Louis it was a hundred and fifty miles they said they could row it in two days without food. And a dozen deep voices roared out across the river:

"Mr. Jefferson, hear that drum!
Here we come, sir, here we come . . . !"

And on they rowed, their bellies empty but their spirits soaring. When they saw cows grazing on the bank one would say to another, "You see what I see?" George Shannon said, "I don't believe in cows any more." Presently they came in sight of the village of Charrette and the men in all the boats fired three rounds from the guns and raised a great cheer. Those on the shore responded. Here the captains were able to buy beef and pork and two gallons of whisky. Residents of the village swarmed round the men; householders begged them to come and be their guests for the night. All these people were avid to learn about the unknown land, and in some of the houses citizens and their guests talked all night. Everywhere the men heard over and over the words, "We sure thought you were dead. Tell us all about it." Tell them about it! George Shannon thought. How could they be made to understand it!

The men saw white women here and looked at them as Gravelines had looked at the captains. The next day they saw white women again, waving to them from the banks; and the men in the pirogue, led by Frazier, behaved like lunatics. "Do you see what I see? Is it real?" It was George who had said, "I don't believe in white women any more." "Lay-dees!" one of the men cried, and drew a great breath into the deepest part of him. "Honest to God laydees!" The Corps saluted another village with three rounds, and the village responded; and when the men landed the same old questions were asked again. White women came up and looked gravely at the eyes of these bearded creatures dressed in skins, their gaze shifting from eye to eye and falling at last down over the face to the lips. Their own lips would say softly, "We thought you were all dead. Tell me, was it so horrible?"

Bob Frazier would sweep an arm in lordly fashion towards the western lands and sing to the fair one a few of his rimes: "Madam, we clumb the mountains, we clumb till we were blind and deef and dumb! We waded in rivers till our feet were shredded bones and shredded meat! We fought with the monstrous grizzly bear, we waded knee-deep in prickly pear. . . ."

Bob Frazier did not exaggerate much, Lewis reflected, while lying in the pirogue. As the men rowed and sang he liked to close his eyes and look back—back across the whole fabulous four thousand miles of it. Was rain falling on the shakes of Fort Clatsop, did it look roundabout as if a gray sky had fallen on the black forests? It was autumn again. In the three forks and Shoshone country bushes were again heavy with black and yellow currants, gooseberries, chokecherries, serviceberries; and mountain summits all around were again white. From St. Louis to the ocean he could see it all. He had only to close his eyes to see and smell and hear the vast herds of buffalo, elk, antelope, deer and wolves, covering the broad rolling prairies in all directions, clear to the skyline; and the mountains and mountain rivers, the peaks and pinnacles and crags; the immense forests with their billions of magnificent trees; the untold millions of beaver, otter and muskrat in the unnamed thousands of streams. . . .

"Mr. President, if they have said, 'Oh, they are dead, hell yes, they're dead,' because for two years we were mum! But look at the land we're coming from . . . !"

It was Frazier and his oarsmen singing Frazier's ditties.

Yes indeed, Lewis thought, look at the land we're coming from! What a magnificent panorama it was! He hoped the President would be pleased. He hoped the Federalists would stop their snarling and realize that all this—all this and more—would be needed to make the United States the nation that it someday must be. He tried to imagine the extent of it, the wealth of it, the variety of it: how many states would there be when the last one was named; how many nations would send their sons and daughters to homestead it; what cities would rise on its prairies and plains, its riverbanks and mountainsides . . . ?

"And nothing to eat, sir, not a crumb in all that land we're coming from! Nothing to look at but rain and fogs, mosquitoes and lice and squaws and bogs. . . ."

There would be skeptics, of course, for it was all so much bigger than belief—especially for those who had never looked west of Washington, and for whom France or England was a broad land. The scoffers would jeer, the timid would draw back, and Jefferson's political opponents would still argue that it was all a wasteland that not even the British would want. But tall lanky freckle-faced Tom Jefferson would know better. Behind the light in his large full eyes his imagination would be encompassing the whole immense wonder of it and he would be looking into the future more clearly than any other man looked. Gravely he would say, "Captain Lewis, you say the country is much bigger than we thought it was——" "Much bigger, Mr. President." Then, with a sly twinkle, "You don't think we paid France too much for Louisiana? And by the way, how would you like to be its governor?"

Startled by his fancies, Lewis opened his eyes and looked round him. For a moment his gaze met Will Clark's. Clark was in another boat a few feet away and the men with him were also singing. Well, the President might say that. Yes, he might even say that. But if ever he said it he would have to offer Captain Clark a position of equal rank, for in this long journey to the ocean and back Lewis and his friend had been equal in all things and they must continue to be equal in all things. . . .

"What was it the people said? 'The Blackfeet got them, they are dead!' But, Mr. Jefferson, hear that drum! Here we come, sir, here we come . . . !"

Again Lewis glanced over at Will Clark, and then lay back to listen to the words the men were singing, to close his eyes and dream. In the distance he had seen the smoke of St. Louis. It was September 23rd and the journey was almost over.

What Happened to Them?

What happened to most of them we seem not to know. We don't even know how Meriwether Lewis died. Becoming Governor of the Louisiana Territory, he soon found himself in financial difficulties: he overspent his own private resources in buying land, but far more serious than this was the rejection by the War and Treasury departments of his official vouchers. His creditors closed in on him and, desperate, he set off for Washington to try to talk some sense into the heads of his superiors in the government. While crossing Tennessee he killed himself or was murdered, October 11, 1809.

Clark soon was commissioned a general; became superintendent of Indian affairs; was for several terms Governor of the Missouri Territory; and again superintendent, and in this capacity his services to his nation were no less than brilliant. He won "Judith," whose name was Julia and whom he called Judy; and when she died he married the second of the two girls (now a widow) whom years before he had helped with a balky horse. True to his promise, he paid for the education of Pomp (one of his sons he nicknamed Pompy) and became guardian of Lizette, Charbonneau's daughter either by Sacajawea or otter-girl. Clark died full of serenity and honors in 1838.

Of the sergeants, Pryor became a captain in the War of 1812, married an Osage squaw and died among her people in 1831. Ordway turned to farming and apparently died in Missouri, leaving no children. Gass was in the War of 1812 and was wounded at Lundy's Lane; became for a time a drunkard; at sixty married and sired seven children; and after "getting religion" in his old age became something of a national character, dying at the age of ninety-eight.

Drewyer went back up the Missouri and in 1810 was ambushed by the Blackfeet and killed, the evidence showing that he fought bravely to the end. George Shannon was graduated in the law class with Sam Houston; became a judge and died while holding court in 1836. Shannon was in the party under the command of Pryor that attempted to return Big White and family to his people. Attacked by the Arikaras, Pryor had to turn back. Shannon was shot in one leg, and after he spent a year and a half in a hospital the leg was amputated. By some he was known in later life as Pegleg Shannon.

Bratton was in the War of 1812, became a justice of the peace, and died in 1841. Willard was also in that war; was for years a friend and neighbor of Clark; married in 1807 and had seven sons (naming one for Lewis, another for Clark) and five daughters; and at last crossed the plains with ox-teams to the Sacramento Valley, where he died in 1865. Gibson settled in St. Louis and seems to have died there as early as 1809; Werner became a sub-agent under Clark; Windsor appears to have been in the Army as late as 1819. Frazier got into various difficulties, such as beating up a sheriff and fighting with Indians, from which Clark rescued him. For a while he helped to gather evidence against Aaron Burr. One authority thinks he must be the Robert Windsor Frazier who was living in Vermont in 1834.

John Colter, one of the boldest of American frontiersmen, and generally regarded as the discoverer of Yellowstone Park (though one writer disputes this), came to an untimely end. Some think it was Potts with him when he was surrounded by the Blackfeet in the three forks area. His companion was killed while trying to escape. Colter was given a chance at his life. Stripped naked, including his moccasins, he was told to run for it, and the entire band took after him. We have only his account of it but just the same this must have been one of the most incredible footraces in history. He says he ran for six miles over those cactus-studded hills. Seeing that an Indian was gaining on him, Colter stopped, ducked the hurled lance, picked it up and, running back, spiked the Indian to the earth with it. Gaining the river, he hid under a great pile of driftwood with only his mouth above water, until the Indians gave up the search. Then, still naked, he walked for seven nights, hiding by day, until he reached Manuel Lisa's fort. Some time later he married and seems to have turned to farming but died in 1813.

Charbonneau came at last to St. Louis with his family and for a while was employed by Clark as a government interpreter. Wearying of civilized life, he went back up the river to the land and the people he loved. It is said that his passion for young squaws never left him and that as late as his eighty-first year he married a young Indian girl. One legend says that somewhere along the line Sacajawea decided that she had had enough of his brutality and left him. Though books have been written about her, this woman vanishes into the mists after her sojourn in St. Louis. Her biographer thinks that she died in the Wind River area in Wyoming in 1884.

Pomp, it is thought, died the following year, the last member of the Corps. Clark had given him an education of sorts by employing a private tutor and at least during a part of his life Pomp served as an interpreter and guide to curious persons, usually from abroad, who wanted to see the wild west. Prince Paul of Württemberg seems to have taken a fancy to the youth when he visited this country, and took him to Europe with him, returning him to this country when the Prince made a second visit, in 1829.

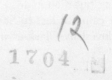